THE YOUNG AMERICAN WRITERS

The

FUNK & WAGNALLS   *New York*

Young American Writers

❦

FICTION,
POETRY, DRAMA,
AND CRITICISM

❦

SELECTED AND INTRODUCED

BY *Richard Kostelanetz*

The author wishes to express his appreciation for permission to reprint the following:

RENATA ADLER: "Polemic and the New Reviewers." Copyright © 1964 by The New Yorker Magazine, Inc. Revised by the author. Reprinted from *The New Yorker* (July 4, 1964), by permission.

BILL BERKSON: "Breath," from *Saturday Night, Poems 1960–1* (Tibor de Nagy, 1961). Copyright © 1961 by Bill Berkson. Reprinted by permission of the author.

ROBERT BOYERS: "A Very Separate Peace." Reprinted from *Kenyon Review* by permission of the author and publisher. Copyright © 1966 by Kenyon College.

JAMES BRODEY: "Door to the River." Copyright © 1965 by Art and Literature, S.E.L.A. (Lausanne). Reprinted from *Art and Literature,* No. 6 by permission of the publisher.

JEROME CHARYN: "Faigele the Idiotke," from *The Man Who Grew Younger and Other Stories.* Copyright © 1963 by Jerome Charyn. The story, which originally appeared in *Commentary,* is reprinted by permission of Harper & Row, Publishers.

FRANK CHIN: "Food for all His Dead." Copyright © 1962 by Frank Chin. First published in *Contact.* Reprinted by permission of his agent, Dorothea Oppenheimer.

TOM CLARK: "Eleven Ways of Looking at a Shit Bird." Copyright © 1966 by Tom Clark and reprinted from *Airplanes* (A Once Book, 1966) by his permission.

KEITH COHEN: "Water," reprinted by permission from *Art and Literature,* No. 10; "You Froze the Light and Flew," Copyright © 1966 Columbia University. Reprinted through the courtesy of the *Columbia Review.*

JONATHAN COTT: "A Hard Day's Knights." Copyright © 1965 by Jonathan Cott. Reprinted from *Ramparts* (October, 1965) by permission of the author.

R. H. W. DILLARD: "Tanjong Malin," from *The Day I Stopped Dreaming About Barbara Steele.* Copyright © 1966 by R. H. W. Dillard. Reprinted by permission of the University of North Carolina Press.

ERIC FELDERMAN: "Black's Theme." Copyright © 1965 Columbia University. Reprinted through the courtesy of the *Columbia Review.*

AARON FOGEL: "Gardens gardens Gardens, Toads." Copyright © 1964 Art and Literature, S.E.L.A. (Lausanne). Reprinted from *Art and Literature,* No. 3 by permission of the publisher; "Vietnam." Copyright © 1965 Columbia University. Reprinted from *Columbia Review* (Spring, 1965) through the courtesy of the publisher.

NORMAN FRUCHTER: "An Act of Comic Revenge." An extract from "A Realist Perspective" in *Studies on the Left,* Vol. 4, No. 2. Reprinted by permission of the author and publisher.

KENNETH GANGEMI: "Olt" (originally titled "The Snow-Lobsters"). Copyright © 1966 Art and Literature, S.E.L.A. (Lausanne). Reprinted from *Art and Literature,* No. 8 by permission of the publisher.

MICHAEL L. GLENN: "The Room." Copyright © 1966 by The Hudson Review, Inc. Reprinted by permission of the publisher and author from *The Hudson Review,* XVIII (Winter, 1965–66), 4.

LOUISE GLÜCK: "Firstborn," "Pictures of the People in the War," and "Solstice." Copyright © 1967 by Louise Glück. "Solstice" originally appeared in *New American Review.* Reprinted by the author's permission; "Grandmother in the Garden," from *Poetry* (March 1967), CIX, No. 6. Copyright © 1967 by The Modern Poetry Association. Reprinted by permission of the author and the Editor of *Poetry;* "The Racer's Widow." Copyright © 1967 by The New Yorker Magazine, Inc. Reprinted by permission of the author and publisher.

STEVEN GUARINO: "The Perimeter Walker," from *For Now,* No. 6. Reprinted by permission of the publisher, Donald Phelps.

ROBERT HEAD: *Sanctity,* first published in the *Tulane Drama Review,* 8 (Winter 1963; T22), 2, and reprinted by permission of the author and publisher. Copyright 1963, assigned 1967 to The Drama Review.

MICHAEL HELLER: "Fragment," reprinted by permission of the author and publisher from the *Paris Review,* No. 38 (Summer 1966).

DICK HIGGINS: "Intermedia." Copyright © 1966 by Something Else Press, Inc. All rights reserved. Reprinted by permission of Something Else Press, Inc.

ARNO KARLEN: "Rain." Copyright © 1967 by Arno Karlen. Reprinted by permission of Arno Karlen, c/o Lynn Nesbitt, Marvin Josephson Associates, Inc.

WILLIAM MELVIN KELLEY: "Cry for Me," from *Dancers on the Shore.* Copyright © 1962 by Fawcett Publications, Inc. Reprinted by permission of Doubleday & Company, Inc.

KENNETH KING: "SuperLecture." Copyright © 1966 by Kenneth King. Reprinted by permission of the author. This was originally the prose-score to m-o-o-n-b-r-a-i-nwithSuperLecture (scenario, direction, production, and performance by Kenneth King; general assistance, lighting, and film by Jeff Norwalk) which was presented November 10–13, 1966, at The Gate Theatre, New York City.

RICHARD KOSTELANETZ: "The New American Arts," from the introduction by Richard Kostelanetz to *The New American Arts.* Copyright © 1965 by Horizon Press, Inc. Reprinted by permission of the publisher.

PETER MICHELSON: "I Dream Profuse." Copyright © 1967, *Chicago Review*. Reprinted by permission of the author and publisher.

HEATHER ROSS MILLER: "Chel," reprinted by permission of the publisher and author from *Red Clay Reader II*. Copyright 1965, Class A, No. 861780, by Mrs. Charleen Whisnant.

ROBIN MORGAN: "The Improvisors." Copyright © 1965 by Robin Morgan. Reprinted from *Sewanee Review* (Summer, 1965) by permission of her agent, Creative Management Associates, Ltd.

CHARLES NEWMAN: "A Dolphin in the Forest, A Wild Boar on the Waves; Three Scenes." Copyright © 1964, the *Chicago Review*. Reprinted by permission of the publisher.

JOYCE CAROL OATES: "Upon the Sweeping Flood." Copyright © 1964 by Joyce Carol Oates. Reprinted from MSS (1964) by permission of the author.

JOHN PERREAULT: "Boomerang" and "Heart," from *Camouflage* (*Lines*, 1966). Copyright © 1966 by John Perreault. Reprinted by permission of the author.

JACQUES PRÉVERT: "The Straight and Narrow Road," as translated by Lawrence Ferlinghetti. Copyright © 1947 by Les Éditeurs du Pont du form. Reprinted from *Paroles* (City Lights, 1956) by permission of City Lights Books.

ED SANDERS: "Poem from Jail." Copyright © 1963 by Ed Sanders. Reprinted by permission of City Lights Books.

DAVID SHAPIRO: "Canticle," from *January* (1965). Copyright © 1965 by David Shapiro. Reprinted by permission of Holt, Rinehart and Winston, Inc.; "Six Poems," first published in the *Chicago Review*. Copyright © 1967, Chicago Review and reprinted by permission of the publisher; "For Son." Copyright © 1965, Columbia University. Reprinted through the courtesy of Columbia Review.

MITCHELL SISKIND: "On a Sculpture of Dr. Albert Einstein." Copyright © 1964 by Art and Literature, S.E.L.A. (Lausanne). Reprinted from *Art and Literature*, No. 3 by permission of the publisher.

RONALD TAVEL: *Shower*. Copyright © 1965 by Ronald Tavel. All Rights Reserved. Reprinted by permission of the author.

ALDEN VAN BUSKIRK: "Last Will And," from *Lami*. Reprinted by permission of his literary executor, David Rattray.

TOM VEITCH: "The Luis Armed Story." Copyright © 1967 by Art and Literature, S.E.L.A. (Lausanne). Reprinted from *Art and Literature*, No. 11 by permission of the publisher.

LEWIS WARSH: "Moving Through Air." Copyright © 1966 by Lewis Warsh. Reprinted by permission of *Angel Hair* magazine.

EUGENE WILDMAN: "The Subway Singer." Copyright © 1967, by Chicago Review. Reprinted by permission of the publisher.

For Julianne,
Mews and more

The United States is becoming a very young country indeed, with half the population already less than twenty-six years old—and most of them highly educated and with experiences and expectations that differ markedly from those that still underlie our social, political, and economic politics. By 1972 more than half of all Americans old enough to vote will be under thirty-two.

—PETER DRUCKER (1966)

THE STRAIGHT AND NARROW ROAD

At each mile
Each year
Old men with closed faces
Point out the road to children
With gestures of reinforced concrete.

—JACQUES PRÉVERT (*trans. Lawrence Ferlinghetti*)

Preface

Young blood doth not obey an old decree.
—WILLIAM SHAKESPEARE, Love's Labour's Lost (*c. 1595*)

The purposes of this book are at once modest and pretentious. Ostensibly, it collects some of the best literature by Americans born 1937 and after—those who happened to be thirty or less in 1967. Its emphasis is upon literature—poetry, fiction, drama, as well as criticism more or less about literature—to the exclusion of political writing, journalism, or criticism of the nonliterary arts, not because I object to any of those genres (indeed, I have labored in each of them) but because the last would splay its focus, the second is by definition unworthy of later reprinting, and the political criticisms of the young have already been much anthologized as well as analyzed and publicized. More important, I hope that this book contributes to instilling a generational sense among chronological accidents; for in contrast to the radical political youth whose suspicion of people over thirty is a pet piety and the young Englishmen waging war against an older generation, the young writers in America today have less collective awareness than any generation in recent memory. The scarcity of young literary magazines which are more eclectic than coterie is evidence of this; another sign is the absence of writers who coalesce the sensibilities of my literary generation as well as F. Scott Fitzgerald and Ernest Hemingway, Saul Bellow and Norman Mailer at once represented and educated their own contemporaries. The *Young American Writers* is the first book of its kind; and for no other reason, I hope that younger readers, in particular, discover that its selections collectively create a resonance they find relevant.

I use the phrase "best literature" advisedly, for it would be disingenuous of me not to confess that my selections reflect a distinct taste for writing that is stylistically more modernist than old-fashioned and more challenging to my perceptions than comforting. I am likely, for instance, to excuse a degree of surface obscurity that inadvertently results from highly original ambitions; and I am probably more inclined than most critics to relish a piece that is clearly like nothing I have ever read before. My bias presupposes that as times today are different from times past, so the young writers today are shaped by a culture hardly resembling that of their elders; thus, the literature attuned to our years will measure its integrity by its stylistic distance from previous work. The dimensions of my literary taste, let me add, I have more thoroughly elaborated in the introductions to *On Contemporary Literature* (1964) and *Twelve from the Sixties* (1967); so reviewers intending to quarrel with my selections should check the principles and examples discussed in those essays.

Some seven years ago, while still an undergraduate, I realized that the writings of his exact contemporaries should be a major interest of an aspiring critic; and with that purpose in mind I have since read and reviewed all that I possibly could, implicitly preparing for this project long before it ever took shape. This book should reflect literally years of considering the problems the task poses and my wide reading in little magazines and other esoteric sources, as well as a taste too various to subscribe to any clique or established and/or narrow point of view. Nonetheless, I regret that space limitations forbade my choosing no more than either one piece or a few pages from each contributor; that foolishly avaricious publishers and/or agents excluded, against my wishes, Richard Tillinghast, Stephen Koch, and Arthur L. Kopit, Lanford Wilson, and Barton Midwood; that a year or two in age put beyond my choice such fine writers as Lee Baxandall, John Yount, Frederick Seidel, Kenneth H. Brown, Robert Mezey, Jonathan Kozol, Claude Brown, Edward W. Said, Jack Marshall, Kathleen Fraser, Thomas E. Adams, and Jean-Claude van Itallie. Barbara Garson never responded to my requests to consider something other than her best-selling *Macbird;* Thomas Pynchon, his agent writes, "will allow no reprints of anything he published in the past"; and disagreements over taste or suitability kept me from including pieces by Andrew Field and Ely Stock. Were the book a little fatter, it would contain works by, among others, Norma Klein, Jeremy Larner, David Galloway, James Gatsby, Jay Neugeboren, Jay Featherstone, the late Richard Fariña, Clark Coolidge, Rudolph Wurlitzer, Kathryn Perutz, Sam Shepherd, Bruce Kaywin, Peter S. Beagle, Michael Fried, Arthur Freeman, Charles Mee, Henry Taylor, Keith Lowe, Aram Saroyan, S. K. Oberbeck, the late Diane Oliver, Joseph Cerevolo, and Ron Padgett. Although I am personally a rock enthusiast, not even the best lyrics manage, as poetry, to transcend conventional, if not prosaic, ways of putting words together. My apologies in advance to all other young writers whose work has evaded my research. Finally, although I should like other readers to find the following selections as interesting as I do, let me disclaim any definitiveness for this collection; for I sincerely hope that other editors will contribute in the common cause with similar anthologies that in no way duplicate my own.

Nothing more conclusively substantiates the huge labor this project demanded than the number of people to whom I am indebted—scores of agents and publishers and writers who kindly extended me permission to reprint works within their control, publishers of both books and periodicals who supplied me with their produce (less than one percent of which could be included here), friends too numerous to credit individually who directed me to material I might not have otherwise considered, my Funk & Wagnalls editor, Emile Capouya, for his faith in a book as unfashionable as its editor's taste, and to Julianne, who pushed me to work, pulled me away, tolerated my habits, criticized my selections, kept the faith, and warmed my heart. The dedication I offer her hardly measures my love.

R.K.
New York City
14 May 1967

CONTENTS

PREFACE xi

INTRODUCTION: *The Young American Writers* xvii

Renata Adler: *Polemic and the New Reviewers* 3

Bill Berkson: *Breath* 25

Robert Boyers: *A Very Separate Peace* 27

James Brodey: *Door to the River* 35

Jerome Charyn: *Faigele the Idiotke* 39

Frank Chin: *Food for All His Dead* 55

Tom Clark: *Eleven Ways of Looking at a Shit Bird* 68

Keith Cohen: *You Froze the Light and Flew* 71
        Water 75

Jonathan Cott: *A Hard Day's Knights* 83

R. H. W. Dillard: *Tanjong Malim: 1934* 91

Eric Felderman: *Black's Theme* 93

Aaron Fogel: *Gardens gardens Gardens Toads* 111
        Vietnam 117

Norman Fruchter: *An Act of Comic Revenge* 123

Kenneth Gangemi: *Olt* 128

Michael L. Glenn: *The Room* 137

Louise Glück: *The Racer's Widow* 156
        Pictures of the People in the War 157
        Grandmother in the Garden 157
        Solstice 158
        Firstborn 159

Steven Guarino: *The Perimeter Walker* 160

Robert Head: *Sancticity*   168
Michael Heller: *Fragment*   189
Dick Higgins: *Intermedia*   191
Arno Karlen: *Rain*   197
William Melvin Kelley: *Cry for Me*   204
Kenneth King: *SuperLecture*   221
Richard Kostelanetz: *The New American Arts*   238
Peter Michelson: *I Dream Profuse*   253
Heather Ross Miller: *Chel*   255
Robin Morgan: *The Improvisors*   261
Charles Newman: *A Dolphin in the Forest, a Wild Boar on the Waves*   265
Joyce Carol Oates: *Upon the Sweeping Flood*   276
John Perreault: *Boomerang*   294
            Heart   296
Ed Sanders: *Poem from Jail*   298
David Shapiro: *For Son*   301
            Six Poems   302
            Canticle   304
Mitchell Siskind: *On a Sculpture of Dr. Albert Einstein*   307
Ronald Tavel: *Shower*   310
Alden Van Buskirk: *Last Will And*   335
Tom Veitch: *The Luis Armed Story*   336
Lewis Warsh: *Moving Through Air*   351
Eugene Wildman: *The Subway Singer*   353

The Young
American Writers

For a few years now I have been haunted by the question of what has happened to my literary generation. Considering how many people go to college nowadays and how many of those at college take creative writing courses; how many of the more talented receive fellowships for research, if not writing and/or travel, after college; and how economic affluence, as well as unemployment benefits, should provide budding young writers with more potentially creative leisure than their predecessors had, I wonder why there are so few under-thirty writers of note in this country today. The mystery can hardly be attributed to the absence of individual talent, which the educational institutions of this country systematically ferret out as never before. Indeed, as potential talent always exists, the sources for this cultural deficiency must lie in the culture itself, particularly in the institutions that influence literary activity. No single explanation will sufficiently explain the absence; yet certain forces strike me as clearly inhibiting.

One is the universities themselves, whose impact upon the creative culture of our time is at once beneficial and threatening. Without doubt, the schools do more to support the people and products of culture than any other kind of institution in our society; indeed, without them, the "cultural boom" would have no base. On the other hand, let me suggest that the universities extend more support to the literary culture that already exists than encourage the creation of new writing. For the young, college is now more difficult than it used to be; for not only has the sum of important knowledge in every field increased, but the same impact of Sputnik that made anti-intellectualism unfashionable also allowed universities to shamelessly increase the work loads they expect of their students. Studenting nowadays takes considerably more time and effort than, say, twenty years ago; and the same leisure that fraternity men once exploited for getting drunk was also used by the incipient poets as free time to write. Today, the budding writer instead takes a creative writing course, which offers two immediate advantages—as a substitute for a strictly academic venture, "creative writing" endows the student with hours to scribble; by insisting upon pages to judge, the class forces him to translate conceptions and dreams into words.

After that, creative writing courses may be more detrimental than beneficial, precisely because success as well as unsuccess can be inhibiting. Failure may stem from inability to write at all, an unfortunately barren period in a young person's life, or an unwillingness to write in the style(s) the instructor prefers; and although a mediocre performance in such a course may permanently discourage an incipient writer, a more determined novice, I would like to believe, shall persist. During my own freshman year at college, I cannot forget, one of America's most-touted novelists informed me with benevolent regret that I had no talent for words, and several friends who are now practicing writers have told me of similar experiences. For reasons I can no longer remember, I took four courses in creative writing; and looking back, I would say that all I ever got out of them were two permanent enemies and one valuable friend.

Success in creative writing classes is probably more detrimental than failure; for the student invariably earns the best grade by repeating the formulas evident in his teacher's own work. Indeed, emulation is such a natural process in student-teacher relationships that the participants should be more aware of it than they usually are. Not only is the favored young writer often discouraged from experimenting with other approaches, but his writing usually resembles in style the work of the teacher's other favorite students. Nothing makes this phenomenon more clear to me than the experience of receiving every year for review another novel written by the student of a certain professor, a novelist himself but more famous as a critic and teacher; and not only does each book contain the teacher's blurb, if not his introduction, but they all display the same formula of a first-person narrator whose defect (blindness, crippling, madness, etc.) endows him with both a grotesque perspective upon experience and an affected prose style full of far-fetched metaphors. The authors of these novels are invariably themselves teachers of creative writing at either their mentor's university or one nearby—sometimes they even hold advanced degrees in the field—as the reputation of the senior professor very much depends upon the success and influence of his students. Moreover, certain departments of creative writing develop collective artistic personalities—a midwestern center propagates realism, a far-western school anti-realism, and so forth; so that a student either tunes in to the established style or takes his manuscripts elsewhere.

Most of the incipient writers of my generation who get through college degrees then go on to a liberal arts graduate school, which seems at first a natural extension of their undergraduate education but is really something else: not an educational institution designed to impart significant knowledge, but a licensing mill to distribute certificates to practice—Ph.D. equals M.D. equals LL.B. Furthermore, graduate education usually insists that the student's intellectual activity become narrower in scope, less adventurous (and more "definitive") in its interpretations, more subservient to the prejudices of a single sponsor; and where a pluralistic situation limits the power an individual teacher has over an undergraduate, in graduate school the student's fate is usually at the mercy of a few men, if not one man. Beyond that, the concept of "standards" insures not only that he does his work in the correct way but that it consumes a good deal of the young writer's twenties; and for all these reasons, I find it indicative that of the important writers thirty and under in this country, only one known to me possesses a doctoral degree—R. H. W. Dillard. Indeed, most dropped out of graduate school, a quitting which is considerably more prestigious nowadays than leaving college.

The world of publishers and periodicals is in its own way as uncordial to the literary young as graduate school; indeed, the situation is so discouraging that I personally regard any book published by my contemporaries as a stroke of fortune that overcame the system. Although I have frequently asked around, I know of no editor under thirty in New York with a particular reputation for, or interest in, discovering the literature of his generation; indeed young men on the make in publishing usually establish themselves by courting their elders. This situation persuades writers in their twenties to take whatever arrangements they can find; significantly, no single publisher has on its lists more than two of the many writers included in this book.

The older diversified literary journals exhibit a somewhat contradictory attitude to young possible contributors; for although the editors of each one will piously announce that they would like to infuse "new blood" into their pages, they would also prefer that the fresh juice flow to the beat and direction their magazine established long before. My recognition of this contradiction stems from my own experience: My contribution to *Kenyon Review* was critical of the New York intellectual Paul Goodman; in *Sewanee Review*, I praised Oklahoma-born Ralph Ellison's essays and massacred New York-born Edward Albee's adaptation of Georgia-born Carson McCullers' *The Ballad of the Sad Cafe;* in *Partisan Review*, I favorably surveyed the publishing achievement of New Directions (which printed several *Partisan* writers, and vice versa); and my essay critical of minority militancy in American letters appeared in *Hudson Review*. In each case, my contribution more or less jibed with the literary world view of the journal; yet to each magazine I later sent essays that would not have blended in so neatly and every one was rejected. Those young writers who do appear regularly in the older literary journals are, one discovers, invariably former pupils of one of the editors; and the easiest way for a reader to discern a protégé from a real independent is to notice that the first appears only in his benefactor's magazine(s).

The intellectual weeklies and fortnightlies are, except for *Commonweal*, in general no more open to young contributors than the

quarterlies; for in addition to a history of inviolably established positions or biases (which every writer respects or suffers exclusion),
they generally have "a stable" of regular contributors of long
standing. Most of the new literary magazines in America are un-
ashamedly coterie in purpose—founded to publish the work of
the editor and his friends; and although many of them print first-
rate work, particularly poetry, their concern for their generation
extends no further than their immediate circle. I know of only
two journals whose editors are young and roster of contributors
eclectic—Charles Newman's *Tri-Quarterly* and Robert Boyers'
Salmagundi; merely because young writers clearly prefer to contribute to journals edited by their peers, rather than beg the charity
of their elders, the health of the culture demands at least a dozen
more similarly youthful and diversified magazines.

Where do the young writers come from, one is often asked; and
the only true answer is the profoundly American one—everywhere, which is to say nowhere in particular. Although the nation-
wide tests of intellectual talent are supposedly more effectively
prognostic than ever before and the major eastern colleges sometimes boast that through their classes pass the cream of American
youth, a survey of the undergraduate origins of the young writers
I admire reveals more diversity than unanimity:

Renata Adler—Bryn Mawr
Robert Boyers—Queens
James Brodey—The New
  School
Jerome Charyn—Columbia
Frank Chin—California
  (Berkeley)
Tom Clark—Michigan
Keith Cohen—Columbia
Jonathan Cott—Columbia
R. H. W. Dillard—Roanoke
Andrew Field—Columbia
Norman Fruchter—Rutgers
Kenneth Gangemi—RPI
Michael L. Glenn—Princeton

Louise Glück—Columbia
  (General Studies)
Steven Guarino—Brooklyn
Michael Heller—RPI
Dick Higgins—Columbia
  (General Studies)
Arno Karlen—Antioch
William Melvin Kelley—
  Harvard
Kenneth King—Antioch
Stephen Koch—Minnesota
Arthur L. Kopit—Harvard
Peter Michelson—Whitman
Heather Ross Miller—North
  Carolina

Charles Newman—Yale
Thomas Pynchon—Cornell
Joyce Carol Oates—Syracuse
John Perreault—Montclair
State

Ed Sanders—NYU
David Shapiro—Columbia
Alden Van Buskirk—Dart-
mouth
Lewis Warsh—City College

The fact that Columbia is the only college with more than two alumni represented here suggests that most American writers (unlike, say, the English) did not go to school with other budding writers, and these observations in turn imply that they educated themselves largely outside classwork, if not after they left college. The crucial truth is that in America, as nowhere else, the individual, rather than the environment, makes the man a writer.

Any generalization I can attempt about the young writers clearly defies certain old dichotomies. The distinction between academic and nonacademic, the common currency of fifties' criticism, has no relevance today; the fact that the poet Robin Morgan and the playwright Robert Head never matriculated or that Louise Glück and Bill Berkson never graduated hardly explains how their work differs from that of, say, Aaron Fogel and Arno Karlen, Kenneth Gangemi and Michael L. Glenn, all of whom have bachelor degrees. Likewise, I suppose that my own writing and Renata Adler's, as well as Thomas Pynchon's and Kenneth King's, are more academically pedantic than, say, Joyce Carol Oates's and William Melvin Kelley's, Jerome Charyn's and Charles Newman's; yet they are all currently professors and we have not taught at all. Most of us who now remain outside the academy work in the collateral trades—journalism, editing, even printing; and only three of us, to my knowledge, live solely off our serious writing—Pynchon, Kopit, and myself, they through the royalties of one successful work and I through the sheer volume of my handicraft. Usually, at any past time, more young American writers were wholly sufficient.

A reader sensitive to the minority backgrounds of writers will have trouble distinguishing the young Southerners from the Northerners, the homosexuals from the heterosexuals, and the Jews from the Gentiles (although not the Chinese and the Negroes), perhaps because nearly every young person nowadays owes more to the common experience of America than to the parochial influence of a particular ethnic subculture or geographical area. Indeed, the postwar electronic media, which cumulatively function as a third parent, so effectively minimize ancestral heritage, while secular education so often stamps more shape on the sensibility than does parochial background, that young writers who cultivate their "origins" seemingly will an affectation. For instance, even though William Melvin Kelley is a brown-skinned American who writes about other Negroes, the style of his fiction, I would judge, owes more to his teachers at Harvard—John Hawkes and Archibald MacLeish—than to his racial coloring. Finally, the literary young in general have little connection with the political young, who emerged from wholly different traditions and aspirations, as well as became active in response to different stimuli; for not only is their best literature as apolitical—by implication, usually anarchist—as literature has always been, but out of the new left movement has come only one realized piece of literature—Barbara Garson's satirical *Macbird* (1966), whose attitudes are likewise anarchist.

What little I know about the personal backgrounds of these writers (only a third of whom I have personally met) suggests that more of them grew up in the suburbs of the larger metropolises than within the large city itself, in smaller cities, or in rural areas; and although those of us who passed our teen years in the suburbs were quite sure that nothing significant could come out of such cultural aridity, we have since discovered that most of our literary friends passed through similar places and felt similar antipathies. Indeed, I suspect that a distaste for the affluent suburbs may be the shared awareness of my literary generation, although only a writer slightly older than us, Philip Roth, has successfully translated the experience into literature. Curiously, aside from Roth (in *Letting Go* [1962]), no young writer I know has yet made either graduate school or creative writing classes a viable literary subject: and that, I suppose, reflects either an unwillingness to make immediate problems the stuff of literature or the general decision to leave the common environment to political writers and critics whose genres are more appropriate to those subjects. Indicatively, autobiography no longer seems a viable interest for imaginative writing, for self-exposure rapidly becomes as commonplace as self-aggrandizement. Right now, most of us live in the larger cities or, if elsewhere, in university communities; and although many of us have studied abroad, no major young writer considers himself an expatriate, just as none has made the American in Europe the subject of a major effort.

I discern considerable significance in the fact that many of us have published in more than one genre and some have worked in entirely different media. Arno Karlen has published poetry, fiction, translations, criticism, and pure journalism, while I find that examples of my own writing fit into such standard categories as intellectual history, journalism, social thought and criticism of fiction, theater, poetry, art, music, and intermedia. Kenneth King has written criticism, collaborated in dance companies, and choreographed his own dance-theater pieces (one to his own prose-score, reprinted here); Dick Higgins has composed music, staged happenings, written plays and poems and polemics, as well as founded a publishing house; John Perreault paints and writes poetry and art criticism; and Jonathan Cott has published poems and criticism of film, literature, and music in addition to producing his own radio shows about music. All this suggests that perhaps young writers today find polyliteracy a more worthy ideal than monoliteracy.

In the literature itself, no theme seems as pervasive as the discontinuity of experience—the unwillingness of the writer to make what he portrays fall together into the neat linear patterns of traditional literature; and the vehicles of this theme are as much a work's content as its style. The thorough disconnectedness of David Shapiro's poetry, as in the opening stanza of "For Son," exemplifies the theme:

> I kept spinning in all kinds of grass. An unmarried woman
> came and pointed out the stems to me. In my light fast
> motor-cycle, she read each letter in order. My hands are
> resting on an arched roof, horse allowed to roam at night.

A similar strategy shapes these lines from Bill Berkson's "Breath":

> So we went walking in our breath—denying the tooth of it,
> it was the sandwich hopelessly sighingly

color delection propellors
the conditioned button on our ears, we fastened it, shinily,
being smart.

Here Berkson achieves an ironic relation between the semblance of coherence, if not the *sound* of significance, and the actual content of his words.

The same principle, by extension, informs several recent works of fiction, such as Michael L. Glenn's "The Room," which portrays a narrator's inability to fit his experience into a continuously coherent pattern, even though he knows that linear form is the primary convention of fiction: "If I am to tell stories," he says, "I shall have to apply some order to the process. I shall have to tell them from beginning to end, or from end to beginning, for that is how stories are told." His persistent digressions cause him to blunder in his aspirations; but his failure becomes the theme of an extraordinary piece of fiction. Thomas Pynchon exhibits a similar preoccupation in his *V.*, probably the greatest single extended work by a young American; for here Pynchon uses his early training in science to create a realized image of the quantum theory of matter. Where Isaac Newton and the literature of the Newtonian centuries regarded both physical matter and worldly experiences as flowing linearly in a predictable fashion, the literature attuned to post-Newtonian physics portrays discontinuous batches of energy flowing haphazardly across a space. In *V.*, Pynchon writes of both the adventures of certain people and of modern history as a whole; and just as the pattern of one realm duplicates the pattern of the other, so the picture of experience created in the book duplicates the imagery of the new physics.

Discontinuity, one hastens to add, does not mean incoherence; for disconnected narratives achieve, usually through repetition, their own kind of coherence. The author may weave a consistent vision through numerous examples, as William Burroughs does in *Naked Lunch* (1958); or the persistent failure of the narrator to find or create unity may actually unify a particular fiction. Moreover, formal discontinuity as a perceptual mode duplicates both the omniattention that we experience in our ordinary lives, as well as the marijuana and psychedelic experience that is now more prevalent than a decade ago. Similarly, just because a literary work does not cohere in a linear fashion does not at all mean that it cannot be understood; rather, as our recent literature accustoms us to its particular ways of organizing experience, we learn to confront a new work with expectations wholly distinct from those we honed on traditional literature in order to comprehend it in entirely different ways. Discontinuous stories are more rereadable, if only because we are liable to catch coherences and juxtapositions we missed the first time through.

The young writers exhibit a completely uninhibited attitude toward literary form; for they are probably the first literary generation in history to *feel*, not just know, that literally anything can be done with words—that they can be put together in any way. Aram Saroyan, for instance, makes poems of one verbal unit, which reveal his artistry by the ingenuity of his distortion:

eyeye

Or:

nnausea

The kind of giant-stepping over space and time that David Shapiro achieves is probably indebted to Apollinaire's *Zone* (1913); yet his work transcends its model, simply because Shapiro has assimilated a true freedom from the constrictions that a half century ago Apollinaire appeased as he challenged. Neither Apollinaire nor any of the Dadaists could have written the following stanza:

Enchantment is not vulgarity;
Somewhere, at the moment, a man is grasping gloom
While giraffes smooch April branches in my mind.

A poet's profound sense of meter and diction, along with an unfailing resistance to cliché, keeps such "free" arrangements of words from sinking into doggerel. In contrast to Shapiro's leisurely tone, Robin Morgan regards formal opportunity as an invitation to experiential compression and a heightened texture:

always it ends with me among them,
too swift to tell
which arms embrace women, which men,

> caressing beards, full breasts, until we fall
> to the carpet
> of living bodies, some dismembered,
> calves haired and soft,
> torsos planed unlike a woman's.

Such an intensity, itself a rare excellence, reveals an awareness of poetic possibilities that strikes me as distinctly contemporary,

In short fiction, the measure of formal freedom is the degree of distance not only from the conventional arc-story of traditional writing but also the epiphany story of early modern literature. Most of the stories here are flat in form—they open pretty much at the same place, with the same tone, that closes them; and they cohere, as well as make their essential points, less through time, as in the sequences of narrative, than across space—the relationship that the various details have to each other. Even if the prose evokes the semblance of a plot, as in Jerome Charyn's "Faigele the Idiotke," the linear story functions more as an ironic convention than a revelatory structure; for the themes that we learn at its end have actually informed the story from the start. Finally, the scrambled narratives of, say, Mitchell Siskind and Tom Veitch epitomize the young writer's awareness of absolute formal freedom.

The best literature of my generation reveals a literacy as diverse and individual as our habits; for not only is it difficult to trace most of the writing included here to a particular influence— the era of Faulkner's overwhelming example seems past—but the echoes I hear in individual works are usually various. Pynchon's novel, for instance, seems indebted to Thomas Mann, Nathanael West, Lawrence Durrell (whom Pynchon parodies), Henry Miller, John Barth (particularly for the yo-yo image), picaresque verse traditions, and much else; and works by the two poets Louise Glück and Robin Morgan defy my attempts at ancestry-tracing. Even when I hear the influence of certain authors, the list of apparent mentors is more catholic than parochial. Joyce Carol Oates strikes me as closest to Flannery O'Connor, Arthur L. Kopit to Eugene Ionesco, Michael L. Glenn to Samuel Beckett, Charles Newman to Nathanael West, Frank Chin to Tillie Olsen, Jerome Charyn to Isaac Babel, David Shapiro and Bill Berkson to John

Ashbery, Aaron Fogel and Mitchell Siskind to Kenneth Koch, Arno Karlen to William Faulkner, Ed Sanders to Allen Ginsberg. The explanation of such diversity may well be university education which, if nothing else, exposes the incipient writer to so many possible influences that each of us makes a highly individual choice.

What ideas might unify this literary generation I cannot yet discern; the evidence is too insufficient to support the kind of generalizations I should like to make. One way of grasping tendencies is to regard those older minds that appear to have great influence —say, Marshall McLuhan, Paul Goodman, and Allen Ginsberg. McLuhan has made visible dimensions of reality that were previously invisible and yet are so pervasive and contemporary that he is the educator we all respect. We admire Paul Goodman for his insights; for few explanations of the world around us are as immediately perceptive as *Growing Up Absurd* (1960); but beyond that, Goodman represents personal integrity and devotion to self-purpose in a society whose institutions and leaders are constantly foisting purposes and projects upon the young; indeed, as Goodman makes clear, the problem is not that the young lack direction but that their world offers them more directions than they can possibly pursue—saying no can be as positive a decision as saying yes. Allen Ginsberg is the only truly public poet of his time, the author of lines everyone of us remembers, as well as the prophet of pot, who represents a kind of honesty and freedom from inhibition that most of us admire but cannot yet achieve. The fact that these exemplars influence not only the young writers but many more besides leads me to suspect that the literary young more clearly represent the attitudes and aspirations of their generation than the political young, perhaps because most of the young writers regard themselves as similar to their peers rather than different.

American writers born in 1937 and after comprise the third literary generation of the postwar period. The first came of age just after the war; and perhaps because the world of literature was eagerly looking for a war novel to match the earlier ones, writers such as Norman Mailer, Gore Vidal, James Jones, and John Aldridge established themselves quickly—indeed, precisely because they owed their original fame to the beneficence of critics, no group of writers is as hyperconscious about the press they receive. The second group came of age early in the fifties; less concerned with a particular historical event, they also eschewed realism in literature for more ironic and fantastic modes. As a group on the literary scene, they were a thoroughly disorganized force —some joined movements that were then emerging, such as LeRoi Jones and the "beats," while others were picked up by reigning establishments, such as Philip Roth and Susan Sontag by the New York literary circle and John Updike by *The New Yorker*. Others like John Barth developed wholly outside coteries, only to find themselves acclaimed by everybody. In close retrospect, I would judge that my own literary generation is even less defined and organized than its immediate predecessor; and in their failure to create their own institutions lies the model for our own deficiency. Our memories of the depression and World War II—events that haunt our elders—are negligible, and no subsequent historical occurrence has had such a universal impact upon our collective consciousness. The example of the Vietnam conflict all but deceives us into believing that no war was ever worth fighting (and probably convinced publishers that fiction about a recent war could no longer command an audience); and although we sense the desire to do things differently from our elders, very few of us seem able to act on his knowledge. Just as we have not founded many of our own magazines or found funneling editors in publishing, so we have neither organized into cliques nor acclaimed our spokesmen. Finally, I detect in writers such as David Shapiro and Aaron Fogel, both of whom were born after the War and came of age entirely in the sixties, a wholly different kind of sensibility; for that reason, I suspect that they may represent the fourth postwar generation.

My prejudices notwithstanding, I think this is a talented generation, more thoroughly educated and culturally sophisticated than earlier chronological sets; and although we are hardly cautious, the mistakes of our elders, particularly their vulgarisms, oppress us. The fact that we are not better known has less to do with our talent or the relevance of our work than the foci of the literary establishments (in America, there are always *several*) and the major machinery of reputation-making, neither of which has displayed much care about our work. Early recognition, one remembers, usually results from fortuitous connections and an achievement at once extraordinary and fashionable; and at the moment, the purveyors of fashion are not ourselves but our elders. To my mind, few poets today are as consistently excellent, or as productive, as David Shapiro and Louise Glück, few prose stylists as predictably fine as Joyce Carol Oates and Arno Karlen, or as clever and courageous as Eric Felderman and Frank Chin. Michael L. Glenn and Thomas Pynchon, Tom Veitch and Mitchell Siskind are all writing fiction unlike anything we have read before. Andrew Field has already established himself among the very finest American critics of Russian literature, and rare today is the critic who risks reading contemporary poetry as profoundly as Robert Boyers does. Although Renata Adler has published only a few essays, each one exhibits a dazzling style and enough intellectual force to make eyes turn and heads roll. Of the poets, as an experimenter with minimal materials Michael Heller has no peer; few can turn hackneyed subjects to original ends as successfully as Aaron Fogel or can make the imaginative leaps of John Perreault and Bill Berkson. All these writers are functioning and productive; soon they will be joined by the Ph.D. alumni, whose dormant talents may then blossom. The sixties was probably a more fortunate time than the fifties or forties in which to come of age, and as statistics remind us, by 1972 one-half of the voting population will be under thirty-two. Even though the institutions of our elders seem doggedly reluctant to taks us as we are, the future is very much ours.

THE YOUNG AMERICAN WRITERS

RENATA ADLER*

❦

Polemic and
The New Reviewers

In literary criticism, polemic is short-lived, and no other essay form becomes as quickly obsolete as an unfavorable review. If the work under attack is valuable, it survives adverse comment. If it is not, the polemic dies with its target. A critic is therefore measured not by the books he prosecutes but by the ones he praises (we turn to Edmund Wilson for Proust, Joyce, Eliot, and Hemingway, not for Kafka), and it is surprising that among a younger generation of critics polemic should be so widely regarded as the most viable and rewarding kind of criticism. Three recent works—*The Sense of Life in the Modern Novel*, by Arthur Mizener; *A World More Attractive*, by Irving Howe; and *Doings and Undoings*, by Norman Podhoretz—may provide an explanation.

Arthur Mizener is the most affirmative critic of the three, the least polemical, and the least interesting. His book is little more than a splicing together of enthusiasms. He recounts plots (from Trollope to Updike), lists dates, quotes and compares passages (good ones, from many sources); he seems tempted to pick up the novels whole and deliver them to the reader. His critical sympathies, in short, are strong; his critical intelligence, however, is weak or self-effacing. Mr. Mizener seldom explains or analyzes,

* RENATA ADLER, *born in Milan, Italy, received her B.A. from Bryn Mawr and her M.A. in Comparative Literature from Harvard. A staff writer on* The New Yorker *since 1962, she has written reportage and criticism for its pages, as well as fiction for* Harper's Bazaar.

3

and whenever he does, his prose neatly strangles whatever his thought may have been:

> The problem for writers like Dreiser is apparently how to release from deep beneath the viscous and muddy surface of their conscious minds their imaginative apprehension of their experience, and the only way they seem able to do so is, paradoxically, by a slow roiling of the muddy surface.
>
> What criticism of the novel is is a theory that will put at the center of our attention the world envisioned by the novel, which will then serve to limit and discipline the exercise of our metaphysics upon it. Our lot would very much like to circumambulate the novel's charms for the nearly exclusive purpose of keeping our metaphysics warm. The only valid source of discipline for this corrupting impulse to metaphysical speculation is the unique object that is the novel itself.

What the second of these paragraphs seems to recommend is that the critic leave theories alone and let literature speak for itself. And Mr. Mizener, for one, is clearly well advised to do so. The effect, however, of his constant citing of excerpts from the works themselves is to make his book almost a scrap album. Or a whirlwind tour of the sights. ("And on your left, ladies and gentlemen, the beautiful opening passage of *Across the River and Into the Trees*. . . . And, on your right, the historic scene from E. M. Forster. . . . Notice, in particular, the portico . . .") The effect is also, on a slightly higher plane, that of a benign, unanalytic book column in a reviewing section of the Sunday newspapers, to which Mr. Mizener is a frequent contributor.

While Mr. Mizener subordinates himself so completely to the works he admires that his intelligence becomes invisible, Irving Howe does the reverse; he dominates a book and wrenches it to suit his concern of the moment. And his concern is nearly always extraliterary—sociological or political. The title of his new book, *A World More Attractive*, suggests a utopian outlook, and even in his literary essays he is primarily concerned with social action —"images of war and revolution, experiment and disaster, apocalypse and skepticism; images of rebellion, disenchantment, and nothingness." When a writer—Wallace Stevens, for example—

seems less preoccupied with these "images" than Mr. Howe himself, Mr. Howe discerns them as a "premise," or a "background," or a "pressure upon all subjects":

> Stevens does not examine society closely or even notice it directly for any length of time; he simply absorbs "the idea" of it. . . . A perspective upon history is brilliantly maintained; history as it filters through his consciousness of living and writing at a given time.

This line of argument can, of course, be used to demonstrate that anyone is really writing about anything whatever—"as it filters through his consciousness of living and writing at a given time"—and the author of *A World More Attractive* makes frequent and imaginative use of what we might call the ascribed, or foisted, premise: "Dostoevski had not read Max Weber. But the anticipation is there." For Mr. Howe seeks, above all, to establish a *position*, and he uses his intelligence to force that position upon the literary work. (If the work resists, so much the worse for it; Mr. Howe will find it lacking in "moral style.") Yet it need not be supposed that this exercise of intelligence gives Mr. Howe an advantage in clarity over Mr. Mizener:

> The ideal of socialism has become a problematic one, but the problem of socialism remains an abiding ideal.
> But if one turns from the immediate political struggle to a kind of socio-cultural speculation by means of which certain trends are projected into an indefinite future, there may be some reason for anticipating a society ruled by benevolent Grand Inquisitors, a society of non-terroristic and bureaucratic authoritarianism, on top of which will flourish an efficient political-technical elite—a society, in short, that makes Huxley's prophecy seem more accurate than Orwell's, except insofar, perhaps, as Orwell's passion and eloquence helped invalidate his own prophecy.

Whatever these two sentences may mean, their vocabulary, at least, suggests that we are in the presence of an intellectual—a radical intellectual, of the sort that was identified in the thirties with such "little journals" as *Partisan Review*. And as an intellectual of the thirties Irving Howe has become, if not an interesting critic, at least an interesting criticism of the predicament of letters in the sixties—particularly in the little journals, to which *he* is a frequent contributor. Most of these journals were born of the depression and defended underdogs, who seemed at the time to fall into two broad categories—the artists and the poor. After the Second World War, old issues began to cloud, old protégés made good, and expository writers with a low tolerance for complexities were at a loss. A good part of the thirties' poor had become the fifties' bourgeoisie; most genuine depression artists had become the culture heroes of an age of affluence. Whom to defend? A stalwart revolutionary, Mr. Howe seemed to find himself without a cause, a comrade, or an enemy. He soon started a magazine of vaguely Socialist persuasion, called *Dissent,* and the dissenting position he has taken is a paradoxical one. He has turned upon old protégés to begrudge them the successes that time has brought. He now assails the former underdog, now part of the post-depression middle class, for everything—its new comforts, its tastes, and its morals. He now wishes to bar from "the raids of mass culture," and from the "contamination" of the "middle-brow," the "serious culture" that the radicals sought in the thirties to bring to the people. At the same time, he wants to bar to the artists and intellectuals the success—"this rise in social status"—that he sought in the thirties to help them achieve. If only, he seems to be saying, the middle class and the artists might become befriendably poor again:

> Today, in a sense, the danger is that the serious artists are not scorned enough.
> Suppose, then, that the goal of moderate material satisfaction is reached. . . . What would the intellectuals say? . . . [They would be like Christ, facing the Grand Inquisitor.] He has nothing to say. . . . [His] kiss is a kiss of despair, and He retreats, forever, in silence.

In short, now that the revolution of the thirties has begun to bear fruit, Mr. Howe has come to distrust the notion of progress, and he seeks in literature (or imposes upon literature) that aversion to the modern which he himself feels. Lacking a new direction for his liberalism, he dissents; he seems to bear his banner proudly backward towards the thirties and the "world more attractive" those years represent for him.

An editor of *Commentary* and a regular reviewer for *Show*, Norman Podhoretz inhabits a middle ground between the tame Sunday newspapers of Arthur Mizener and the radical little journals of Irving Howe. He is, in fact, one of those writers for little journals who have of late been assimilated almost en bloc into the magazines of broader circulation, and his adjustment, as a thirties' liberal, to the sixties is a highly pragmatic, even a classic one. The rebel whose cause has succeeded traditionally develops a concern with personal power, and the title of Mr. Podhoretz's collection of critical essays, *Doings and Undoings*, implies a faith in the power of the critic to affect, or even determine, the fate of authors and literary works—"to correct," in Mr. Podhoretz's phrase, "what he considers to be an egregious error in the prevailing estimate of a book or a literary reputation."

Doings and Undoings is not, Mr. Podhoretz points out, a unified collection. "How many people wrote it, then? Two, I think, or possibly three." The first estimate seems accurate; there are two distinct personalities at work in this book—one a literary critic far more canny than Mr. Mizener, the other a post-revolutionary, extra-literary polemicist far more effective than Mr. Howe. Essays on Faulkner, Edmund Wilson, and Nathanael West seem to reflect the first personality; essays on Norman Mailer, Mary McCarthy, Hannah Arendt, and John Updike, among others, seem to reflect the second. Since the second personality—the author, one supposes, of *Undoings*—is the more recent chronologically, and since his work clearly dominates the collection, it might be well to begin with his position, as Mr. Podhoretz defines it in the piece entitled "Book Reviewing and Everyone I Know." In praise of contributors to a new periodical, *The New York Review of Books*, Mr. Podhoretz remarks:

> All these reviewers inhabit much the same intellectual milieu, and what they have in common, apart from talent and intelligence, is an attitude toward books and an idea about the proper way to discuss them. This attitude might be characterized as one of great suspiciousness: a book is assumed to be guilty until it proves itself innocent—and not many do. . . . The major premise behind such suspiciousness is that books are enormously important events, far

too important to be confronted lightly, and certainly too important to permit of charitable indulgence.

The argument that a sign of a book's importance is that it should be "assumed to be guilty until it proves itself innocent" is a curious one, since our whole legal system rests upon the opposite premise—that the sign of an individual's importance is that he should be assumed innocent until he is proved guilty. But Mr. Podhoretz conceives of this position of "great suspiciousness" as an antidote to the "bland and uncritical" reviewing columns of the Sunday newspapers (so much for Mr. Mizener) and as a solution (here he agrees with Mr. Howe) to "the problems of mass culture . . . and . . . the need for an embattled struggle against the deterioration of literary and intellectual standards." Finally, he pinpoints what he considers the salient quality of *The New York Review* reviewers: "A book for them is, quite simply, an occasion to do some writing of their own." And he adds that if only *"The New York Review* were to succeed in establishing itself on a permanent footing . . . everyone I know would certainly be happy."

There are several remarkable things about this essay and the point of view it represents. First, "everyone I know" occurs fourteen times (aside from its appearance in the title), and "someone I know," "no one I know," "someone I *don't* know," and "everyone they know" make one appearance each. Although it must be admitted that repetition is a rhetorical device of which, in any case, Mr. Podhoretz has always been inordinately fond ("what really happened in the thirties" occurs nine times in another essay, and "tells us nothing about the nature of totalitarianism" several times in a third), it seems quite safe to say that "Book Reviewing and Everyone I Know" is pervaded by a sense of comradeship and solidarity; Mr. Podhoretz clearly does not consider himself a speaker in isolation. On the other hand, such terms as "embattled," "struggle," and "suspiciousness" seem to indicate, on behalf of the group, a feeling of beleaguered hostility. Moreover, such unembarrassed statements as "Among our most talented literary intellectuals (including just about everyone I know) reviewing is regarded as a job for young men on the make" and "A book for them is, quite simply, an occasion to do some writing of their own" imply that the New Reviewers regard criticism less as a sympathetic response to literature than as an opportunity for an assertion of personality. (One conclusion is inescapable here: A book is going to have an exceedingly difficult time "proving itself innocent" if the reviewer "assumes" it "guilty" and then uses it, "quite simply," as "an occasion to do some writing of [his] own.") Finally, a glowing nostalgic reference to "the back files of magazines like *Partisan Review* and *Commentary*," combined with an expression of despair over the present ("But except for Dwight Macdonald and one or two others, everyone I know—indeed, everyone who writes—is often afflicted with the feeling that all he is doing is dropping stone after stone down the bottomless well of American culture. Who listens? Who cares?"), seems to complete a picture, a philosophical adjustment, an answer to the predicament of Mr. Howe. The radical child of the thirties, the contributor to the back files of little journals, finding himself at present directionless, embattled, and perhaps even unheeded, achieves a solidarity in numbers in the security of "everyone I know." The political fervor of the ex-revolutionary is not lost; it is simply redirected into literary channels, where it appears as a certain hostility toward books ("assumed guilty"), a pronounced defensiveness toward presumptive readers ("the bottomless well of American culture"), and an attitude toward the job at hand— reviewing—as an opportunity to assert personal ambition ("young men on the make . . . do some writing of their own"). In short, the rebellion has succeeded, the junta is in power, and it is now the era of the purge.

To interpret a whole collection on the basis of a single essay would be, of course, to oversimplify, and Mr. Podhoretz is a more complicated and interesting writer than this single essay might suggest. But "Book Reviewing and Everyone I Know" does announce a group, a program, and perhaps even the emergence of a new critical school, and since Mr. Podhoretz is a singularly articulate spokesman for that school, it might be well to explore his program as it recurs in some of the other essays in *Doings and Undoings*, and in the work of other New Reviewers—those who share what Mr. Podhoretz calls "the same intellectual milieu."

Mr. Podhoretz, to begin with, clearly regards reviewing as a continuous dialogue, and he devotes, in his reviews, considerable attention to the opinions of previous reviewers. In the essay "In Defense of James Baldwin," he writes:

> With few exceptions, the major reviewing media were very hard on *Another Country*. It was patronized by Paul Goodman in *The New York Times Book Review*, ridiculed by Stanley Edgar Hyman in *The New Leader*, worried over . . . by Elizabeth Hardwick in *Harper's*, summarily dismissed by *Time's* anonymous critic, loftily pitied by Whitney Balliett in *The New Yorker*, and indignantly attacked by Saul Maloff in *The Nation*.

And in "A Dissent on Updike" he cites not only written opinions but spoken ones as well:

> When his first novel, *The Poorhouse Fair*, came out in 1958, I remember arguing about it at great length with Mary McCarthy. . . .
>
> I cannot for the life of me understand what there is about him that so impresses people like Mary McCarthy, Arthur Mizener, and Stanley Edgar Hyman—to mention only three critics. . . .

The "Defense" in one case and the "Dissent" in the other might seem to require such a roll call, but it is Mr. Podhoretz's method throughout the collection to orient his point of view in terms of what he calls "the prevailing estimate of a book or a literary reputation." And he is not the only one to do so. There is a kind of reciprocity along the reviewing circuit that, while it occasionally imparts a pleasing continuity to critical discussion (the reader who suspects that the reviewer does not do justice to the book under consideration may be consoled by the knowledge that the reviewer has read at least all previous reviews of it), more often resembles nothing so much as a ticker-tape compendium or a caucus in an airless convention hall. "Irving Howe and I discussed this tendency some time ago, and wrote . . ." says Lewis Coser in *Partisan Review*. "The last time I remember talking about the novel was a year ago last June or July," Norman Mailer writes in *Esquire*, "and it was in a conversation with Gore Vidal." "Even Norman Mailer," Alfred Chester writes in a review of William Burroughs' *Naked Lunch*, "unpredictably mislaid himself long enough to write: 'Burroughs is the only American novelist living today who may conceivably be possessed by genius.'" "It was from Sartre that I first heard of Jean Genet," Lionel Abel writes in *The New York Review;* and "These have been duly underscored by her critics," says another contributor to the same periodical, "notably Lionel Abel, in a long and trenchant essay in . . ." "I have only once had the privilege of meeting Paul Goodman," another reviewer remarks in *Commentary.* "I stress 'privilege.' There is no one whose encounter flatters in a more exacting way."

This elaborate system of cross-references is one to which Mr. Podhoretz—at least in *Undoings*—subscribes, and when he feels he must disagree with what he frequently calls "the serious critics," he does so warily. His essay on James Baldwin continues:

> Three of these reviewers—Goodman, Hardwick, and Hyman —are first-rate critics, and I therefore find it hard to believe that their wrongheaded appraisals of *Another Country* can be ascribed to a simple lapse of literary judgment. How could anyone as sensitive and knowledgeable as Elizabeth Hardwick have been so led astray . . . ? How could a man of Stanley Edgar Hyman's sophistication have been so fooled . . . ? How could Paul Goodman, who most assuredly knows better, have taken. . . .

Mr. Podhoretz is not, of course, the only reviewer to feel so bewildered by his own divergence from the mainstream of critical opinion that he must temper his remarks with "sensitive," "sophistication," and "knows better." Occasionally, such differences are bridged with the elaborate courtesy of a junior executive introducing his immediate superior at a Rotary banquet. "This collection of essays . . . reflects the amazing catholicity of Mr. Schlesinger's tastes and interests," Lewis Coser begins his attack on Arthur Schlesinger, Jr. "His range is wide indeed." And Frank Kermode, concluding an ambivalent review of Mary McCarthy's essays, concedes himself "aware that one is incomparably less honest, as well as less clever, than she," and adds, "I can think of no writer whose silence would be more damaging to our moral and intellectual hygiene." A more relaxed approach, along the reviewing circuit, to the moment of painful dissent is manifest in the use of first names: Norman Mailer, in attacking Nelson Algren, calls him "Nelson"; Alfred Chester, in disparaging Henry Miller, calls him "Henry"; Paul Goodman, in disagreeing with Harold Rosenberg, calls him "Harold"; and Lionel Abel, in discussing the misdeeds of the ghetto leader Chaim Rumkowski, refers to him familiarly as "Chaim." Mr. Podhoretz is more formal. "On the other hand, Macdonald, Rahv, and Kazin," he concludes his summary dismissal of their essays, "even in their perfunctory moments, have more to say than most of us when we are trying hard." The apparent source of such affectionate concern with the opinions of other reviewers is a conviction that the value of an opinion can be defined by the admiration one feels for the holder of that opinion. "Not *which* idea but *whose?*" the reviewer seems to ask himself. The original judgments of respected critics quickly acquire an aura not only of self-evidence but of finality (*they* at least are assumed innocent until they are proved guilty): "I admire [Edmund] Wilson greatly," Lionel Abel writes, in an essay on Alfred Kazin, "from which it will be seen that I do not . . ." And, says Dwight Macdonald, "As a conscious artist, O'Neill was stiff and crude, as Mary McCarthy has established." The New Reviewers hastily stand up to be counted, and reviewing becomes not merely a circuit but a cartel.

Apart from the group orientation of *Doings and Undoings*, the book is interesting primarily for its arguments. In his introduction, Mr. Podhoretz establishes the premises on which his critical arguments are based:

> Most often the event [that produced these essays] was the appearance of a new book that seemed to me to raise important issues . . . and almost always it was the issues rather than the book itself that I really cared about. Is that a damaging admission for a literary critic to make? . . . We may be looking in the wrong place for the achievements of the creative literary imagination when we look for them only where they were last seen— in novels and poems and plays. . . . These may all be of great interest to me as a student of literature, and they may be of some interest to me as an habitual reader. But they are of no interest to me as a man living in a particular place at a particular time and beset by problems of a particular kind.

This position is a consistent and audacious one, and Mr. Podhoretz adopts it with full awareness of its implications. But, again, particularly in his lapse of faith in pure fiction, he does not speak entirely in isolation. "I wonder, who reads short stories?" writes John Thompson in *Partisan Review*. "When you pick up a magazine, do you turn to the short story? What is it doing there, anyway? It looks as boring as a poem, and probably it is. Maybe if you yourself write short stories, yes, you take a quick slice at it, to see who's doing it now, is he one up on you or not, what's he copying. . . ." "The novel is having a hard time," Alfred Chester remarks in *Commentary;* and in *Show* Kenneth Lamott observes, "People who care about such things have agreed for as long as I can remember that the novel is in a bad way." "Her book is memorable to me," Julian Moynahan writes of Brigid Brophy in *The New York Review*, "only because halfway through reading it I was seized by a cramping suspicion that the novel as a viable literary form might after three hundred years of life be ready for burial." And, referring to a statement made by Paul Goodman, a reviewer writes, "Such an observation calls into question the validity of fiction itself."

Mr. Podhoretz, however, does not go quite so far; he does not discount fiction altogether. He has simply, in his words, "lost my piety toward the form in its own right, which means that I do not feel an automatic sympathy for the enterprise of novel-writing," and he continues:

> A large class of readers . . . has found itself responding more enthusiastically to . . . non-fiction (and especially to magazine articles and even book reviews) than to current fiction. . . . And what the novel has abdicated has been taken over by discursive writers. Imagination has not died (how could it?) but it has gone into other channels. . . . What I have in mind—and I cheerfully admit that the suggestion sounds preposterous—is *magazine articles*.

The suggestion does not sound preposterous at all, particularly in a passage pointing out the literary takeover by "discursive writers." (It explains, for one thing, why reviewers pay so much attention to other reviewers, and it attempts to explain, for another, why Mr. Podhoretz's magazine articles should have been published in book form.) One result, however, of a conviction that imagination has been diverted from fiction into expository writing is that the expository writer, particularly the reviewer, is often tempted to press his *own* imagination upon the work of fiction, to prescribe for the novelist the kind of work that the reviewer thinks he ought to have written. Thus, Mr. Podhoretz berates John Updike for having written about old age, and not having written a reminiscence of childhood, in *The Poorhouse Fair,*

> . . . In any case there was something that gave me the creeps about the way he had deliberately set out to reverse the usual portrait-of-the-artist-as-a-young-man pattern of the first novel.

And he further instructs the novelist (as though Mr. Podhoretz's pains necessarily resembled Updike's, and as though Mr. Podhoretz himself were writing a novel including a description of them):

> Severe pain in one part of the body does not travel through the system, either on wet wings or dry; on the contrary, after the first flash of burning sensation, its effect is actually to focus one's entire consciousness on the hurt spot. . . . Consequently the appropriate images for rendering such an experience . . . would be . . .

He reproaches Saul Bellow for the ending of a novel ("If, however, Bellow had been ruthless in following out the emotional logic of *Seize the Day,* it would almost certainly have been murder—and *Seize the Day* would almost certainly have been a great book"), and he suggests his own ending for Joseph Heller's *Catch-22.* He even rebukes Harry Truman for not "admitting" in his autobiography that he was the "ambitious, perhaps lonely boy who dreamed of greatness" that Mr. Podhoretz thinks he must have been. In his conviction that it is the business of criticism to prescribe for literature, Mr. Podhoretz is again not quite alone: "It is the Orestes-Iphigenia story, we see here, that Salinger all along had been trying to rewrite," Leslie Fielder (himself much occupied with myth) prescribes for Salinger, "the account of a Fury-haunted brother redeemed by his priestess-sister." "He could become the best of our literary novelists," Norman Mailer prescribes for another author (as opposed, one wonders, to our *non*-literary novelists?), "if he could forget about style and go deeper into the literature of sex." (A "forgetting" and a "going deeper" that, *bien entendu*, Mailer himself has managed to achieve.)

A difficulty, however, in pitting the reviewer's imagination against the author's, in assuming that critics have an obligation to correct not merely, in Mr. Podhoretz's words, "the prevailing estimate of a book or a literary reputation" but the book itself, is that the relationship between writer and reviewer soon becomes a contest—and a contest, occasionally, of a highly personal sort. The book under review is not written as the reviewer would have written it; he begins to speculate as to what personal deficiency in the author could possibly account for this lapse. If the author has received widespread public recognition, the line of personal attack is clear: he has been corrupted by success in the mass media —and New Reviewers will go to enormous lengths to ferret out references to the author in *Life*, *Time*, *Newsweek*, best-seller lists, and so on, in order to establish some kind of guilt by non-obscurity. More commonly, however, the reviewer's attack upon an author is quite direct—an allegation that his personality, particularly in its sexual and moral attitudes, must be somehow diseased. Alfred Chester, for example, confidently impugns Henry Miller's sexual prowess: "Miller, in fact, never makes his reader raise more than a blush and, more often than not, the blush is for Henry's delusions of grandeur." Leslie Fiedler, on the other hand, attempts psychoanalysis: "Finally, like his characters, Salinger is reconciled with everything but sex. . . ." And another reviewer impugns the personal competence not of the author but of previous reviewers: "Except for Middleton Murry, who for reasons all too transparent found *Aaron's Rod* 'the greatest of Lawrence's novels,' and F. R. Leavis, who for reasons almost as transparent is extremely indulgent toward the novel, no one has ever considered either *Aaron's Rod* or *Kangaroo* successful." (To the reviewer, perhaps, the reasons are transparent; the reader scarcely dares admit that he finds them opaque.) The reviewer hastens, however, to assure the reader that his *own* house is sexually and morally in order. "I just don't want to give up my skin," Alfred Chester informs us, in a rather tangential comment on a book under review. "It feels so good, especially in the sun or in the woods or in the sea or against another." And Mr. Podhoretz himself, in the essay "My Negro Problem—And Ours," while he admits that his own moral stand is not irreproachable, excludes the possibility that most other right-thinking people can be better off. Having outlined the violent and unhappy childhood that left him, to his dismay, with a residual fear and envy of Negroes, he begins to claim for his feelings a certain universality:

> This, then, is where I am; it is not exactly where I think all other white liberals are, but it cannot be so very far away either.

The pervasiveness, assurance, and self-congratulation of that "I" in *Doings and Undoings* and in the works of other New Reviewers lead occasionally to a highhandedness that is almost grotesque. Mr. Chester writes:

> I think I am precisely the man for whom serious modern novels *are* written, since I am one of the men they are written about. Look at four of the most influential novelists of the last twenty years. . . . By influential I mean, of course, that which has impact on the thinking of those capable of thinking, and this, at least in France, is without reference to sales or to the behavior patterns of beatniks and college students.

Having excluded "sales" (i.e., the buyers of books) and "college students" (i.e., some of the most avid readers of them) from the category of "those capable of thinking," Mr. Chester is naturally left with himself, the reviewer, as the man for and about whom "serious modern novels" are written. But one danger in the assumption that it is the reviewer who occupies the center of the literary universe is that he begins to regard everything about himself, however tangential to the book under review, as of universal interest and importance. "Nearly everyone I know would rather see a movie than read a book. . . ." Mr. Chester writes. "And I count among my friends . . ." (And he counts among his friends, we may safely assume, Leslie Fielder, whom Podhoretz notes as having said that "the sight of a group of new novels stimulates in *him* 'a desperate desire to sneak out to a movie.'") Despite this tendency to express in criticism all the reviewer's little feelings and preferences—his delight in movies, the predilections of his friends, the situations in which his skin feels good—New Reviewing personalities are not, in general, so idiosyncratic that a reader cannot find one quality they have in common:

> Yet the truth is that the great national "debates" that the New York *Times* daily calls upon us to consider are invariably puerile from an intellectual point of view and far beneath the consideration of any sophisticated mind.

> Showing up their weaknesses is child's play for a sophisticated critic.

> Granted that painters and actors need not—indeed should not —be capable of discussing their respective arts with genuine sophistication, is it really necessary. . . .

> He is in the presence of a writer who is very sophisticated indeed and who therefore cannot possibly be as callow and sentimental. . . .

> Now, this black-and-white account, with the traditional symbolisms reversed, is not the kind of picture that seems persuasive to the sophisticated modern sensibility—the sensibility that has been trained by Dostoevski and Freud, by Nietzsche and Kierkegaard, by Eliot and Yeats, to see moral ambiguity everywhere, to be bored by melodrama, to distrust the idea of innocence.

> On the other hand, of course, there are equally sophisticated critics like Robert Brustein and Kenneth Tynan who have arrived at opposite conclusions, finding [Lenny] Bruce not. . . .

> Those who find Bergman profound and sophisticated (as if the artist who could move them deeply had to be a deep thinker) are very likely to find Satyajit Ray rather too simple.

> Apart from its truth, I find this very refreshing indeed, because most of us are too sophisticated to have written it or thought it. . . . We all believe and know these things, but we fear that to say them out loud would be to evoke the superior smile.

What these passages (the first five by Mr. Podhoretz, the remaining three by assorted contributors to *Partisan Review* and

Commentary) have in common is a keynote of sophistication—or, at any rate, the mention of the word. Sophistication, one gathers, is a quality lacking in *Times* editorial writers, illusory in Bergman films, absent in artists and actors talking about their work, present in Robert Brustein and Kenneth Tynan, and conditioned by Dostoevski, Freud, Nietzsche, Kierkegaard, Eliot, and Yeats (although in what sense Dostoevski can be said to train the modern sensibility to be bored by melodrama, or Nietzsche to see moral ambiguity everywhere, or Yeats to distrust the idea of innocence, is something that Mr. Podhoretz is too sophisticated to explain). Richard Chase points out the sophisticate's fear of evoking "the superior smile." The definite article is puzzling. *The* smile? Whose smile? Why, the communal smile of Norman Podhoretz, Alfred Chester, Lionel Abel, and the rest—the collective smile of the New Reviewing school.

And the stimulus for that sophisticated, perhaps not altogether winning smile is, when it is not the author of a literary work, none other than the reader, who is allowed occasionally to believe that he is in on an exclusive circuit secret but more often is reminded that he is hopelessly out—a child permitted to eavesdrop on the nocturnal conversation of his elders. No opportunity is lost to cast aspersions on the mind and the behavior of that child. "Who listens? Who cares?" Mr. Podhoretz inquires rhetorically, and he deplores the dwindling of "a reading public literate enough to understand a complicated exposition." Concern, in fact, about the mental caliber of a hypothetical reader slurred as middle-class, middle-brow—indeed, middle-everything—is so widespread that Fiedler professes himself disappointed because he cannot find a novel "which might have caught once and for all the pathos and silliness of middle-class, middle-brow intellectual aspiration;" and even the publisher of *Esquire* feels impelled to announce in his column that " 'The mindless dictatorship of the audience' was the most provocative single sentence uttered at Princeton during the entire *Response Weekend*." (Calling "the mindless dictatorship of the audience" a "sentence" is but one indication of the publisher's concern.) "Is it really so difficult to tell a good action from a bad one?" Frank Kermode inquires in *Partisan Review*, and he answers with a ringing New Reviewing anti-Everyman cliché: "It would seem so, since most people appear to be wrong most of the time." "People like to think Eichmann mediocre," says Lionel Abel. "I think they also like the idea of Miss Arendt, implied by her subtitle, that evil can be banal. Perhaps they are flattered to believe that in the ordinary and dulling conduct of their lives they are at the very least doing something wrong." Here Mr. Abel delivers a threefold vote of no confidence in readers: with the carelessness of his grammar ("Miss Arendt" for "Miss Arendt's"); with the shakiness of his assumption (that the reader's conduct is any more "ordinary and dulling" than Mr. Abel's own); and with the injustice of his insinuation (that the reader would accept the invalid-conversion fallacy—evil is banal, therefore banality is evil, as one might say all dogs are animals, therefore all animals are dogs —which Mr. Abel permits himself). Not merely readers, however —*everything* is on the wane. A New Reviewing Cassandra seems to have issued an encyclical announcing that the sky is falling—a conclusion that has traveled ever since, in slightly diluted form (as in the childhood game of "Whisper"), around the whole reviewing circle. "Is 'the sickness of our time' a literary hoax?" Benjamin DeMott inquires in *Harper's*. "Are the writers who call the present age a cesspool mistaking personal whiffiness for objective truth?" The questions are purely rhetorical; Mr. DeMott's answer, needless to say, is No.

> The multiplication of commodities and the false standard of living, on the one hand, the complication of the economic and technical structure in which one can work at a job, on the other hand, and the lack of direct relationship between the two have by now made a great part of external life morally meaningless.

Thus, knotting unintelligibly together a few strands of defeatist cliché, George Steiner exemplifies both a prose style and a world view: Everything is bad, science and technology advance, moral values are in permanent eclipse, and there is no hope. (There is no syntax, either—only jargon to express the futility of it all.) "I . . . suppose, they talk about plot and character, style and setting," John Thompson speculates mournfully of the universities. "Maybe it is just too late."

This generalized cultural alarmism has created among the New

Reviewers a forensic device that we might call not name- but catastrophe-dropping. Whenever a reviewer's exposition is in danger of disintegration, he simply mentions a calamity to distract
the reader's attention (much as a member of a debating society
might cry "Fire!" in a crowded auditorium when his argument is
going badly). In his discussion of his Negro problem Mr. Podhoretz makes repeated reference to the *violence* of his feelings, as
if in evidence of their universality. And Norman Mailer, inveigh-
ing querulously against modern architecture, has a comparable in-
spiration:

> That rough beast is a shapeless force, an obdurate emptiness,
> an annihilation of possibilities. It is totalitarianism: that totalitari-
> anism which has haunted the twentieth century, haunted the ef-
> forts of intellectuals to define it, of politicians to withstand it,
> and of rebels to find a field of war where it could be given battle.

Totalitarianism. Haunted. Annihilation. Beast. The reader
gasps. What has the analogy to do with modern architecture?
Nothing. But Mr. Mailer is ready with another gambit: "Our
modern architecture reminds me a little of cancer cells. Because
the healthy cells of the lung have one appearance and those in the
liver another. But if both are cancerous they tend to look a little
more alike." What has cancer to do with architecture? What
"sameness" is there between, say, Edward Stone and Le Corbus-
ier? None. But the reader is meant to agree, in a state of typo-
graphical shock.

"I write the sentence, *six million innocent people were slaugh-
tered,*" Irving Howe writes in *Commentary*, "and for a person of
adequate sensibilities may it not be as affecting as an embodiment
in a conventional narrative?" Well, no, Mr. Howe, but it may
give the illusion of shoring up a sickly argument. "It is dead. It is
evil, like racial prejudice," Alfred Chester writes of the comedy
of Vladimir Nabokov. "Less evil . . . were the Eichmann jokes
making the rounds last year which mocked and trivialized the
death of six million Jews—and which, nonetheless, even I and
other Jews could laugh at." Racial prejudice. Dead. Evil. Eichmann. What relevance have they to the comedy of Vladimir Nabokov? None. They are simply a reviewer's form of literary

demagoguery. Other devices on the same order are the frequent use of obscenity and a kind of strident excremental prose that masquerades as a perpetual assertion of manliness. Norman Mailer, for example, writes in a review. "A bad maggoty novel. Four or five half-great short stories were buried like pullulating organs in a corpse of fecal matter;" and Alfred Chester, addressing the author of a book on homosexuality, barks, "Better cut out all that ceaseless groping, Jack, and get down to work!"

Mr. Podhoretz, however, is seldom coarse or shrill. On the contrary, he seeks, by his own account, "a language in which it is possible to talk sensibly and with due proportion about new books." Here is Mr. Podhoretz arguing "sensibly and with due proportion" about the works of John Updike:

> His short stories—which I usually find myself throwing away in disgust before I can get to the end—strike me as all windup and no delivery.

How Mr. Podhoretz can detect the "delivery" if he throws stories away "before I can get to the end" is a problem that he seems not to have posed himself. Nor need he bother to pose it, for although there may be considerable discussion among those in the milieu, there is little dialectic, and arguments of extraordinary inventiveness are permitted to flourish unchallenged. The warm, permissive climate of the New Reviewing is sealed protectively against all intellectual discipline, and it has managed to foster in comfort a whole new genre of fallacy. Lionel Abel, for example, in disagreeing with Hannah Arendt about Adolf Eichmann, takes an argument of Miss Arendt's own, treats it as his, and arrives at a new form of argument altogether, a kind of pre-emptive bid— agreement-as-refutation: "Is there any contradiction between being morally monstrous and also comical?" he asks. "I am inclined to think that there is none, that anyone who considers the comical traits of Iago and Richard III must be of my opinion." Precisely, and of Miss Arendt's as well—but one must concede Mr. Abel the novelty of his argument; he simply restates, in less subtle terms, what Miss Arendt has said, and expects her to cry *"Touché!"*

"On the subject of Trotsky," Lionel Abel writes, in another article, "Mr. Kazin exhibits a harshness, intemperateness, and insensitivity which he does not show at all in responding to Herman Melville's Captain Ahab. And this is all the more striking to me since everything Mr. Kazin has to say against Trotsky could be said with equal or greater force against Melville's hero." This appears to be some sort of art/reality interchange, whereby everything that can be said against Mr. Abel can probably be said with equal or greater force against Dogberry. We might call it, perhaps, the argument-from-socio-critical-ineptitude.

Alfred Chester, on the other hand, touches all the forensic bases, and doffs his cap at every one:

> So *Tropic of Cancer*, says I, isn't a great book. So? There is a consolation prize, however, think of what pleasure it is to disagree with Karl Shapiro. And what pleasure it is to disagree with that long and laudatory list of eminent names that appears on the dust jacket like a list of vitamins and minerals: Eliot, Pound, Durrell, Anaïs Nin, Orwell, etc. And what pleasure to disagree also with the whole of the beat generation and their sycophants who have learned from Miller . . . to posture at revolutions that even *Time* Magazine approves of.

This passage, despite its strange, uncertain irony, calls into being the argument-from-the-stature-of-the-people-with-whom-one disagrees.

"The sum effect is that *The Glass Bees* puzzles," writes Theodore Solotaroff, "by its technique of steadily delimiting and generalizing its particulars, to the point of turning them into abstractions that could mean this or could mean that, and producing eventually a type of moral sensationalism and sentimentalism." "Delimiting . . . particulars to the point of . . . abstractions . . . producing . . . moral sensationalism"—the sum effect is that this argument puzzles by its technique of steadily ensnarling and obfuscating its terms that could mean this and could mean that, and producing eventually a kind of logical surrealism and vertigo.

And, finally, Mr. Podhoretz himself has argued in *Show* that if two authors "had really wanted to give us a profile of the art of acting, rather than a profile of the practitioners themselves, they would have tried to induce these people to talk candidly about each other's work instead of about their own lives and careers."

The argument that a book is improved when its subjects "talk candidly about each other's work" is—"for reasons," as the reviewer of *Aaron's Rod* and *Kangaroo* would say, "all too transparent"—a characteristically New Reviewing prescription. "Hamlet," Mr. Podhoretz says in the same piece, "would exist without John Gielgud to play him, but would the heroine of *Sweet Bird of Youth* have existed without Geraldine Page? For me, the fact that I can't remember her name is answer enough." Answer enough, perhaps, for Mr. Podhoretz. The reader may detect the birth of the argument-from-personal-amnesia.

It is hardly necessary to go on citing instances of the inexhaustible variety of argument along the reviewing circuit. There are signs, in any case, that the cloud (catastrophe-droppers might say "the *mushroom* cloud") is passing. Or, in purely mechanical terms, there are beginning to be some short circuits in the New Reviewing system. Steven Marcus, in *The New York Review*, crosses three wires (anti-Everyman cliché, reviewer centrality, and catastrophe-dropping), with this result:

> It is almost as if for three hundred years the literature of Western culture had not, so to speak, conducted a campaign to demonstrate that the middle class family is about as close as we have come to achieving hell on earth.

"The literature of Western culture," as represented by Henry James, Thomas Mann, and Jane Austen—to name authors of but three nationalities—has conducted no such "campaign." Mr. Marcus has confused "the literature of Western culture" with the expository writing of Norman Podhoretz, Leslie Fiedler, Lionel Abel, and the rest of the New Reviewing school.

One can view Mr. Podhoretz as an exponent of a group program only because, in his polemic, or *Undoings*, he insistently invites one to do so, and because (aside from an ill-informed and poorly reasoned piece on Hannah Arendt and his well-intentioned but poorly reasoned essay on the Negro problem, both of which have a kind of negative fascination) the *Undoings* have no interest *except* as examples of a school of critical writing. And the principles that unite the New Reviewing school are—if it is possible to call them "principles" at all—an elaborate system of cross-references that amounts to mutual coattail-hanging; a stale liberalism gone reactionary in anti-Everyman snobbery and defeatist cliché; a false intellectualism that is astonishingly shabby in its arguments; a hostile imperiousness toward fiction that results in near megalomania on the part of expository writers; and a withering condescension toward authors and readers that finds expression in a strident tendency to shout the opposition down. The New Reviewing is, more generally, a pastiche of attitudes and techniques vying to divert the attention of the reader from the book ostensibly under review to the personality of the reviewer, striving intrusively and valiantly to hold the line against the arts. And the *Undoings* in this collection are, for the most part, models of New Reviewing principle.

In the essays, however, in which Mr. Podhoretz is least interesting as a member of, or spokesman for, something—in his *Doings*, in short—Mr. Podhoretz does manage to assert himself as a genuine critic. Most of these *Doings* are included in a section called "Traditions"—nontopical, nonpolemical, even noncontroversial essays—and they are the considered, sympathetic works of a young man more interested in interpreting books than in pitting himself against them. There are not enough of them to constitute a volume of three hundred and seventy-one pages, but they are evidence that the critical writings of Norman Podhoretz may yet result in a worthwhile collection.

BILL BERKSON*

❧

Breath

*November! November! smoke outrunning branches, reefs
turning hideous and cold, windows accepting,
porches accepting the draught, the dust, its vacancies like the
    artic
desert* . . . the lead-dogs in heat, thirst of adventurers
for elastic Moorishness—the slow bench, walk and fountain
        certainties.
It looks like a palace like the top of something, the pole!

So we went walking in our breath—denying the tooth of it,
it was the sandwich hopelessly sighingly
color deletion propellors
the conditioned button on our ears, we fastened it, shinily, being
        smart.
November will not outlast it, it is a straight
red line around the heart's jacket, forming a grey one, cold
it is fur, fur for steel as ourselves—run it on your finger-tip grate
Like picking up a pencil, aware of the next-door cellar of fire,
Mush! pull from out under the cellophane considered knocking,
        was it

* Bill Berkson, *born in New York City in 1939, studied at Brown,
The New School, Columbia, and The Institute of Fine Arts (New
York University), and yet holds no degree. He has published poems
in several magazines, collected his early verse in* Saturday Night
(1961), and contributed criticism of art, poetry, and films to Art
News, Arts, Kulchur *and elsewhere. Since 1964, he has conducted a
poetry workshop at The New School.*

candy, glue, a stick of bells? Snows snow on the mountain pedals—
and not here yet? "They will be late as scissors"
                    "they will be early as the knob"

The drawer finished and the collection not yet burned,
beginning a new crossing with real paint this time,
lacking as would have it hinge a real armies with which to deal
Love comes but once to a shoe
and must be stepped on
if we, any of us, are to survive . . .
in its tracks, the moth
capered like his sailor-suit photo against
old speedy dessert season, an armistice wrested
from the trees

ROBERT BOYERS*

❧

A Very Separate Peace

Miss Iris Murdoch has written that the greatest art "invigorates without consoling, and defeats our attempts to use it as magic." The poetry of Theodore Roethke constitutes an artistic achievement of a very high order. It is a poetry suffused with magical transformations suggesting the fluidity of human experience and the metamorphic facility of the creative imagination. It is, moreover, a poetry which invigorates precisely in proportion to Roethke's insistent attempts to console both himself and his readers.

Roethke's *Collected Poems* may be described by one of the poet's favorite metaphors, that of the journey. From his earliest published verse to the final posthumous volume, Roethke strove to recapture both the remembered childhood past of peace and organic security and the archetypal past—the slime and torment of the subconscious. He grasped for these not as absolute ends in themselves but as means to accepting the inevitabilities of change, the dying of passion, and ultimate finitude. His best poems permit us to embrace the principle of change as the root of stability. Through rhythm and syntax and diction, they so evoke passion that we are able actively to sympathize with his sense of loss, and we can feel, with him, how "all finite things reveal infinitude."

* ROBERT BOYERS, *born in New York City in 1942, received his B.A. from Queens College and his M.A. from New York University. Editor of the literary journal* Salmagundi, *he has contributed essays on literature and politics to* Kenyon Review, Dissent, *and* The New Leader, *as well as compiled a collection of essays on Robert Lowell (1968).*

Whoever wishes to write of Roethke is faced with multiple problems. It is not that Roethke is as diversified in his concerns as other poets, or that his language presents obstacles to the rational intellect. Rather, it is his shifts of mood that weary us, though they never cease to fascinate and please. Just beneath the surface of the love poems lurks an almost obsessional concern with death; yet for every step toward the primeval sources of existence, there is a shuddering retreat toward the daylight world. Even in the middle of that magnificent "North American Sequence," published in *The Far Field* after his death, Roethke is uncertain of how far he wishes to go, how great a journey into his murky interior he is willing to undertake. In "The Long Waters," he moves confidently toward "The unsinging fields where no lungs breathe," but cries at last: "Mnetha, Mother of Har, protect me/ From the worm's advance and retreat, from the butterfly's havoc/ . . . The dubious sea-change, the heaving sands, and my tentacled sea-cousins." In such poems, there is a powerful tension between Roethke's desire to explore the depths of his sensibility and his natural reticence before the specter of hideous possibilities which may be revealed. The demands of the poet's nature seem to vie with the projects of his imagination. Fortunately, the projects are not ultimately scuttled in the interests of safety, and Roethke goes as far as his imagination can take him.

Nonetheless, what I should like to do here is to suggest the peculiar limitations of Roethke's vision, and to draw close attention to those particulars in which he especially excels. We all know that, with the possible exception of Yeats, our poetry has not for some time produced a more melodious singer than Roethke. Nor, I think, need we dwell on the wonderful, quick humor which so distinguishes Roethke's lighter poems and permits him to get such rare effects as he manages in a love poem like "I Knew a Woman," in which the lady's "choice virtues" are to be articulated by "English poets who grew up on Greek/ (I'd have them sing in chorus, cheek to cheek)." Roethke's own choice poetic virtues are too well established to require constant repetition.

A basic approach to Roethke's work should question the direction of his consoling qualities. Roethke was profoundly conscious of impending death, but perhaps even more concerned about the ineffectuality of old age, the fragrance of life and passion lingering in the nostrils without any ability to affect or rouse a benumbed sensibility. In other poets such a fearful premonition might be construed as a nervous apprehension of the loss of imaginative daring and insight. Wordsworth and Coleridge shared this orientation with the approach of middle age. Roethke's nostalgia for youth is a complex element which somewhat resembles the longing of the nineteenth-century Romantic poets. The child's fundamental innocence is a common factor, though Roethke embraces this not as a universal principle. Rather, he sees it as unavoidably attendant upon the benevolent circumstances in which he spent his childhood. In the poem "Otto," named for his father, Roethke recaptures the sense of pride he felt in a parent who controlled a rural environment immersed in the sounds and stinks and inconsistencies of nature. Roethke's fond remembrance amounts almost to hero-worship: "Once when he saw two poachers on his land,/ He threw his rifle over with one hand;/ Dry bark flew in their faces from his shot,—/ He always knew what he was aiming at." The natural man who "does not put on airs" is also a crack shot!

Roethke's childhood, spent in the environs of his father's greenhouse, becomes for the poet an emblem of an intimacy with the elements that he knows he must maintain. It is not reality in a naturalistic sense that he values, in which he wishes to be immersed. He covets the limited detachment that permits contemplation, and finally imaginative projection beyond the boundaries of the patently real. He strives to cultivate in a distinctly Wordsworthian way "a wise passivity." In such tranquil receptivity, as he reports in "The Abyss," "The Burning lake turns into a forest pool"—the violence at the heart of all creation is resolutely transformed into an acceptance of flux and perpetual restoration.

Roethke's is an essentially anarchic personality, thoroughly amorphous and shifting. In his poems he associates himself most completely with water, always changing in the intensity and direction of its internal movement, always rhythmic in its perpetual ebb and flow. The aridity of conventional life, the expedient veneer called civilization, is effaced by the poet's ability to get out of himself, the self which has been erected as a mask between his nature and his awareness. In "The Song," first appearing in *Words for the Wind,* the poet retreats from an image of a "ragged man" whom we associate with Roethke himself: "I stared at a fissure of ground/ . . . The old house of a crab/ . . . I sang to whatever had been/ Down in that watery hole/ . . . And the sweat poured from my face/ When I heard, or thought I heard,/ Another join my song/ With the small voice of a child,/ Close, and yet far away./ Mouth upon mouth, we sang,/ My lips pressed upon stone." The terrible, because impossible, longing for identification with the child, or the crab, and ostensibly other creatures of the deep, is nowhere more poignantly evoked than in those last two lines. Roethke was not unaware of his inability to achieve union with "the other" which is the lost self, and it is his awareness which makes the perpetual longing so noble and moving.

In the poems of Roethke's maturity, written during the years of his marriage (he married relatively late in life), the other becomes identified with his wife. The subject of Roethke's love poems is interesting largely because of the anachronistic reticence before eroticism displayed in many of them, despite the full-bodied frankness of his memorable work. The reticence is nowhere clearer than in an early poem like "To My Sister," in which the poet becomes virtually hysterical. The movement is nervous and halting—there is a shuddering apprehension of irremediable loss and even sin in lines like "Keep faith with present joys refuse to choose/ Defer the vice of flesh the irrevocable choice." The surrender implicit in the sexual act, the abandonment of what Roethke calls "the proud incredible poise," is a frightening prospect for him at this early period, though it is transformed into an absolutely ruthless self-revelation in the later work. This peculiar strain, peculiar especially for a passionate singer of erotic love, never quite disappears. In "Love's Progress," the warm expectation of sexual union and the eager call to action: "Love me, my violence,/ Light of my spirit, light/ Beyond the look of love," dwindles to the plaintive note of "Father, I'm far from home," and finally, "I fear for my own joy;/ I fear myself in the field,/ For I would drown in fire."

It is rather strange to find such a progression in the poems of a man who often wrote with lyrical abandon and hysterical warmth. Of course, the combination of opposites is an integral feature of Roethke's work. As M. L. Rosenthal has noted, the laughter which rings in Roethke's voice is most frequently "the pathetic hilarity of the unbearably burdened." His assertiveness is neither defiant nor forced, but a natural expression of his need for release from an introspection which often verges on the obsessive. Roethke is not unintellectual—one is aware of ideas revolving in his brain and crossing the page. At the same time, it is his ability to intoxicate with sound patterns and to make his images pirouette and dissolve without any concomitant exhaustion of clarity that first arrests our consciousness. With what energy and passion Roethke drives forth lines like "I could love a duck./Such music in a skin!/ A bird sings in the bush of your bones./ Tufty, the water's loose./ Bring me a finger. This dirt's lonesome for grass./ Are the rats dancing? The cats are" (from "Give Way, Ye Gates"). Poems like these, intensely playful and reverent of life, soon become more erotic, more focused on the promise of sexual embrace and the transference of energy from the self to the beloved. There is only the slightest vestige of that reticence previously discussed. For the most part, Roethke rollicks freely in unabashed sensualism, as in "Words for the Wind": "I kiss her moving mouth,/ Her swart hilarious skin;/ She breaks my breath in half;/ She frolics like a beast;/ And I dance round and round."

What is involved for Roethke in the surrender to sensualism, in the willingness to lower his guard, is the refusal to intellectualize his condition. He opens his arms to existence and lets it wash over his sensorium. In one poem Roethke reports that "She kissed me out of thought." There is a lightness in such an assertion which is not to be confused with flippancy or whimsy. Roethke truly yearns for the passivity of the observer who feels involved but profoundly unconcerned: "Fingering a shell,/ Thinking:/ Once I was something like this, mindless" (from "The Far Field"). Death becomes an acceptable prospect for the romantic feeding his imagination on visions of transcendence and reconciliation with the nature from which he is sprung. The frenzy characteristic of Roethke's reminiscence is replaced in his later years by a serenity that reflects the poet's confidence in his vision, as in "The Rose":

"And I stood outside myself,/ Beyond becoming and perishing/ . . . And I rejoiced in being what I was."

Roethke's love poems frequently reflect the poet's desire to get beyond himself by achieving identification with the beloved. In "The Other," he wonders aloud: "Is she what I become?/ Is this my final face?" And in "Four for Sir John Davies": "Did each become the other in that play?/ She laughed me out and then she laughed me in./ . . . We played with dark and light as children should." One thinks of the child and his eagerness to pass rapidly from role to role in play, his wondrous ability to project himself into realms of giants and fairies and sparkling elflike *Wunderkinder*. The image of the self is as yet marvelously flexible, and the newest role can demand a sincerity of absorption unknown to the average mature personality. It is this kind of absorption that Roethke wants to achieve in his maturity, but he eventually discovers that the love of woman is not the ultimate mode for him. True, the speculation evoked by erotic involvement becomes less and less draining, more and more spontaneous and improvisatory, but there still remains a level of self-consciousness that is unsatisfactory. Roethke gropes toward an imaginative ambience in which all significations seem tentative, in which the will is no longer operative, anxious to achieve an intense pleasure which may constitute an evasion of its true destiny. In "The Longing," written near the end of his life, Roethke wonders "How to transcend this sensual emptiness?/ . . . And the spirit fails to move forward."

Roethke finally affirms the primary importance of accepting experience on its own terms, without evasion. When we are free, he says in "Journey to the Interior," we can be "Delighting in surface change, the glitter of light on waves," "Unperplexed in a place leading nowhere." There is an element of static resignation here which is somewhat unsavory. Roethke wants to stand solidly rooted in the earth he loves, gathering everything to him, all sensation, every trace of loveliness, like the rose "Rooted in stone, keeping the whole of light,/ Gathering to itself sound and silence —/ Mine and the sea-wind's." We must learn to be explorers of the knowable, the finite, the perishable, if we "would unlearn the lingo of exasperation." Such resignation is neither ignominious nor unpleasant in itself, but the implications are likely to seem unsatisfying to a modern audience still smarting from the rigors of Robert Lowell's latest sequence.

It is perhaps gratuitous to refer to Robert Lowell at the conclusion of a piece which has deliberately restricted itself to Roethke, and yet I find the reference unavoidable. There are qualities in Lowell's best work that seem to me essential elements of modern poetry, and these are clearly lacking in Roethke. One is not surprised to discover this absence in the later verse, for the object of Roethke's strivings often seemed rather inane and impossibly idyllic, particularly in the early volumes. Roethke soars happily when he beholds "The cerulean, high in the elm,/ Thin and insistent as a cicada,/ And the far phoebe, singing,/ . . . A single bird calling and calling." The landscape is exotically rural. His vision is landscaped with images out of the poetic past. He refuses to make himself intimately conversant with the materials of the modern world, which is, after all, an urban universe. It is one thing to speak of a timeless ambience unconstrained by a devotion to the particularisms of specific times and places. It is another thing to write as though all times and places were alike, and as though the tone of the atomic age were interchangeable with that of the nineteenth century. From our vantage point, we are in a position to know more about the horrors of the human heart than has been possible at any previous time. Our nightmares are in no respect perfectly equivalent to those of our fathers, whether in scope or ferocity. Surrounded by a gaudy affluence, we are beset by intimations of global disaster and the pitiless exploitation of millions of men. The appalling apathy and lobotomized drift of the average man are specters as frightening as any that have clouded the poet's vision.

That a poet like Roethke can "overlook" such undeniable elements of the human condition is lamentable. I do not call for commitment to a political position, nor for a resolute determination to reform the state of the world. Robert Lowell would properly indict such strictures as blatant, vulgar, and irrelevant to the poet's true function. I do feel justified in demanding that the poet tell what he knows, what we all know. How he tells it and from what orientation constitute the texture and framework of his uniqueness, and ultimately the test of his validity. We can sympathize, in purely human terms, with a poet's inability to maintain an indefinite spiritual militancy, but his exhaustion must not be tantamount to repression. The attention Lowell pays to particular varieties of the human experience enables him to bring a more comprehensive perspective to his exploration of the human heart. Roethke's speculations appear to be of the defiantly hothouse genre by comparison—they are carefully cultivated, rather lush in themselves, but somehow lacking the vitality of context. It seems to me that the surrender of the modern sensibility to things as they are, to Experience in the archetypal mode, must be preceded by a thorough acknowledgment of precisely what such acquiescence involves. Otherwise, the resignation is disappointing in its insignificance. One admires and is moved by the energy of Roethke's struggle to get beyond morbid introspection, but one is not convinced that the battle was fought along spiritually fruitful lines, at least insofar as we are concerned. There is irony in the strange spectacle of an ostensibly "university" poetry impressing us with the basic privateness and limitation of its relevance.

JAMES BRODEY*

❦

Door to the River

The child's book at the window throws wood on the circle
this yellow between splinters in the circle on which there is a
    slipper
leather beside the yellow bay where he wants to lounge
with gas wood a prescription on top, the cage. a telephone book
    outside.
This cloak of yellow outside beside the terminal chairs between us
I'm going to come down on you you're responsible for the shoes
yellow inside the brick the chair the necklace on your ripe brown
    flower
feathers a wall of sunrise

The brown transcription over shoeboxes the eagle above begin-
    ning change
comes down into that coming down
corners let us known when. Responsible tin can my life is in the
    banister
with lines the chairs recover the intrigue we released as children
incinerator cowboy rolls out of that certain shadow in the west
not a well! or I'll mountain! this is all too ecumenical

* JAMES BRODEY, *born in Brooklyn, New York, in 1942, attended
various colleges, among them the New School where he won the
Dylan Thomas Poetry Award for 1966. He edits* Clothesline *and
runs Clothesline Editions which published his collected verse,* Fling
Madly South *(1967). His poems have appeared in* Art and Literature,
City Lights Journal, C, *and other magazines.*

2.

version, mainly yours. he's typing he can't sleep the cats are in
    the circle
in the chair, the manuscripts are all around us,
                                        the violin is on the table,
when she begins again it's time to leave, the pipes before breakfast
thank god for the yellow!
                        up on the avenue you're not only out of sight
but the canal, the lights above the beach are infested, a switch
    inside the collection

3.

the book again, two crazy wheels, is in it? you're not very sure
    about
personal hygiene, or what to do with the yellow
at leisure in the University.
                        we are devoted to the yellow

4.

the yellow article prefers the table on which there are some ash-
    trays
there were yellow blankets on the bed,
                                an aviator passes our table
he is picking a yellow toy to eat to jump on as if it were a tree
the new scenery is in place for the evening performance
the proper position rolls across
                        there is dirt in the circle
copies of it, the dirt, in our conversation, book titles on the collar
    have faded
the child's book is back on the window partly hidden,
                                a jug of destination.
our destination is the circle
the present full of lots of wood, onions, oak inside the painting
a book alongside the room,
                        the evil comes back

clothed in the waitress' decision there is a necktie inside the vase
the level country precedes our decision

about the aviator's speech.
the pipes a telescope feeds us, on us, crushable cardinals in the
stamp
terrible lines come through the post through the mail the federal
services
went out

5.

this destination the typewriter cannot concentrate on what news-
print manifest
the raccoon cup remains beneath our wallpaper surrender

a rhapsody of pits
how can I end this poem? with stringbeans? a chinese sanitation
officer
or the yellow
what is it with this yellow what's really with cheese
outside of the painting I love or am "in love" with polished cheese
like the unopened can of pretzels at Edwin's table
or the landscape of creamsicles, taxis outside the building
waiting for barriers to come to an end

5½.

an almanac of campsites on fire
(this has nothing to do with the poem, but I'm tired of arranging
cattle drives)
bridges begin wednesday to become difficult to become an assurance of quality
the same announcement comes in the mail

not as unscrupulous
the medieval houses you will be the only recipient of the first
railroad bridge
in great detail
23 photographs; 26 line drawings those seagulls have lighted

furnished with cables
the yellow cover after excavation the painting took fifteen minutes

6.

the George Washington Bridge over the Hudson River
                              at New York City, is
fast becoming
              to the young generation of Americans,
                        the symbol of its civilization
the machine has been invented
The Manhattan Bridge, completed six years after the Williams-
      burg is much more pleasing (after the painting)
                              in its design.
The yellow beside the white makes brown the beauty an erection
      Manhattan comforts
This bridge is the ambitious dream of a governor
                        in the remote province
      once it was the color of alteration:
our last hours
              were made happier by the efficient view,
                              a small replica
of the bridge as it leaves us

7.

As this poem is a monument to the opal originality,
                              courage,
and true pioneer spirit that reigns over in
the superhuman neighborhood
                    in which,
              I study the painting, as if by subscription

JEROME CHARYN*

❧

Faigele the Idiotke

The Nazis were marching all over Europe and I could already see them crossing the Atlantic and capturing the Empire State Building or holding maneuvers in Central Park. "Manny," my mother kept telling me, "join up with the merchant marines or get a job in a defense plant," but I sat home. Phil was talking about going to New Orleans. We had both just finished high school and we knew that in a month or two we would be shipped off to the army. If only we'd had ten more years to live, we both solemnly agreed, we would have been the greatest painters in the world. "One month," Phil said, "gimme one month in New Orleans and then they can take me away." He wanted me to go with him, but I had never been away from home even for a day and I was scared. New Orleans was like the end of the world. "Manny," Phil said, "who knows where we'll be in another three months. They'll bury us both in Africa somewhere." He was right, but I was still afraid to go. "Phil," I said, "if you want to paint, you can paint in the Bronx too." So he went by himself.

I sat home and didn't say a word to anybody and every time I heard the air-raid sirens wail I could feel my heart contract and dig all the way down to my bowels, looking for some place to hide. It was no joke. I couldn't paint or eat or anything. And then in about a week I got a letter from Phil. "Manny," he said, "it's

* JEROME CHARYN, *born in New York in 1937, attended its High School of Music and Art and later graduated from Columbia College. He has published three novels,* Once Upon a Droshky (*1964*), On the Darkening Green (*1965*), and* Going to Jerusalem (*1967*), and a collection of shorter fiction,* The Man Who Grew Younger (*1967*). He teaches at Stanford University.*

39

great." And he told me stories about dark and fragrant women with melon-shaped breasts and soft, honeyed lips, and I dreamed about them day and night. Every day I got another letter from Phil with stories about even more fantastic women. "I gotta get out," I said, but I knew I could never work up enough courage to go to New Orleans.

I had to have at least one little adventure. So I stuffed three pairs of pants, some T-shirts, and a whole arsenal of paints into my duffel bag and I took out the hundred dollars that I kept in a shoe box under my bed—who could trust a bank with the Germans only three thousand miles away?—and one morning, when no one was home, I sneaked out without even leaving a note. I knew that if my mother had been home she would have been able to stop me in a minute. And then, feeling like Leif Ericson or Daniel Boone, I took the "D" train down to Delancey Street. I tried to find a room, but everywhere I went I was told that all the rooms were reserved for soldiers and sailors on leave. "Be a patriot," one woman told me, "sleep out in the street." I found a vacant telephone booth on Second Avenue and immediately called my mother. At first she laughed, but when I told her I wasn't coming back, she started cry. "Manny, come home," she said. "No. Ma, I'm not a million miles away, I'm down near Delancey Street. I'll call you every Tuesday. . . . Ma, I have to get out . . . so send the cops after me . . . Ma, listen . . ." There was no use talking anymore, so I said a quick goodbye and hung up. It started to rain and I panicked and sat inside the telephone booth, clutching the duffel bag. A woman wanted to make a phone call, but I glared at her and finally she went away. I saw a "Rooms for Rent" sign hanging from a fire escape across the street and I felt a little better. I opened the door of the telephone booth tentatively, popped my head out like a wily turtle, felt the rain beat harmlessly on my neck and face, and then ran across the street.

The front of the house was dark and some of the windows were boarded, but I went inside anyway. A woman with a bald spot on the back of her head and a patch over one eye met me at the door. Two black cats stood next to her with their backs humped threateningly. I almost dropped the duffel bag. Staring dumbly at her I somehow managed to communicate the fact that I wanted to rent a room. She took me up three flights of rickety stairs. The floorboards creaked, and the two black cats followed us wherever we went. I took the first room she showed me, and I figured that after I got rid of her I'd pick up my duffel bag and sneak out. She came up close to me and I thought I saw a fang mark on her neck. I would have screamed or thrown the duffel bag at her or just simply started to cry, but then she smiled a little shamefacedly and said, "Tell me, you're a Jewish boy?" I wagged my head.

"Good," she said. "I usually rent out this room for fifteen dollars but for you let it be ten." The two cats brushed against my shoes and started to purr. I felt as if I had been living in the room all my life.

"If you need any soap or towels, don't be ashamed to ask. There's a toilet on every floor but if it gets to be like Grand Central Station just come downstairs to me. Be my guest. My name is Mrs. Geller."

"Mrs. Geller," I said, "the room, is that ten dollars a week?"

"What do you think this is, the Waldorf?" She clapped her hands and smiled. "It's a lucky thing for you you're a Jewish boy. Tell me, it's the first time you're in New York? You never rented out a room before? Don't be a schlemiel, it's ten dollars a month." She started laughing to herself; the patch over her left eye moved up and down. "Sonny," she said, "be careful, or somebody'll steal off your pants." She straightened out her patch, picked up both cats, and left.

I inspected the room. The walls were chipped and cracked and the ceiling sagged miserably. There was a sink near the door with two leaky faucets. An unvarnished chest with a missing drawer and a lumpy bed with four crooked legs faced each other uneasily in one corner of the room. I killed two giant roaches and then approached the bed. I punched the mattress twice and waited eagerly for the bedbugs to appear. I turned the mattress over and punched it again. "Wait," I said to myself, "maybe they're just a little shy." I searched through my duffel bag and remembered that I had left my roll of canvas on top of the closet in my mother's room. A wrinkled shade was attached to the top of the win-

dow. I tore the shade off the window, removed one of the draw-
ers of the chest, found a nail and four pins, and tried to stretch the
shade across the back of the drawer. But the shade began to crumble, and I flung the drawer across the room. Two gigantic plaster
chips fell from the ceiling and almost took out my eye. I was
ready to run home.

And then I closed my eyes and had a vision of myself crawling
across the ceiling of the Sistine Chapel with a paint brush in my
mouth. I opened my eyes and stared at the ceiling and the walls. I
felt inspired. I moved the chest over to the center of the room,
loaded my pockets with tubes of paint, and climbed on top of the
chest. A woman called, "Faigele, get off the fire escape." I heard a
loud clank outside my window and the chest began to wobble.
Pieces of plaster rained from the ceiling and struck my shoulders
and the back of my head. I jumped off the chest and ran to the
window. The fire escape was shaking violently and I thought the
world was coming to an end.

I saw a girl who must have been at least six feet tall climb up the
fire escape three steps at a time. Her skirt flared unevenly and
exposed her bony kneecaps and her unwashed underwear. She
stopped for a moment in front of my window and pressed her
angular face against one of the panes. I stepped back. She smiled
queerly and climbed up to the roof, the steps of the fire escape
trembling in her wake. I took two deep breaths and went down to
Mrs. Geller. I asked her for a room without a fire escape. "Shah,"
she told me. "It's only Faigele. She's harmless."

I was furious. "How can I get any work done with her running
around like that?"

"Sonny," she said, "you'll get used to her."

"Why don't you have her arrested or something?"

"Arrested? She's only twelve years old."

Mrs. Geller's cats started arching their backs and right away I
calmed down. "Well, why don't somebody tell her father?"

"Father? Her father is dead. He was killed in the war. And her
mother, she works all day and when she's not working who
knows where she is? So what can I do? Who else would take her
in with a daughter like that? Should I throw them out in the street
better? After all, Faigele's a Jewish girl. This I can guarantee." I

don't know what she expected me to say, but now she was the one who was getting worked up. "Go, if you want, pack up and go. I don't care if the whole house moves out. Who needs boarders? Faigele stays! That's final!"

"All right, Mrs. Geller, all right. But could you tell her to stay away from my fire escape?"

"No! The girl goes wherever she wants." Then she backed down a little. "Sonny," she said, "you know why they call her Faigele, hah? Faigele, it means bird in Yiddish. I myself gave her that name. Why? Because she reminds me of a bird the way she runs around and hops all over. And she's kind like a bird too. The lousy kids around here they make up other names for her. But if you ask me, they're the ones who are the dopes."

She looked me at me pleadingly, so I slapped my sides, and said, "Let her use the fire escape, okay?" and I went up to my room. I wrote a letter to Phil and gave him my new address. "Phil," I said, "Second Avenue is not New Orleans, I know, but a little freedom is better than nothing. All I've met so far are an idiot girl and a woman with a patch over her eye, but I've only been here for half a day." I had nothing fantastic to tell Phil, so I made the letter short. "I'll mail it tomorrow," I said, and using my pants for a pillow, I went to sleep. I thought I'd have some kind of nightmare about Faigele or Mrs. Geller's cats and I'd start screaming in the middle of the night, but I slept soundly.

When I woke up I started to sneeze. Half my body was covered with plaster chips. I heard somebody shout, "Faigele, Faigele, the Idiotke," from the roof. The ceiling began to bulge in about five or six places and I protected my head from the bombardment of falling chips. "That's enough," I said, and after putting on my pants, I went up to the roof. Six kids were up there and they stood around in a circle and all of them were shouting at Faigele. Five of them wore black skullcaps. The other kid wore a sailor hat. He was the ringleader and his name was Hymie. Faigele was sitting on the tar floor of the roof with her skirt hitched up to her knees. She was searching for her shoes. Hymie started pumping his arms and said, "Fly, Faigele, fly!" Then the other kids joined in, "Fly, Faigele, fly." One kid said, "Let's play hot potata," and he tossed something up in the air that looked like a gigantic loaf of bread or maybe a football. Then I took a closer look. It was one of Faigele's shoes.

"Hey," I said to Hymie, "why don't you give her back her shoe?" "No," Hymie said, "not until she flies for us." And then the other kids joined in again. "Fly, Faigele, fly." I tried to grab the shoe, but the kids kept tossing it over my head and shouting, "Hold on to the hot potata." Finally one of the kids dropped the shoe, and I snatched it up before any of them could run over. Now Hymie called the other kids over for a huddle. They let out some kind of a crazy cheer and then they all separated. Faigele was still sitting on the tar floor and I wanted to warn her and give her back her shoe, but the kids started picking up dried lumps of tar and they threw them at Faigele and me. "Revenge from the Maccabees." Some of the lumps were as big as an egg. Faigele was an easy target because she was sitting on the floor, so most of the kids aimed at her. She kept getting pelted and she didn't even hide her head. I figured it was time for a little action.

I couldn't catch all six of the little bastards at one time, so I went after Hymie. He kept dodging in and out of the clotheslines, but I caught him and I gave him a good hard kick in the can. Hymie's chums had surrounded Faigele and they were getting ready to bombard her. When they saw me coming, they ran over to the next roof and started throwing tar from over there, but they were too far away to do any damage. Faigele's other shoe was still missing and I looked all over the roof for it. I couldn't find it, so I helped Faigele lace up her one shoe, and then she stood up, limped a little, and started somersaulting crazily across the roof. I guess she was performing for me. She ran nimbly along the ledge, making a noise that sounded a little like a moo. "Faigele," I said, "you'll fall off," but she didn't listen to me. Then Faigele climbed down the ladder that led to the fire escape and disappeared. I went back to my room.

About ten minutes later I heard a thumping sound in the hall, and I figured that maybe Faigele was coming up to pay me a visit. But I should have known better. She would have come through the fire escape. And like a fool I opened the door and was ready to put on a little performance of my own, when somebody grabbed me by the shirt and threw me across the room. It was Hymie's father. He couldn't have been much more than five feet tall, but his shoulders were almost as wide as the door, and, standing there with his arms dangling down almost to his knees, he looked like King Kong. I wanted to open the window and join Faigele on the fire escape, but I was too scared to move. King Kong wore an apron that was smeared with dried blood, and I figured that he must be a butcher.

"You," he said, pointing one of his stubby fingers at me. "You like to go around kicking kids, huh?" Then he noticed a few tubes of paint that I had left on top of the chest. "A painter boy." He picked up one of the tubes, tossed it once or twice, and began to squeeze it. The cap popped off and a snaky string of cobalt blue shot out of the tube and fell with a plop on the uncarpeted floor. He seemed to be enjoying himself, and one by one he went to work on my tubes of paint. I turned around for a second and saw Faigele peering sadly through the window, and then King Kong, laughing wildly and squeezing out my last tube of paint, started coming toward me, and I must have fainted or something, because the next thing I knew, Mrs. Geller was leaning over me and slapping my face with a lumpy rag. The two black cats were climbing all over me.

"Look at him, he's turning blue. Sonny, get up!"

"I'm all right," I said, "and stop hitting me with that rag, huh?" I shooed the cats away from me and then stood up. The whole room was cluttered with lumps of paint.

"I know the whole story," Mrs. Geller said. "We'll fix him, wait. He thinks he's the boss around here, that gorilla. I'll have him dispossesed, wait. Out in the street he'll go. And Hymie, that little gangster, he'll catch it from me too."

"Thanks, Mrs. Geller, I appreciate everything, but I'm a little tired, and . . ."

"I understand, Sonny. Come down later and I'll make you some soup."

I examined myself in the mirror, but I couldn't find a bump or even a bruise. Then I heard a light tap on the window. I opened it and looked outside, but no one was around. I noticed a cracked pigeon egg and a rotten carrot on the landing of the fire escape. Presents from Faigele? The egg and the carrot stank unbearably and I wanted to close the window, but I felt that somewhere Faigele was watching me, so I cursed myself, reached out and brought the booty into the room. I wrapped the carrot and the egg in some newspaper and dropped them into the bottom of the chest.

The next morning I woke up with my nostrils stinging. The room smelled worse than a sewer. A dozen pigeon eggs, a wormy apple, and two blackened turnips were sitting out on the fire escape. "Faigele, Faigele," I cried out, but no one answered my call. I went down to Mrs. Geller. Her two cats glared at me and prepared to hump their backs, but I ignored them. "Mrs. Geller," I said, "enough is enough. Tell me where Faigele's mother lives."

Mrs. Geller stared at me for a moment, and after playing nervously with her patch, she said, "On the second floor."

"Which room?"

"The one . . . the one near the stairway. But you won't find her there. She's never home. Tell me, what happened?"

"Later," I said, "later," and I ran up to the second floor. I stood in front of the door near the stairway and knocked on it with my fist. No one was home. I sat at the top of the stairs for almost an hour, and then I went up to my room. I stuffed my nostrils with cotton, and using a rusty tablespoon I scooped the dozen eggs, the wormy apple, and the two blackened turnips into a paper bag. I went down one flight and left the bag with a little note in front of Faigele's mother's door. "The hell with it," I said, "if I stink everybody out of the house, it's Faigele's fault." I heard someone coming up the steps, and I thought it might be Faigele's mother, so I peered down the darkened stairwell and recognized King Kong. I ran up to my room.

The next morning there were no pigeon eggs or turnips outside my window, and I thought the problem of Faigele was solved. King Kong had destroyed all my Venetian red and cobalt blue, but luckily I had kept a few tubes of paint in my duffel bag. I went downstairs, scoured the block, and found several large pieces of cardboard outside an abandoned grocery store. "If Picasso can paint on cardboard," I said, "so can I!" On the way upstairs I stopped off at the second floor, but the paper bag was gone. I was eager to get back to work, and I didn't wait around to see if Faigele's mother was at home. I figured I'd try a self-portrait, so I arranged my remaining tubes of paint on the chest, posed myself in front of the mirror and started to sketch on the cardboard with a stumpy blue crayon. Then, instinctively, I turned around and saw Faigele outside on the fire escape. Mrs. Geller's two cats were with her. "Faigele's friends," I said to myself, but I kept on working. I couldn't help it, I had to turn around again. Faigele was looking at me in a funny way. She opened her mouth wide and made a sound that was somewhere between a caw and a moo, and I dropped the crayon. "Oh my God, she's serenading me," I said, and I walked over to the window and shooed her away. But Faigele stood on the fire escape and kept it up. I tried to finish the sketch, but my hand kept shaking, and Faigele's serenade froze my heart. I charged down to the second floor and beat on the door near the stairway with both fists. The door across the hall opened and Hymie came out. "Ma, Ma, look who's here!" he said, and shaking his can at me, he ran back in. Hymie's mother came over to the door. "What's the commotion?"

"I'm looking for Faigele's mother."

"Faigele's mother?"

"Mrs. Geller told me she lives on this floor. Next to the stairs."

She started laughing. "Mrs. Geller told you that? And you believed her yet? Dummy, Mrs. Geller herself is Faigele's mother!"

"What?" I said dumbly, and then Hymie's mother walked over to the door near the stairway. She just touched the knob and the door opened by itself. I looked inside. It was a storeroom. A monstrous metal crib stood near the door. A metal hoop, some gigantic wooden blocks, and a doll that was taller than I was were piled behind the crib. Faigele's old toys.

"Now you believe me or not?" Hymie's mother said.

"What about Faigele's father? Didn't he die in the war?"

She started laughing again, and I had to wait almost a minute before she calmed down. "Can she make up a story! Dummy, nobody knows who Faigele's father is—not even Mrs. Geller herself, that gypsy!"

I went down to Mrs. Geller. Her cats weren't around, and she looked lost without them. I guess she knew her little game was up.

"Mrs. Geller," I said, "why did you make up such a lie?"

She looked around desperately for her cats, and then she said, "Sonny, I'm sorry." She started to cry. "I didn't want you to move out. Who can find boarders?" A solitary tear appeared from beneath her patch and dribbled down her bumpy face. I think I was ready to cry myself, especially when I saw that tear.

"Don't cry, Mrs. Geller," I said, "I like Faigele, I mean it."

She grabbed the end of my T-shirt and started wiping her eyes with it, and I was a little embarrassed.

"Don't be angry with her, Sonny. You protected her before from those little bandits and she was trying to show her appreciation."

"It was nothing, Mrs. Geller. But please tell her not to leave any more eggs outside my window and to stay away from my fire escape. I mean, if she wants to come around once in a while, fine, but Mrs. Geller, the way it is now, I can't get any work done."

"I'll tell her, Sonny, I swear. She didn't mean no harm."

She wanted to kiss my hands, but I pulled them away quickly and put them in my pocket.

"Don't worry, Mrs. Geller," I said hastily, "who knows, maybe I'll paint Faigele's picture for you one of these days." And without giving her a chance to say anything else, I went straight up to my room. Faigele and the cats were gone, but about an hour later I had another guest. King Kong. I wasn't expecting him, so I opened the door, and he pushed his way in. He was holding some kind of petition.

"Sign it," he said.

"Sign what?"

"It's a petition to get Faigele committed. All we need is one more signature and then maybe we'll be able to get some action on it. Sign it, or I'll break your arm!"

"Go 'head." I offered him my left arm. "Break it if you want, but I'm not going to sign."

He shook his head and walked toward the door, but he changed his mind, came over to me again and started pleading. "What's the matter, ain't you got any sense? The girl's an idiot. Everybody knows it, even her own mother. Look, we'll be doing Faigele a favor if we get her committed. That's a fact. Sure, if she stays around here, one of these days she'll fall off the fire escape and crack her head. I'm telling you, it's better off for everybody if Faigele goes. Mrs. Geller can't rent out a room with her around. The whole second floor is empty except for me and my wife and the kid. Everybody moved out." He took out the petition again. "Come on, sign it. Be a sport."

"No," I said flatly.

I thought he was going to pounce on me. But he waved the petition and said, "Who needs you, creep! We'll get her committed without your help. And lemme tell you, you're the next one to go." He stormed out of the room.

Two days passed. I met Mrs. Geller in the hall and told her about King Kong's petition. She looked a little worried. "You didn't sign it, no?"

"Mrs. Geller, what kind of a guy do you think I am? Sure I didn't sign." And when I told her that, she grabbed me and started hugging me and kissing me, right in the hall. Finally I made her let me go, and I went upstairs. "Sonny," she called up to me, "now they'll never be able to take Faigele away. I have you for an ally!"

I figured I'd continue working on the self-portrait I'd started, so I posed myself in front of the mirror again. I heard something drop down with a plop on my fire escape. "Not again," I said, ready to tear out my hair. "Faigele, Faigele, lemme have some peace." I walked over to the window ready to scoop up turnips or eggs or whatever it was. My fire escape was covered with tremendous lumps of horse manure. This wasn't Faigele's doing. I mean, there's a difference between sending somebody a rotten pigeon egg and a lump of drek! I looked up and saw Hymie's impish face peering over the edge of the roof. I stuck my head out the window and, shaking my fist at Hymie, I said, "You can tell your father that I'll never sign his lousy petition, no matter what!" And then I realized how vulnerable I was with my head sticking out. I closed the window quickly and was ready to charge up to the roof, but I saw Faigele dash past my window, and about half a minute later I heard Hymie cry "Help, help!" I started cheering. "Hurray, hurray, Faigele's fighting back!" I became a little frightened. Suppose she throws him off the roof? After all, it's partly my fault. I protected her before, so now she's protecting me. And I went up to the roof. Faigele was already gone, but Hymies' legs were dangling out of an orange crate that was half filled with horse manure. I laughed so hard that I had to sit down for a minute to catch my breath. "Help, help!" Hymie cried, and finally he managed to climb out of the crate.

"She made you eat your own ammunition, huh Hymie?"

He walked over to the next roof without saying a word.

I bolted my door and put the chest next to it for a barricade, and waited for King Kong to show up. I wasn't going to take any chances. I spent half the day sitting on top of the chest, listening, like some kind of an insane spy, for footfalls outside my room. After a while my chin dropped on my chest and I started to dream. Faigele and I were playing on the roof, pretending to be birds. She kept flapping her arms, and then, all of a sudden, she just took off and started to fly. She flew over the roof, and I cupped my hands over my mouth and called after her. "Faigele, Faigele, come down. People can't fly. Come down, before you fall." But she kept flying higher and higher. And I had to find some way to make her come back, so I started pumping my arms like mad, and believe it or not, here I was, flying too. Nobody knows how wonderful it is to be able to fly. If people could fly, I don't think they'd ever want to do anything else. I can't imagine anyone ever getting tired of flying. My arms moved up and down effortlessly and I followed behind Faigele. "Faigele," I said, "wait up," but I could never catch up with her. And then my arms started feeling a little heavy, and my body began to spin. And no matter how hard I flapped my arms, I couldn't keep myself from falling. But even as I plunged I thought to myself: It's worth it, just to be able to fly for a little while. I heard somebody screaming at me. King Kong was outside my room, banging away at the door. "Lemme in. You saw what she did to my kid, the idiot. And you're the one who's responsible." He rammed the door with his shoulder, but I still didn't give in. And for the first time in a long time I didn't feel guilty about not being in the army. The hell with the Germans; I had a war of my own.

"I'm telling you," King Kong said, "you better sign the petition if you wanna live to see tomorrow. . . . All right, if you're too afraid to come out, here, I'll push the petition under the door. Sign it, and then I'll go away." When the petition came through, I picked it up and tore it into a hundred pieces. With a demonic grin I sent it back piece by piece. I heard King Kong go down on his knees outside the door. He must've been trying to assemble all the pieces. I think he was crying. "Now you're gonna stay inside of that room for the rest of your life. Because if you ever try to come out, I'm gonna tear you apart. Nobody's gonna save you now. I'll be waiting for you." And then he walked down to the next floor.

Luckily I had stored seven cans of tuna fish in the bottom drawer of the chest, or I would have starved to death. Three days passed. I tried to send signals down to Mrs. Geller, but Faigele didn't come near my window, not even once. I was going to ask King Kong for a truce, but I knew it wouldn't work. I was down to my last two cans of tuna fish. And then, during the afternoon of the fourth day of the siege, I heard a knock on the door. Somebody called, "Manny, open up," and it wasn't King Kong. "Phil?" I said, pressing my ear against the door. "Is that you?"

"Who the hell do you think it is? Come on, open up."

Phil was wearing a dirty T-shirt, and he looked as if he hadn't slept for a week. I hugged him anyway, that's how glad I was to see him. I was going to tell him about Faigele and the siege and everything, but he waved me off and said, "Please, Manny, lemme rest up for a minute. I haven't been off my feet for days." I led him toward the bed. He took off his shoes and put them on the window sill. The heels and soles were worn through, and his feet were black. He wanted to fall asleep, but I wouldn't let him.

"Phil," I said, "what happened? Why'd you come back from New Orleans?" He rubbed his feet and kept quiet.

"So?" I said, and I waited eagerly for him to tell me about his adventures. But all he did was look sourly at me and rub his belly.

"I'm hungry," he said. "If you won't lemme sleep, then at least gimme something to eat." So I gave Phil my last can of tuna fish. He gobbled up the whole can in less than a minute. After he licked the oil off his fingers he looked at me with his baggy eyes, and then he turned his head away.

"Manny," he said, looking at the wall, "the first day I got to New Orleans this guy and a girl caught me in back of a bar and stole my wallet and my watch. The girl wanted to take my pants and my shirt, and I hadda beg the guy to lemme keep 'em. I slept out in the street for two nights and I was even arrested for being a vagrant. Don't ask! Manny, the army couldn't be any worse than that."

"Phil, what about those letters you wrote me?"

"Ah," he said, "all lies. I thought maybe you'd come out there if I wrote you all that. It was terrible being by myself, Manny. And after a while I started believing all the crap I wrote, and I felt a lot better. You know. I didn't meet anybody out there. No women, nothin'."

I felt like strangling him.

"Hey Manny," Phil said, stretching his arms lazily, "wake me up after it gets dark."

And that's when I grabbed him by the ankles and threw him off the bed.

"Get out."

"What? Quit it, Manny. I'm tired. Later, huh? Then we'll play games."

"Get out."

He put on his shoes. "You a nut, huh, Manny? First you hug me and now you wanna throw me out. All I wanted to do was stay here for one—"

I pushed him out of the room and bolted the door.

"Manny," he said, standing outside, "you turned into a madman, I mean it. Lemme in. I don't wanna go home. Manny?"

He asked me one more time before he left. I stood near the door for a minute and then I began to panic. I didn't want to stay by myself any more. "I'm sorry," I said, and I opened the door. "Phil." No one answered. I wanted to run down after him, but I was too afraid to leave my room. So I bolted the door again and sat down on the floor, and believe it or not, I started to cry. "Manny," I said to myself, "you're the king of the shmoes!" An artist I wanted to be yet!

And then, almost miraculously, I saw Faigele's face in the window. At first I thought it was only a vision, but when she started to moo I knew that it was Faigele in the flesh! "Faigele," I said, "wait, don't go away!" but she climbed up to the roof. "I'll show them," I said, and gathering up a brush, a large piece of cardboard, and some random tubes of paint, I opened the window and climbed out on the fire escape. I looked around to see if Hymie was spying on me and then I tiptoed up to the roof, gripping the metal banister tightly after every step. I looked down once and got dizzy and almost dropped a tube of paint. Faigele was playing behind a clothesline, so I walked over to her quietly, sat down on the lumpy tar floor, and placed the piece of cardboard against my knees. I watched her play for about ten minutes, and then I took out my crayon.

A pigeon landed on the roof and Faigele started to imitate the way it walked. The pigeon limped for a minute, and Faigele limped too. She smiled at the pigeon, and I stared at her, because it wasn't the smile of an idiot girl. No. Her whole face glowed and her smile was so gentle and warm that even the pigeon was baffled and stood motionless for a moment. She reached out her hand to touch the pigeon, but then she started to moo, and her features coarsened and her smile lost all of its enchantment. She was Faigele the Idiotke again, and the pigeon flapped its wings and retreated to the other end of the roof. Faigele flapped her arms too and ran after the pigeon. "Faigele, Faigele," I cried, "come back." I saw Hymie and a few of the Maccabees standing behind me and I knew King Kong would be up in a minute. I stood up, dropped the paint and the cardboard, and galloped after Faigele. The pigeon stood on the ledge of the roof. Faigele approached the ledge, flapping her arms and mooing. Hymie and the Maccabees started to shout. "Fly, Faigele, fly." The pigeon remained on the ledge for another moment and then flew off triumphantly. "Fly, Faigele, fly!" Faigele stood on the ledge and watched the pigeon, and I could see now she was crying. "Fly, Faigele, fly." She looked at me once, and then flapping her arms rhythmically, she jumped off the roof. I tried to grab one of her legs, but it was too late. Her arms flapped once or twice as her body plunged, and for a minute I thought she really was going to fly, and then her body struck the ground with a heavy thud and she lay motionless out in the yard. Mrs. Geller's cats appeared suddenly, ran over to Faigele, and started licking her body. Hymie and the Maccabees ran downstairs and I remained alone on the roof. I heard the cats begin to howl.

Even King Kong cried later when he saw Faigele out in the yard. Mrs. Geller kept beating her chest and her patch dropped all the way down and exposed the gutted socket of her eye. "I should have sent her away," she sobbed brokenly, and King Kong put his arm around her and comforted her. The two cats kept howling. I signed seven different forms, and I told the story over and over again, and finally the police left. I went up to my room and started packing. I found the pigeon egg and the carrot that I had left in the bottom drawer of the chest, and I dropped them gently into the duffel bag. And then I went downstairs.

I spent half the night wandering through the streets, bent over from the weight of the duffel bag. I kept mumbling to myself. "Let Phil be a birdman if he wants, I'm staying on the ground. I don't want to fly. Faigele, Faigele . . . I should have signed the petition." A taxicab almost ran me over and twice I was stopped by policemen. A drunken sailor offered to buy me a beer, and when I walked past him without saying a word he kicked me in the butt, and I tumbled over and fell in the gutter. The sailor picked me up and told me how sorry he was, and he made me keep his sailor hat. I peed in the middle of the street and was almost arrested, but luckily I was wearing the sailor hat and the policeman let me go. "Save it for Germany," he said with a wink. Finally I settled outside a recruiting station and sat quietly on my duffel bag. I glanced at all the recruiting posters. Uncle Sam pointed his bony finger at me and I heard him say, "Faigele, Faigele, Faigele."

FRANK CHIN*

❧

Food for All His Dead

"Jus' forty-fie year' go, Doctah Sun Yat-sen Free China from da Manchus. Dats' why all us Chinee, alla ovah da woil are cele-brate Octob' tan or da Doubloo Tan . . . !"

The shouted voice came through the open bathroom window. The shouting and music was still loud after rising through the night's dry air; white moths jumped on the air, danced through the window over the voice, and lighted quickly on the wet sink, newly reddened from his father's attack. Johnny's arms were around his father's belly, holding the man upright against the edge of the sink to keep the man's mouth high enough to spit lung blood into the drain. . . .

The man's belly shrank and filled against Johnny's arms as the man breathed and spat, breathed and spat, the belly shrinking and filling. The breaths and bodies against each other shook with hor-rible rhythms that could not be numbed out of Johnny's mind. "Pride," Johnny thought, "Pa's pride for his reputation for doing things . . . except dying. He's not proud of dying, so it's a secret between father and son. . . ." At the beginning of the man's death, when he had been Johnny's father, still commanding and large, saying, "Help me. I'm dying; don't tell," and removing his jacket and walking to the bathroom. Then came the grin—pressed lips twisted up into the cheeks—hiding the gathering blood and drool. Johnny had cried then, knowing his father would die. But now the man seemed to have been always dying and Johnny al-

* FRANK CHIN, *born in Berkeley in 1940, graduated from the Univer-sity of California (Berkeley), where he edited* The Pelican, *the under-graduate humor magazine, and later attended the University of Iowa. He has recently completed a novel.*

ways waiting, waiting with what he felt was a coward's loyalty to the dying, for he helped the man hide his bleeding and was sick himself, knowing he was not waiting for the man to die but waiting for the time after death when he could relax.

". . . *free from da yoke of Manchu slab'ry, in'epen'ence, no moah queue on da head! Da's wha'fo' dis big a parade! An' here, in San Francisco, alla us Chinee—'mellican 're pwowd!* . . ."

"It's all gone . . . I can't spit any more. Get my shirt, boy. I'm going to make a speech tonight. . . ." The man slipped from the arms of the boy and sat on the toilet lid and closed his mouth. His bare chest shone as if washed with dirty cooking oil and looked as if he should have been chilled, not sweating, among the cold porcelain and tile of the bathroom.

To the sound of herded drums and cymbals, Johnny wiped the sweat from his father's soft body and dressed him without speaking. He was full of the heat of wanting to cry for his father but would not.

His father was heavier outside the house.

They staggered each other across the alleyway to the edge of Portsmouth Square. They stood together at the top of the slight hill, their feet just off the concrete onto the melted fishbone grass, and could see the brightly lit reviewing stand, and they saw over the heads of the crowd, the dark crowd of people standing in puddles of each other, moving like oily things and bugs floating on a tide; to their left, under trees, children played and shouted on swings and slides; some ran toward Johnny and his father and crouched behind their legs to hide from giggling girls. And they could see the street and the parade beyond the crowd. The man stood away from the boy but held tightly to Johnny's arm. The man swallowed a greasy sound and grinned. "I almost feel I'm not dying now. Parades are like that. I used to dance the Lion Dance in China, boy. I was always in the parades."

Johnny glanced at his father and saw the man's eyes staring wide with the skin around the eyes stretching for the eyes to open wider, and Johnny patted his father's shoulder and watched the shadows of children running across the white sand of the play area. He was afraid of watching his father die here; the man was no longer like his father or a man; perhaps it was the parade. But the waiting, the lies and waiting, waiting so long with a flesh going to death that the person was no longer real as a life but a parody of live things, grinning. The man was a fish drying and shrinking inside its skin on the sand, crazy, mimicking swimming, Johnny thought, but a fish could be lifted and slapped against a stone, thrown to cats; for his father, Johnny could only wait and help the man stay alive without helping him die. "That's probably where you got the disease," Johnny said.

"Where, boy?"

"Back in China."

"No, I got it here. I was never sick for one day in China." The man began walking down the hill toward the crowd. "Back in China. . . ."

They walked down the hill, the man's legs falling into steps with his body jerking after his falling legs; Johnny held his father, held the man back to keep him from falling over his own feet. The man's breath chanted dry and powdered out of his mouth and nostrils to the rhythm of the drums, and his eyes stared far ahead into the parade; his lips opened and showed brickcolored teeth in his grin. "Not so fast, *ah-bah!*" Johnny shouted and pulled at his father's arm. He was always frightened at the man's surges of nervous life.

"Don't run," Johnny said, feeling his father's muscles stretch as he pulled Johnny down the hill toward the crowd. "Stop running, pa!" And his father was running and breathing out fog into the hot night and sweating dirty oil, and trembling his fleshy rump inside his baggy trousers, dancing in stumbles with dead senses. "Pa, not so fast, dammit! You're going to have another attack! Slow down!"

"I can't stop, boy."

They were in the shadow of the crowd now, and children chased around them.

"Look! There they are!" the man said.

"Dere you're, ladies and genullmans! Eben da lion are bow in respack to us tonigh'!"

The crowd clapped and whistled, and boys shoved forward to see. Old women, roundbacked in their black overcoats, lifted their heads to smile; they stood together and nodded, looking like clumps of huge beetles with white faces.

"Closer to the platform, boy; that's where I belong," the man said. He leaned against Johnny's shoulder and coughed out of his nostrils. Johnny heard the man swallow and cringed. The man was grinning again, his eyes anxious, the small orbs jumping scared spiders all over the sockets. "Aren't you happy you came, boy? Look at all the people."

"Take time to catch your breath, *ah-bah*. Don't talk. It's wrong for you to be here anyhow."

"Nothing's wrong, boy, don't you see all your people happy tonight? As long as . . ." he swallowed and put his head against Johnny's cheek, then made a sound something like laughter, "As I've been here . . . do you understand my Chinese?" Then slowly in English, catching quick breaths between his words, "I be here, allabody say dere chillren're gonna leab Chinatong and go way, but 'snot so, huh?" His voice was low, a guttural mono-tone. "Look a'em all; dey still be Chinee. I taught da feller dat teach dem to dance how to do dat dancer boy. Johnny? dis're you home, here, an' I know you gat tire, but alla you fran's here, an' dey likee you." His face was speaking close to Johnny and chilled the boy's face with hot breath.

The boy did not look at his father talking to him but stared stiffly out to the street, watching the glistening arms of boys jerk-ing the bamboo skeletons of silk-hided lions over their heads. His father was trying to save him again, Johnny thought, trying to be close like he had been to him how long ago when his father was a hero from the war. The man spoke as if he had saved his life to talk to his son now, tonight, here among the eyes and sounds of Chinese.

"I'm sorry, *ah-bah*, I can't help it . . ." was all Johnny could answer sincerely. He knew it would be cruel to say, "Pa, I don't want to be a curiosity like the rest of the Chinese here. I want to be something by myself," so he did not, not only because of the old man, but because he was not certain he believed himself; it had been easy to believe his own shouted words when he was younger and safe with his parents; it had been easy not to like what he had then—when he knew he could stay; then, when the man was fat and not dying, they were separate and could argue, but not now; now he was favored with the man's secret; they were horribly bound together now. The old man was dying and still believing in the old ways, still sure—even brave, perhaps—and that meant something to Johnny.

"An' you see dam bow in respack now, an' da's good lucks to ev'eybody!"

The lion dancers passed, followed by a red convertible with boys beating a huge drum on the back seat.

Johnny knew the parades; the lion dancers led the wait for the coming of the long dragon, and the end. The ends of the parades with the dragon were the most exciting, were the loudest moment before the chase down the streets to keep the dragon in sight. He was half aware of the air becoming brittle with the noise of the dances and the crowd, and, with his father now, was almost happy, almost anxious, dull, the way he felt when he was tired and staring in a mirror, slowly realizing that he was looking at his own personal reflection; he felt pleased and depressed, as if he had just prayed for something.

"You know," the man said, "I wan' you to be somebody here. Be doctor, mak' moneys and halp da Chinee, or lawyer, or edgenerer, make moneys and halp, and people're respack you." He patted the boy's chest. "You tall me now you won' leab here when I die, hokay?"

"I don't know, pa." The boy looked down to the trampled grass between his feet and shrugged off what he did not want to say. They were hopeless to each other now. He looked over his shoulder to his father and could not answer the chilled face and they stared a close moment onto each other and were private, holding each other and waiting.

Policemen on motorcycles moved close to the feet of the crowd to move them back. The boys wearing black-and-red silk trousers and white sweatshirts, coaxing the clumsy dragon forward with bells and shafts could be seen now; they were dancing and shouting past the reviewing stand. The dragon's glowing head lurched side to side, rose and fell, its jaw dangling after the goading boys. As the dragon writhed and twisted about itself, boys jumped in and out from under its head and belly to keep the dragon fresh.

"Maybe I'm not Chinese, pa! Maybe I'm just a Chinese accident. You're the only one that seems to care that I'm Chinese." The man glared at the boy and did not listen. "Pa, most of the people I don't like are Chinese. They even *laugh* with accents, Christ!" He turned his head from the man, sorry for what he said. It was too late to apologize.

"You dare talk to your father like that?" the man shouted in Chinese. He stood back from the boy, raised himself and slapped him, whining through his teeth as his arm swung heavily toward the boy's cheek. "You're no son of mine! No son! I'm ashamed of you!"

The shape of the bamboo skeleton was a shadow within the thinly painted silk of the dragon, and boys were shouting inside.

"Pa, *ah-bah*, I'm sorry."

"Get me up to the platform, I gotta make a speech."

"Pa, you've got to go home."

"I'm not dead yet; you'll do as I say."

"All right, I'll help you up because you won't let me help you home. But I'll leave you up there, pa. I'll leave you for ma and sister to bring home."

"*From da Pres'den, of da United State' 'mellica! 'To alla ob da Chinee-'mellican on da celebrate ob dere liberate from da Manchu. . . .'*"

"I'm trying to make you go home for your own good."

"You're trying to kill me with disgrace. All right, leave me. Get out of my house, too."

"Pa, I'm trying to help you. You're dying!" The boy reached for his father, but the man stepped away. "You'll kill ma by not letting her take care of you."

"Your mother's up on the platform waiting for me."

"Because she doesn't know how bad you are. I do. I have a right to make you go home."

"It's my home, not yours. Leave me alone." The man walked the few steps to the edge of the platform and called his wife. She came down and helped him up. She glanced out but did not see Johnny in the crowd. Her cheeks were made up very pink and her lipstick was still fresh; she looked very young next to Johnny's father, but her hands were old, and seemed older because of the bright nail polish and jade bracelet.

Johnny knew what his father would tell his mother and knew he would have to trust them to be happy without him. Perhaps he meant he would have to trust himself to be happy without them . . . the feeling would pass; he would wait and apologize to them both, and he would not have to leave, perhaps. Everything seemed wrong, all wrong, yet, everyone, in his own way, was right. He turned quickly and walked out of the crowd to the children's play area. He sat on a bench and stretched his legs straight out in front of him. The dark old women in black coats stood by on the edges of the play area watching the nightbleached faces of children flash in and out of the light as they ran through each other's shadows. Above him, Johnny could hear the sound of pigeons in the trees. Chinatown was the same and he hated it now. Before, when he was younger, and went shopping with his mother, he had enjoyed the smells of the shops and seeing colored toys between the legs of walking people; he had been proud to look up and see his mother staring at the numbers on the scales that weighed meat to see the shopkeepers smile and nod at her. And at night, he had played here, like the children chasing each other in front of him now.

"What'sa wrong, Johnny? Tire?" He had not seen the girl standing in front of him. He sat up straight and smiled. "You draw more pitchers on napkin for me tonigh'?"

"No, I was with pa." He shrugged. "You still got the napkins, huh?"

"I tole you I want dem. I'm keeping 'em." She wore a short white coat over her red *cheongsam* and her hair shook down over her face from the wind.

"I wanta walk," he said. "You wanta walk?"

"I gotta gat home before twalve."

"Me too."

"I'll walk for you dan, okay?" She smiled and reached a hand down for him.

"You'll walk *with* me, not *for* me. You're not a dog." He stood and took her hand. He enjoyed the girl; she listened to him; he did not care if she understood what he said or knew what he wanted to say. She listened to him, would listen with her eyes staring with a wide frog's stare until he stopped speaking, then her body would raise and she would sigh a curl of girl's voice and say, "You talk so nice. . . ."

The tail of an embroidered dragon showed under her white coat and seemed to sway as her thigh moved. "You didn' come take me to the parade, Johnny?"

"I was with pa." Johnny smiled. The girl's hand was dryfeeling, cold and dry like a skin of tissue-paper covered flesh. They walked slowly, rocking forward and back as they stepped up the hill. "I'm always with pa, huh?" he said bitterly, "I'm sorry."

" 'sall right. Is he still dying?"

"Everyone's dying here; it's called the American's common cold."

"Don' talk you colleger stuff to me! I don' unnerstan' it, Johnny."

"He's still dying . . . always. I mean, sometimes I think he won't die or is lying and isn't dying."

"Wou'n't that be good, if he weren't dying? And if it was all a joke? You could all laugh after."

"I don't know, Sharon!" He whined on the girl's name and loosened her hand, but she held.

"Johnny?"

"Yeah?"

"What'll you do if he dies?"

Johnny did not look at the girl as he answered, but lifted his head to glance at the street full of lights and people walking between moving cars. Grant Avenue. He could smell incense and caged squabs, the dank smell of damp fish heaped on tile from the shops now. "I think I'd leave. I know what that sounds like, like I'm waiting for him to die so I can leave; maybe it's so. Sometimes I think I'd kill him to stop all this waiting and lifting him to the sink and keeping it a secret. But I won't do that."

"You won' do that . . ." Sharon said.

"An' now, I like to presan' da Pres'den ob da Chinee Benabolen'. . . ."

"My father," Johnny said.

The girl clapped her hands over her ears to keep her hair from jumping in the wind. "You father?" she said.

"I don't think so," Johnny said. They walked close to the walls, stepped almost into doorways to allow crowding people to pass them going down the hill toward the voice. They smelled grease and urine of open hallways, and heard music like birds being strangled as they walked over iron gratings.

"You don't think so what?" Sharon asked, pulling him toward the crowd.

"I don't think so what you said you didn't think so. . . ." He giggled, "I'm sort of funny tonight. I was up all last night listening to my father practice his speech in the toilet and helping him bleed when he got mad. And this morning I started to go to classes and fell asleep on the bus; so I didn't go to classes, and I'm still awake. I'm not tired but kind of stupid with no sleep, dig, Sharon?"

The girl smiled and said, "I dig, Johnny. You the same way every time I see you almos'."

"And I hear myself talking all this stupid stuff, but it's sort of great, you know? Because I have to listen to what I'm saying or I'll miss it."

"My mother say you cute."

They were near the top of the street now, standing in front of a wall stand with a fold-down shelf covered with Chinese magazines, nickel comic books, postcards and Japanese souvenirs of Chinatown. Johnny, feeling ridiculous with air between his joints and his cheeks tingling with the anxious motion of the crowd, realized he was tired, then realized he was staring at the boy sitting at the wall stand and staring at the boy's leather cap.

"What are you loo' at, huh?" the boy said in a girl's voice. Sharon pulled at Johnny and giggled. Johnny giggled and relaxed to feeling drunk and said:

"Are you really Chinese?"

"What're you ting, I'm a Negro soy sauce chicken?"

"Don't you know there's no such thing as a real Chinaman in all of America? That all we are are American Indians cashing in on a fad?"

"Fad? Don' call me fad. You fad youselv."

"No, you're not Chinese, don't you understand? You see it all started when a bunch of Indians wanted to quit being Indians and fighting the cavalry and all, so they left the reservation, see?"

"In'ian?"

"And they saw that there was this big kick about Chinamen, so they braided their hair into queues and opened up laundries and restaurants and started reading Margaret Mead and Confucius and Pearl Buck and became respectable Chinamen and gained some self-respect."

"Chinamong! You battah not say Chinamong."

"But the reservation instinct stuck, years of tradition, you see? Something about needing more than one Indian to pull off a good rain dance or something, so they made Chinatown! And here we are!"

He glanced around him and grinned. Sharon was laughing, her shoulders hopping up and down. The boy blinked then pulled his cap lower over his eyes. "It's all right to come out now, you see?" Johnny said. "Indians are back in vogue and the Chinese kick is wearing out. . . ." He laughed until he saw the boy's confused face. "Aww nuts," he said, "this is no fun."

He walked after Sharon through the crowd, not feeling the shoulders and women's hips knocking against him. "I'd like to get outta here so quick, Sharon; I wish I had something to do! What do I do here? What does anybody do here? I'm bored! My mother's a respected woman because she can tell how much monosodium glutamate is in a dish by smelling it, and because she knows how to use a spittoon in a restaurant. Everybody's Chinese here, Sharon."

"Sure!" the girl laughed and hopped to kiss his cheek. "Didn' you like that?"

"Sure, I liked it, but I'm explaining something. You know, nobody shoulda let me grow up and go to any school outside of Chinatown." They walked slowly, twisting to allow swaggering men to pass. "Then, maybe everything would be all right now, you see? I'm stupid, I don't know what I'm talking about. I shouldn't go to parades and see all those kids. I remember when I was a kid. Man, then I knew everything. I knew all my aunts were beautiful, and all my cousins were small, and all my uncles were heroes from the war and the strongest guys in the world that smoked cigars and swore, and my grandmother was a queen of women." He nodded to himself. "I really had it made then, really, and I knew more then than I do now."

"What'd'ya mean? You smart now! You didn't know how to coun' or spall, or nothin'; now you in colleger."

"I had something then, you know? I didn't have to ask about anything; it was all there; I didn't have questions, I knew who I was responsible to, who I should love, who I was afraid of, and all my dogs were smart."

"You lucky, you had a dog!" The girl smiled.

"And all the girls wanted to be nurses; it was fine! Now, I'm just what a kid should be—stupid, embarrassed. I don't know who can tell me anything.

"Here, in Chinatown, I'm undoubtedly the most enlightened, the smartest fortune cookie ever baked to a golden brown, but out there . . . God!" He pointed down to the end of Grant Avenue, past ornamented lamps of Chinatown to the tall buildings of San Francisco. "Here, I'm fine—and bored stiff. Out there—Oh, Hell, what'm I talking about. You don't know either; I try to tell my father, and he doesn't know, and he's smarter'n you."

"If you don't like stupids, why'd you talk to me so much?"

"Because I like you. You're the only thing I know that doesn't fight me. . . . You know I think I've scared myself into liking this place for awhile. See what you've done by walking with me? You've made me a good Chinese for my parents again. I think I'll sell firecrackers." He was dizzy now, overwhelmed by the sound of too many feet and clicking lights. "I even like you, Sharon!" He swung her arm and threw her ahead of him and heard her laugh. "Christ! my grandmother didn't read English until she watched television and read 'The End'; that's pretty funny, what a kick!" They laughed at each other and ran among the shoulders of the crowd, shouting "Congratulations!" in Chinese into the shops, "Congratulations!" to a bald man with long hair growing down the edges of his head.

"Johnny, stop! You hurt my wrist!"

It was an innocent kiss in her hallway, her eyes closed so tight the lashes shrank and twitched like insect legs, and her lips puckered long, a dry kiss with closed lips. "Goodnight, Johnny . . . John," she said. And he waved and watched her standing in the hallway, disappearing as he walked down the stairs; then, out of sight, he ran home.

He opened the door to the apartment and hoped that his father had forgotten. "Fine speech, pa!" he shouted.

His little sister came out of her room, walking on the toes of her long pajamas. "Brother? Brother, *ah-bah*, he's sick!" she said. She looked straight up to Johnny as she spoke and nodded. Johnny stepped past his sister and ran to the bathroom and opened the door. His mother was holding the man up to the sink with one hand and holding his head with the other. The man's mess spattered over her *cheongsam*. The room, the man, everything was uglier because of his mother's misery in her bright *cheongsam*. "*Ah-bah?*" Johnny said gently as if calling the man from sleep for dinner. They did not turn. He stepped up behind the woman. "I can do that, *ah-mah*, I'm a little stronger than you."

"Don't you touch him! You!" She spoke with her cheek against the man's back and her eyes closed. "He told me what you did, what you said, and you're killing him! If you want to leave, just go! Stop killing this man!"

"Not me, ma. He's been like this a long time. I've been helping him almost every night. He told me not to tell you."

"You think I don't know? I've seen you in here with him when I wanted to use the bathroom at night, and I've crept back to bed without saying anything because I know your father's pride. And you want to go and break it in a single night! First it's your telling everybody how good you are! Now go and murder your father. . . ."

"Ma, I'm sorry. He asked me, and I tried to make him understand. What do you want me to do, lie? I'll call a doctor."

"Get out, you said you're going to leave, so get out," the man said, lifting his head.

"I'll stay, ma, *ah-bah*, I'll stay."

"It's too late," his mother said, "I don't want you here." The time was wrong . . . nobody's fault that his father was dying; perhaps, if his father was not dying out of his mouth Johnny could have argued and left or stayed, but now, he could not stay without hate. "Ma, I said I'm calling a doctor. . . ."

After the doctor came, Johnny went to his room and cried loudly, pulling the sheets from his bed and kicking at the wall until his foot became numb. He shouted his hate for his father and ignorant mother into his pillow until his face was wet with tears. His sister stood next to his bed and watched him, patting his ankle and saying over and over, "Brother, don't cry, brother. . . ."

Johnny sat up and held the small girl against him. "Be a good girl," he said. "You're going to have my big room now. I'm moving across the bay to school." He spoke very quietly to his sister against the sound of their father's spitting.

Sharon held his sister's elbow and marched behind Johnny and his mother. A band played in front of the coffin, and over the coffin was a large photograph of the dead man. Johnny had a miniature of the photograph in his wallet and would always carry it there. Without being told, he had dressed and was marching now beside his mother behind the coffin and the smell of sweet flowers. It was a parade of black coats and hats, and they all wore sunglasses against the sun; the sky was green, seen through the glasses, and the boys playing in Portsmouth Square had green shadows about them. A few people stopped on the street and watched.

TOM CLARK*

❦

Eleven Ways of Looking at a Shit Bird

I

In twenty occupied stalls
The only moving thing
Was the eye of the shit bird.

II

I was of three minds
Like the man who has just seen three shit birds.

III

The shit bird whirled in the flush.
It was a small weight off my pants.

IV

A man and a woman
Are one. Plunk!
A man and a woman and a shit bird . . .

* TOM CLARK, *born in Chicago in 1941, received his B.A. from the University of Michigan and later studied and taught in England. Currently poetry editor of* Paris Review, *he has published two pamphlets of poems,* Airplanes (*1966*) *and* The Sand Burg (*1966*), *and a play,* The Emperor of the Animals (*1967*).

V

I do not know which to prefer,
The sound of my own squeezing,
The shit bird whistling,
Or the splash.

VI

Icicles filled the deep toilet
Beneath my ass.
The shadow of a shit bird
Crossed it
And froze fast to the basin.

VII

I know noble accents
And lucid, inescapable rhythms;
The song
Of the shit bird.

VIII

When the shit bird flew out of sight,
It marked the basin with many circles.

IX

At the sight of shit birds
Flying in a green light
Many would take hiding.

X

He rode over Connecticut
In a glass coach
Without a washroom.
Once, a fear pierced him;

It was the approach
Of the shit bird.

XI

The water is whirling,
The shit bird must be flying.

KEITH COHEN[*]

❧

You Froze the Light and Flew

"... behind the high sustained note, he said he heard now and then the suggestions of a melody."

The next night they were there again. It was difficult to believe that they would stay so close to the building, though a few more yards and they would have been lying against the rusted fenders in the used car dealer's back lot. He did practically nothing at first. Once he was down on the ground with her, it was little different from previous nights. Even after he had unbuttoned her blouse and fumbled with her skirt until it was down to her knees, it seemed ages that nothing happened and that they were more or less still. Then clouds began rushing across the sky near the horizon, about level with the top of the steam stack rising from the huge burner in the adjacent lot. And at the same time, a particular species of black bird began congregating, as they always did when it rained, around the top of the steam stack. They were briefly alighting on the lip of the stack and then re-looping several times in the air and swooping down into the stack itself, when it was suddenly apparent that she had unloosened her garter belt by herself and pulled it down. At once he began to work frenetically on her panties, then on his own pants and underclothes at the same time. Within a few seconds, he had eased himself on top of her. They both had their clothing simply pushed down from the waist to the knees, so that she could barely spread her legs. Nothing

* KEITH COHEN, *born in Quantico, Virginia, 1945, graduated from Columbia College in 1967 and currently studies comparative literature at Princeton as a Woodrow Wilson Fellow. Two of his stories have appeared in* Art and Literature, *and he is finishing a novel.*

71

happened then; again there was no movement. After about five minutes, he moved back over to one side of her. She pulled her clothes back on by herself. They got up rather hurriedly, and he pulled his raincoat up over his head before they reached the sidewalk.

As Katherine walks away and goes through the double glass doors into the apartment building, her hair swings across her shoulders and flashes reflected light in the manner of the three fountains on the front banks of the property. The crests of these fountains are now visible above the low wall that encloses the parking lot. They appear in irregular spurts, sometimes, though infrequently, disappearing altogether below the wall. Their color is constantly changing, probably depending on the light thrown up at them from some cyclical source below. All three fountains seem to be colored by an identical source, since the blue, for example, of the fountain at the left will appear several seconds later on the middle fountain and then in a few more seconds on the fountain at the right. This pattern of horizontal motion, though not at once detectable, can be seen repeated with every color.

"Ten, nine, eight, seven, six, five, four, 3, 2, 1, DONE."

Katherine turned over again, this time getting up on her knees, and pulled the covers from under the pillow down toward her ankles. Before she could sit back down, Alan tucked his fingers into her thin skirt at the waist and pulled down with one swoop all that remained. She slowly flattened out as he dragged the clothes entirely off her legs and then all at once turned herself over to face him. She pulled him toward her at first, but he remained propped up above her by his arms, so she raised her legs and with her feet tugged at his underpants. She got one side partially down. Then with one hand that she unloosened from along her side, she relieved the tension in the front so that the other side would slide down. They both kicked at the underpants until they flew from his ankles.

While Katherine sleeps, an airplane is passing. It crosses the suggested shapes of three radio towers visible from the bed through the window. These towers, formed solely by red lights along their sides, appear to be in the backyard across the street and on the edge of the horizon at the same time. The red lights seem to go out now and then as nearby trees obliterate them. The airplane cruised past their peaks, flashing first a white light on the tail, then two sets of red and blue lights on either wing. The white light continues flashing, and after the plane had passed the third tower a red light near its nose is lit and remains lit.

"He said the crack had started from one point at the bottom of the pane and exploded into thin vessels all across the top."

They were falling from the fifteenth floor. Katherine kept looking up through the hole in the top of the elevator to see the skylight shrink in the distance. They were illuminated by the momentary flash of each passing floor. Alan kept walking over to the control board and pushing the button marked "1."

The drugstore is just beginning to close up when Katherine goes in. Most of the front lights are turned off; then the outside lights. In this way, that which is reflected from the outside disappears almost altogether from the glass, immediately inside of which only the dim lights remain that will stay on all night. They are bluish fluorescent lights, which tint the elastic supporters and half-girdles nearby, at the far left of the window. Some of these foundations simply hang from pieces of cardboard inscribed with tiny diagrams indicating their correct position on the body and arrows indicating the support they provide; others are stretched onto shiny plastic torsos that reflect the lightbulb itself and thus indicate where it is located. The revolving circle to one side of these has a smaller white light of its own. The light shines up from the front of the base, illuminating each side of the revolving disk as it faces forward. On one side is a woman's face, smiling, with bright blond hair in a puffed style that comes in just below the ears; on the other side is another woman's face, smiling, with bright brown hair pushed up tightly on the top of her head and braided. The blonde's face is narrow, and small jowls are apparent in spite of the hair that slightly covers them; the brunette's face is similarly small-jowled, though it is less narrow and more rounded, particularly at the chin. These light eyebrows extend partially across the upper bone of the eye-socket and are uniform in width; these darker eyebrows stretch from two proximate points of thickness to a narrow width beyond the eye-socket. This nose, barely detectable, is formed principally by the two brown oval nostrils; this nose casts a dark shadow to the right that widens above the mouth. These lips are a light pink with streaks of white; these lips are a deep red with circles of reflected light. There are innumerable boxes of facial tissues stretching from this revolving display to the far right end of the window and backing smaller boxes, slightly elevated, of toilet water, cold cream, petroleum jelly, hand lotion, and dusting powder, around each of which is a circle of the same product. The blue cardboard boxes of facial tissues are piled in steps, so that they are eight deep at the bottom, seven deep on the next level up, and so on, the single row being closer to the back of the window than to the front. To either side of the structure, this arrangement becomes irregular, and both the depth and the height are decreased. On the side facing forward of each box that can be seen are printed the name of the tissue in black cursive letters both at the top and at the bottom. The same letters are printed on letters, the first letter, "F," extending out of line with the rest of the top of each box, but on a white rectangular background, the borders of which are perforated. On the end of each box, the name is printed in white letters on a smaller scale. Above the name is a coat of arms, outlined in black and divided into four parts. In the upper left-hand portion is a white bird on a blue background, in the upper right-hand portion a blue sword on a black background, in the lower left-hand portion a blue castle on a white background, and in the lower right-hand portion a black branch on a blue background.

"He told her that the mirror on the opposite wall could be tilted up and down."

From the ruined banks before *Tannhäuser* . . . the horses under green lights . . . green-lit trees . . . sprays of hot swimming, the cobblestone way . . . single-file for the following arias, as the numbing at the heels . . . cascade . . . we eat green grass under Pompey . . . further down the flashlights reveal . . . the "Thunder March" at "demitarif" . . . exhaled by the cannon; at the first stepping wave . . . heads, or rather, skulls . . . these green eyes, are they ours . . . we wanted antiquity . . . from the fumes, the salty recapitulations . . . who hobbled over these dark squares . . . the keys, the window, your friends, the German boys, the gate, the highway, the quai, the well, the coupon, the keys, the window . . . onto firmer cement and blacktop . . . weak wires . . . soil that swelled, or so they said . . . going first . . . "scrambling" . . . would endlessly tell on . . . from one soft point to another . . . these pans on the ledge, but has he gotten over them . . . "friends" . . . the warden, the warden . . . posters frozen on Lake . . . rising, the ground out back . . . sprays . . . from the first reflected shoulder . . . would the final aria have . . . we were on the . . . I am in the . . . the keys, check . . . that light . . . is she . . . flew. . . .

(The hairline at the back of the neck consists of two slight curves, almost scallop-shaped, that make a long sharp point in their meeting. A small drop of sweat rolls out from under this point of hair and slides haltingly down the length of the neck. It stops for several seconds at the top of the back, where the spinal column barely begins to make itself seen. It then continues more or less regularly down the back, decelerating with each new ridge of the spinal column and then, once past it, regaining speed. The drop rolls faster down the lowermost portion of the spine, where it suddenly disappears in the thin sheet of light-colored hair.)

Water

The water in the ponds was clear in most places. It seemed green and heavy only because the concrete bottoms of the ponds were painted dark green. The texture of the concrete, rough and irregular, reflected up through the water, giving it an uneven quality, especially when the water was moving. The water was almost always still, however. Certain varieties of pond lilies and swamp weeds dominated small areas of the ponds. They grew generally in small clumps and were often surrounded by flat masses of pollen and dead leaves from the flowers. The point at which the dry masses met the rest of the water was somewhat foamy and made a clear distinction between the two parts. The plant growth was thickest around the small central statues, which were made of the same concrete as the bottoms from which they rose, but which appeared to have been well smoothed down and rounded.

Luis sped from the top of the mountain road that led, all downhill, into Ax-les-Thermes. He kept pedaling. Usually, he coasted down and enjoyed the slow spiraling of the road through the high green hills that surrounded him. Just before the last turn he would cross a bridge, the only level portion of the road, which linked the hills with the pass where Ax-les-Thermes was located. Because of the many trees level with the bridge, the bottom of the narrow gorge below it seemed dark and cool. A few of the boards creaked as tires would go over the bridge. They creaked in rapid succession this time as Luis, still pedaling, flew past toward the last turn before Ax-les-Thermes. Though many branches of trees leading down the banks of the gorge spread out toward the roadway of the bridge, none of them was close enough to be blown by the breeze of the speeding bicyclist. Only the creaking, in fact, of a few loose boards revealed to any greater extent the passage of the bicyclist, who stopped pedaling only now as he skidded around the sharp turn. The Hôtel Thermal-Soleil flicked before Luis' eyes.

Toriña's long black skirts swished as she walked along the dim hallway. The pile of fresh white linens that she pressed against her with her left hand and the bottle of Vichy water she held in her right were surrounded by vague halos caused by the bits of sunlight that came out from under the closed doors along the hallway. It was as if the linens and the bottle were moving by themselves down the dim hallway. Toriña gave a sharp knock at the door of the master bedchamber and walked in.

Mme. Baratin did not stir in the bed. Her eyes were opened, fixed on the bedpost at the lower left corner of her bed. Toriña put the things she was carrying on the main bureau and busied herself with their preparation. Still Mme. Baratin did not move. The top of the mahogany bedpost, where the sunlight from the window was also focused, was shaped like a pine cone. Burned into its surface was a crisscross design that ended several inches from the peak in a horizontal row of a laced vine design.

"Such a hurry," she said.

The smell of lilac oil that Mme. Baratin had used lingered in the room before Toriña began to rub her forehead and temples with alcohol. She helped her into the white bathrobe and then into the sandals that Mme. Baratin wore to the springs.

"Such a hurry," she said, standing up.

She took the towels that Toriña handed her and started out of the room.

"I was on my way to an unusual ceremony. The new resident was arriving that day to take his honored place at the Pantheon. It was the ashes of Jean Moulin, a hero of the French Resistance. I remember it was an unusual day for March—bright, no wind—so I decided to get off at the Luxembourg Gardens and walk from there. As I was walking I noticed an old woman standing off the sidewalk at a corner, carefully trying to cross. I went over to help her, since I knew I would have to cross a few blocks further down anyway. I gave her my right arm and started across. About the last thing I remember is her holding tightly to me with her left arm. She edged her right hand toward me, as if she were cold, and then there was a sudden sharp pain in my right arm above the elbow."

"So even old women now, eh?" said Luis.

"Yes," she said, "she was pretty safe as a decoy, but she still had the normal incompetence of old age. It was only because she injected too much of the damned stuff into me that there were complications. They got scared, and, as a result, I was saved at the last minute."

"In any case," said Luis, putting his head against her breasts and repeatedly squeezing her upper arm near the shoulder, "I could hardly imagine you kneeling by the bed of some rich lord in Tibet."

"No?" she said and then laughed.

Even the highest statue could not be seen from outside the back property, which was surrounded by very high, thick hedges.

I can't see really having anything more to do with this idiocy . . . at the pond nearest the East woods . . . this idiocy . . . did she say four satin cushions?—and the lilac oil . . . after all, he's a compatriot of mine . . . the oil paint, orange, on his hands . . . I might intercept him at the lane off the road—I know he's noticed me—and there in the woods, in the gardener's shed . . . fool—in the end, I'm affected myself by this . . . and the sangría . . . this idiocy . . . the large pitcher . . . the bicycle and the lane off the road to Ax . . . the bicycle . . . I've got to hurry . . . the bitch—the common bitch—the rich bitch— common! . . . she said the pond near the East woods? . . . she wants to be sure I see it all . . . the bicycle leaning against the gardener's shed . . . the time he hadn't left and his orange hands . . . sangría with plenty of lemon rind . . . his tanned thighs and the door . . . at the back property . . . hurry . . . the bicycle—ha! not there for twenty minutes . . . he flies . . . oh, the cushions . . . this idiocy . . . he flies. . . .

Mme. Baratin had taken off her robe and sandals as soon as she got there, for the preparations had already been made. The spring gurgled, and the sun showed metallically through the glass roof. She sat for a while on the smooth stone steps that were hapazardly constructed down into the spring. For support she leaned her hands back onto the smooth concrete foundation that appeared behind the stones. This portion was made up of several square sections separated by even cracks, like sidewalks. The concrete was very dry because the sun had been so strong all morning. Vague circles of white and sandy shades appeared in each square and were abruptly cut off at the cracks. In some places small grains could even be loosened by rubbing the surface.

Mme. Baratin raised her right knee and pulled herself slightly out of the water. Leaning on her left hand, she tilted her body a bit to the left and undid her hair with her right hand. A few locks of dusty, only partially gray hair fell to her shoulders as she took out each pin. It did not come down evenly, since some remained tangled against her head. The tears that fell from her eyes landed around one of the cracks in the smooth concrete. They turned the concrete a deep gray and were quickly absorbed. Some fell directly into the crack and raised a little of the dust that had collected there from the surface over a long period of warm days.

Mme. Baratin pushed herself off the stone steps and back into the spring waters. She immersed herself up to the neck and, putting her head straight back, soaked her hair. The pulsating sun dried her face.

This wind that flattens out my lips . . . metal . . . skin beginning to hang . . . for the white slave trade . . . did she say an old woman? . . . the hotel . . . on the elevator . . . this wind . . . hanging and too soft like the skin of a dead chicken, plucked . . . "I can stay now" . . . this wind . . . all I can do is pedal . . . touching her neck again and . . . white slave trade . . . the heavy serum . . . to recover . . . on the elevator . . . fresh air and sunlight . . . buses around some other *station thermale* . . . sticking . . . her neck . . . the heavy serum . . . .

"Cataluña, however—didn't you notice it?—is different because it's more open to the rest of Europe than the rest of Spain."

Toriña flared up when she came into the shop where Luis was speaking French to the proprietor. A young girl with long brown curly hair and very pale skin was holding his right arm. Luis' hands, filled with small tubes of oil paint, remained stationary as he spoke. He did not seem to recognize Toriña, who still could say nothing.

"But besides spending a few months here to recuperate, I am profiting from the free time by studying anthropology under Dr. Butlegeia from the University. You probably know about the caves, not only near Ax but also directly under the town, which date from several thousand years B.C. Well, at the present, we're working to arrive at a supposition that humanity did not begin by the brain but by the hand. (Although I'm familiar with the theory of evolution, in this case it doesn't help me too much. But on the other hand, the lucid reasoning—scientific rather than philosophical—of Dr. Butlegeia will, perhaps, finally convince me of it.) It's all connected with these springs, one of whose main sources appears to be located near the *Gorge des Indes* just on the other side, you know, of Ax. We'll be making, the doctor and I, some small excursions down there soon."

"That's where the mountain road comes into Ax from the West, isn't it?" said Luis.

"Yes," she said, "and there's a little bridge just above it."

Same skin . . . some chicken skin . . . green . . . pressing or raw . . . wet or raw . . . "I didn't think the back property" . . . ponds against dark walls . . . after the trip . . . white slave trade . . . white or water . . . the woman in the second-floor window. . . ponds . . . the woman with the statues . . . "and the Spaniards" . . . a dim pond or a dark wall . . . some chicken skin . . . or the white slave trade . . . the woman: the new canvas . . . the statue in the window . . . the orange sky . . . "I thought you said sangría, *por supuesto!*" . . . between the panes . . . glasses . . . white, water, or red . . . against a dark wall . . . no, a blank canvas . . . orange in the . . . no, a blank canvas . . . after the white slave trade . . . sticking and the red chicken . . . glasses . . . through Cataluña . . . the woman or Cataluña. . . the oils . . . no, a blank canvas—the new canvas . . . "Spaniards—didn't you notice it?" . . . after the elevator . . . the gorge . . . but this skin . . . marble bones . . . the woman of the window . . . no, a blank canvas . . . or orange concrete . . . no, a blank canvas . . . or this skin . . . no, a blank canvas.

It was a very old boat that crept along the Yangtze. Its orange sail was attached to the main mast in four places with wooden screws and stone cotter pins. The cabin extended slightly above the two lower points of attachment and, like the deck, was made of the same light, grainy wood that the screws were made of. The only metal visible on the boat was a long cable attached to the stern, to both sides of the boat as far as the cabin, and then across the back of the cabin. This was needed as foundation for the wire screening, the only other material that was apparently of metal, which stretched from this base to the top of the mast, where it was finished off at a single point.

Mme. Rose Nao-Chaung, a large old woman, who usually stationed herself at the rear door of the cabin, had no underwear on, as Claudette pointed out to Jeanne-Marie, under her abundant orange skirts. It later dawned on Claudette that she actually reminded one of a giant Buddha.

"A Buddha of the female sex!" asserted Jeanne-Marie.

But this was the greatest extent of the girls' pleasures. Already three of their number had died from lack of nourishment, leaving the figure at 183. Many of the rest were in a constant state of fatigue, the others shouting complaints with what little energy they had left. What kept most of them in submission, however, was their lack of all clothing except for the oblong strip of cotton fabric that Mme. Nao-Chaung had handed out in exchange for their clothing as they pulled out of Marseilles.

"We are now passing the famed *Yangtze Gorges*," announced Mme. Nao-Chaung. "These natural wonders that stretch between the kingdoms of Chungking and Ichang have been lauded in all parts of the known world for their unusual depth."

As if she had just spoken a signal word, the girls felt a sudden jolt beneath them. The boat tilted onto one side and was swiftly dragged from its course into the region of the gorges. The mast cracked and fell, spreading the metal screening over the 183 naked girls and the old woman.

Spanish green, leek green, serpentine green, attic green, mignonette, glaucous green, artillery green, sea green, Veronese green, corbeau, lacquered green, cucumber green, lily green, statue green, Schweinfurt green, Vienna green, bottle green, onion green.

One of the first times, soon after she had been sent to Ax-les-Thermes, Dr. Butlegeia led her underneath the bridge to the West. He said that he wanted to show her the creek at the bottom of the narrow gorge below. But she said that she was already pretty familiar with the underground springs and that she didn't yet feel up to scaling the steep hill. When they climbed back up to the bridge and walked into the sun of the roadway, she smelled lilac oil in the air.

The empty glass on the tray next to Mme. Baratin was stained a light red. Along its sides were small dried pieces of lemon pulp. The other glass was filled with the same deep red liquid that the pitcher contained. At the top of the liquid, carefully sliced rinds of lemon were floating. Mme. Baratin was half-reclining against two silk cushions. Her eyes were closed. Her right leg was in the pond. When she rubbed the rough bottom of the pond with her toes the water moved.

Luis Caseras had several shows in the Ariège area before returning to his native Cataluña.

JONATHAN COTT*

❧

A Hard Day's Knights

INTRODUCTION

"Come Balthazar, we'll hear that song again."
—*Don Pedro in* Much Ado About Nothing

The surprise of the Beatles' film is that you need to see it
again and again. A friend of mine met a WAC who had seen it
fifty-two times: she was standing in the lobby of a movie theater,
waiting out the second bill until the Beatles would come for her
fifty-third. I have seen *A Hard Day's Night* five times and I will
see it again. What does my, and perhaps your, repetition-
compulsion mean? Great films like *Ivan the Terrible (Part II)*,
Day of Wrath, Pickpocket, Rules of the Game—these are movies
you see many times. The Bogart, Mae West, and Tarzan fans remain entranced with their idols after innumerable viewings. And
films of negligible quality such as *One Eyed Jacks* have their de-
votees: one friend has seen the Western twelve times. But the
Hard Day's Night syndrome is hardly cultish or eccentric. The
second-run showings are usually packed with persons seeing the
film for the third or fourth time. It is not unusual for you to
return to one of the great films three or four times when you
consider their technical quality and emotional power and your

* JONATHAN COTT, *born in New York City in 1942, earned his A.B.
at Columbia and his M.A. at the University of California (Berkeley).
He has contributed the chapter on recent poetry to* The New American Arts *(1965), published poems in* Paris Review *and* Angelhair.
*produced radio programs about music for WNYC (New York) and
KPFA (Berkeley), and published essays on film and music in* Ramparts *and* Sunday Ramparts.

newer awarenesses of this power. But there is a law of diminishing returns here; after the fourth viewing of Becker's *Nightwatch* of Olmi's *The Fiancés*, you rest for a while before you return. I suppose you need them just so much, even as you realize their magnificence. The question is: why do we need *A Hard Day's Night* so much that we keep showing it as often as we do?

NAKEDNESS

Undrape! you are not guilty to me, nor stale nor discarded,
I see through the broadcloth and gingham whether or no,
And am around, tenacious, acquisitive, tireless,
and cannot be shaken away.

—*Whitman*, "Song of Myself"

On hearing the girl's screaming, you would imagine that the gods of fire, dawn, night, and thunder were manifesting themselves: "Let us adore this Wind with our oblation." But the girls scream so that they do not tear the Beatles' clothes off, for by screaming they alert the police who in turn set cordons up to block them from their desire. The Beatles have come running from the Garden: "I heard Thy voice in the garden, and I was afraid, because I was naked; and I hid myself." The girls think Adam's words. They are naked under their sweaters and skirts and desire to become one flesh with the undressed Beatles. So they are ashamed of this desire and scream loudly enough to be enjoined from their wish.

A Hard Day's Night tempts us with the excruciating hope that, when we see the film again, this time, surely, we shall see the four boys naked.

CHILDHOOD AND DEPENDENCY

When the world is reduced to a single dark wood
for our four eyes' astonishment,
—a beach for two faithful children,
—a musical house for our pure sympathy,
—I shall find you.

—*Rimbaud*, "Illuminations"

Childhood is our goal. Concomitant with being a child exists the pleasure one gets from playing and the intolerable displeasure one gets from realizing one's dependency on others. Thus the Beatles play on the rugby field in that most pleasurable scene which you want to see again and again. Four boys mock space and time—the sequence lasts under three minutes—as they play to "Can't Buy Me Love." Every moment seems spontaneous and joyful. Actions and movements are speeded up and slowed down. What we see is how we truly wish we felt or remember how we once felt or how we once wanted to feel. "Genital organization is a tyranny in man because his peculiar infancy has left him with a lifelong allegiance (i.e., fixation) to the pattern of infantile sexuality" (Norman O. Brown). If this is correct, why does the playing terminate? After that beautiful scene of exhaustion when the Beatles—lying on the grass, hands under their heads—count or talk silently to themselves? The answer is that 1) Mr. Genital Reality orders them off his field; and that 2) the Beatles have a TV rehearsal waiting for them. They have escaped from their duties: no job, no "Money"—which song comments obversely on that working-day world situation which "Can't Buy Me Love" attempts to fantasize away. The balding TV director ("It's a young man's business") depends on the manager who depends on the Beatles who depend on both, even when they do not wish to admit it. When Ringo gets led astray by the clean old id man, he assumes independence, and, in the tramp sequence, appears comic to us—the Bergsonian object-butt—but we have lost our goal, we laugh at the child in us now. The jokes are on Ringo, but he does not enjoy them. For the Beatles are boys, not bums, and they try their best not to "grow up."

REACHING OUR GOAL
OR GOODBYE TO BEAUDELAIRE'S OWLS

Such was that happy Garden-state
While man there walked without a mate.

—Marvell, "The Garden"

Thus *A Hard Day's Night* does not, in Keats' words, unperplex bliss from pain; still, it strives honorifically towards our longed-for goal of childhood by focusing on the four boys in action. The great Sung neo-Confucianist philosopher Chu Hsi wrote: "Nature is the state before activity begins, the feelings are the state when activity has started. . . ." The verb "to act," in fact—which, in a general sense, means "to begin," "to lead," and eventually "to rule" (from the Greek *archein*) and also "to put in motion" (from the Latin *agere*)—suggests the Beatles' style of life. Their actions and their songs are impelled not from what they know but from what they are—from feelings rather than from states of mind. Boys and girls are naturally active, and it takes a bit of acculturation before they become bored, depressed, and hung-up. Talking at press conferences, taking a bath, dancing, singing, playing cards, running in and out of jail (even the car thief and the cops become game-playing boys again—society's standards are demolished)—all these actions are invested with pleasurable feeling. The Beatles need only themselves for their own resources. Most important is the fact that each Beatle makes an ideal of himself; and that is why we suddenly realize in amazement that the Beatles sing love songs like "If I Fell" and "I Only Want to Dance with You" only to themselves. "You" means "me" in these songs. There is no "other," but they can say "we" to themselves and to each other. The Beatles' state of nature—to refuse Chu Hsi for a moment—is just this state of self-idealized and self-absorbed activity. The Beatles pinch chorus girls backstage, they get married, but that is, as Gatsby said, "merely personal." It doesn't matter. The Beatles' songs are full of feeling because the Beatles like to sing; but it is the singing that is important, for the "feeling" is the state when the singing has started. The girls are screaming, but, as one of the pupils of Heraclitus said perhaps, is this screaming not part of the song?

LOVE

"... dearest M / please come.
There is no one here at all."

—*Robert Creeley*

The Beatles love what they do, so they love themselves. The screaming girls love the Beatles, and the Beatles are the receptacle or container of their love. They also resemble the Greek god of love, in the sense that Kierkegaard speaks of him:

> It is a genuine Greek thought that the god of love is not himself in love, while all others owe their love to him. If I imagined a god or goddess of longing, it would be a genuinely Greek conception, that while all who knew the sweet unrest of pain or of longing, referred it to this being, this being could know nothing of longing.

But the Beatles not only embody love, they are the Incarnation of Love. As Kierkegaard writes:

> In the Incarnation, the special individual has the entire fullness of life within himself, and this fullness exists for other individuals only in so far as they behold it in the incarnated individual. (From *Immediate Stages of the Erotic*)

The Beatles are as extraordinary as they are because they not only represent Love but also contain the "entire fullness" of Love within themselves. They are thus an embodiment and container of Love, and they are also the Love which they contain. There is no one there at all but themselves.

PHYSICALITY

> *Should time be gone,*
> *and all that is impermanent a mere lie?*
> —*Nietzsche*, "Thus Spake Zarathustra"

It has been observed that *A Hard Day's Night* is not strong on plot. This is of course true. But it is not jokes—"campy," anti-Nazi, anti-cops—as good as they are that hold your interest. Rather it is the director's total dependence on showing the physical immediacy of the events and persons observed that generates the film's excitement and pleasure. I can think of no major feature film other than Dreyer's *Passion of St. Joan* that emphasizes the physical fact in such an unmitigated fashion. In Dreyer's film, the fly on Joan's eye, the warts on the interrogator's face, the cripples hanging around, the child sucking the mother's breast just when Joan, about to die, says: "Where will I be tonight?"—all these observed events heighten Dreyer's outraged sense of the flesh, all the more heightened as they contrast with Joan's saintliness. And yet her face, revealing all the confusion and suffering, is the most excruciating of physical facts.

The Beatles' faces and the parts of their faces, however, are the exultantly observed images—if not the heroes—of *A Hard Day's Night*: eyes, noses, hair, teeth. The image of a hand caressing a guitar, first seen on the studio's TV screen, is as close to suggesting a sense of sexual love as the film allows and so eerily reverberates with more force than had it been employed in a different context—say in an Italian comedy, where everyone is touching. The surprise and exhilaration you feel is similar to how you feel at that beautiful moment in Kurosawa's *High and Low* when you first see the kidnapper in his white clothes—as if he were a princess—reflected in the stream of the Tokyo slum.

Then, too, there are the faces of the girls and women. Their faces reveal as much about them as the humors reveal the characters in Jonson's plays. Just a second's sight of them unimaginably expresses the essence of girlhood. As the Beatles sing on TV, you see the girls in the audience, eyes dilating, each one unique from any other in her ecstasy and the force of her early but veritable sexuality. And if the girls seem womanly, the women seem girlish: the wonderfully shy creature talking to Ringo at the press conference, the women dancing at the party, the sexy secretary putting on her shoes who leads George into the shirt designer's office. The Beatles enable the women to become girls; the girls, women—even if only for a moment or the length of a song.

ROCK AND ROLL MUSIC, OR AT CH'U HILL WHEN THE RIVER STOOD STILL

And we sail on, away, afar,
Without course, without a star,
But, by the instinct of sweet music driven;
Till through Elysian garden islets
By thee, most beautiful of pilots,
Where never mortal pinnace glided,
The boat of my desire is guided:

Realms where the air we breathe is love,
Which in the winds and on the waves doth move,
Harmonizing this earth with what we feel above.
  —*Shelley,* "Asia's Song" *from Prometheus Unbound*

Let us take a roundabout path by examining a beautiful ancient Chinese folk song:

> I heard my love was going to Yang-chow and went with him as far as Ch'u Hill. For a moment, when you held me fast in your outstretched arms I thought the river stood still and did not flow.

The sense of stillness and gentleness of the poem's statement brings out the superficial stillness of the emotion the girl says she feels. For there is no sense of passivity here. Rather, the mind and its experiences have been undifferentiated and everything is bursting out from a single source. The past and future combine, with time superseded, so that the present moment becomes eternal. Everything which is flowing remains rooted in this eternal present so that the stillness she feels, while everything is flowing within that stillness, is a bliss and joy that cannot be expressed, only suggested, which this song does so magnificently. Rock and roll songs almost always last under three minutes. The Beatles' songs, like most rock and roll songs, do not develop their musical materials in the way that the sonata-allegro form develops them or in the way that contemporary serial works develop them through permutation. The simple employment of the diatonic scale, usually two themes, and the relatively uncomplicated chord progressions limit development. (The Beatles' songs hint slyly at modal melodic patterns, but they too are diatonic.) Now the reality of Eternity can be felt only in that paradoxical moment of time when time has been superseded so that the present moment becomes eternal. The limited and limiting musical materials out of which rock and roll is created are perfectly suited to the demands of one's perception of Eternity. Everything in the song—in spite of the strophic tension which is undercut or neutralized by means of the continual 4/4 beat—enables you to remain rooted in the eternal present, so that the "river" does in fact stand still.

In this ambience of three-minute timelessness, we are taken outside of ourselves, if we allow ourselves to be so taken. We are taken back to the Garden where the "tragicomedy of love is performed by starlight" and the fireworks light up the sky. It is the blissful peace of the Diamond Samadhi where you feel, like a gentle rain, the soft petals of multi-colored lotus blossoms and those inexplicable, crazy feelings spreading throughout your gums.

Rock and roll is the new mysticism for those too experienced and cynical to believe much in anything anymore—a mysticism which you can accept for three minutes, a veritable even if noninterpersonal giving of oneself, because there is no fear of losing out. (There is here, too, also a return to the undifferentiated world of early childhood experiences.)

The hard day's night, the race to the train, the playing and singing—this is the passion of the world. But in the end, the Beatles in their helicopter fly up to Heaven. Is this not the Easter revelation we all have need of re-experiencing? *A Hard Day's Night* combines radical innocence and religious revelation, inviting ecstasy and salvation to that soul Yeats wrote about: "self-delighting, self-appeasing, self-affrighting"; whose "own sweet will is Heaven's will." Seeing the film again and again, we are the Vulture King seeing Rama in *The Holy Lake of the Acts of Rama:*

> As he went on, he saw the Vulture King lying on the ground, meditating on Rama's feet and the marks they bore. Raghubir, the ocean of grace, stroked his head with his lotus hands, and when he looked on the wondrous beauty of Rama's face, he felt no more pain.

OF THE COMFORT OF THE RESURRECTION

> *"Bring this boy into the world,*
> *and we'll soon make another."*
> —*Grandgousier in Rabelais'* "Gargantua and Pantagruel"

The Beatles have made another film!

[1965]

R. H. W. DILLARD*

❧

Tanjong Malim: 1934

Rain on the roof, bamboo,
His hand, the glass, splintered
Fingernails and wrinkled suit,
Dirty white, his face, the suit,
And chuk, chuk, chuk, the wooden
Paddles of the turning fan.

Malays, empty faces, rubber pots,
The rows and rows of draining trees,

And now the rain, the heat, his face
Is dry, his eyes are blank, but not

Within

      a dancer, small child, girl,
Her hands are sinuous as her eyes,
Thin thighs, small feet, the ching,
And ching, ching, ching, musicians
Drunk with god and wine, it sways,
Her head, the hollow clong and ching,
Ching.

*R. H. W. DILLARD, *born in Roanoke, Virginia, in 1937, received
his B.A. from Roanoke College and his M.A. and Ph.D. degrees from
the University of Virginia. Currently Assistant Professor of English
at Hollins College, he has published several stories, some scholarly
articles, and a book of poems, *The Day I Stopped Dreaming about
Barbara Steele *(1966).*

Mildewed piano, broken keys, old songs,
Moons, loves that last, broken hearts,

(Outside in the rain, sleek with rain,
Eyes slit toward the light, the sound,
The curve of his knife easy on his finger's
Tip, he crouches, watches, waits, waits.)

Pasteboard lovers, counterfeit love, and baby
Wait for me, for me, old tinkle, clatter
And the negro's hands, his teeth gone,
Sings with tight lips, old songs,

                   the clong,
And clatter, so small in his hands so small,
A child,
          our love,
A moon, Miami in the spring, Paree, Dubuque,

       she moved like silk, was dirty,
Small, ching, ching, no sobs, just silk,
The clong, clatter, cries, and ching.

His hand lies easy on the drink, he doesn't
Drink, his face is dirty white and gray,
And listens to the rain, the rap and tattle
Of the rain, no songs, just rain, and whispers
In the bar (The dark is wet and waits.), his
Eyes are open, teeth yellow in his smile,
Eyes open, chuk, chuk and chuk, the rain,
The rain upon the bamboo shutters and the roof.

A hollow clong, cluk, ching and ching.

ERIC FELDERMAN*

❦

Black's Theme

He didn't look out the picture window toward the beach where the sea didn't break silently through fog. He couldn't think of anything it looked like. He put his hands together like a tiny crown. Ah.

Living in peeyellow walls. Like peagreen boats which he always thought were peegreen boats and he would ask his aunt why his pee wasn't green. He pretends its raining and he's a small papoose on the back of the wind. But he feels his body square and giant. "Be small and soft," he whispers, but his head is weighty and brainless as ruined statues.

Focus my eyes. Furnished room furniture. A wounded bed its intestines white as sheets. The crooked floor patched through the green paint of some been-here-and-gone ambitious tenant.

Complacence of objects. Of reptiles. Nothing's working to-night.

My thoughts die like planets obsessing a dinched sun. My thoughts revolve like closets around a painted king.

They promised me I would be king. They promised me.

He looks at the bulging painting-zigzags and gouged oils. The only thing I want to write is that I want to be a great writer.

What had he expected of these lines and colors?

He tries to imagine weightless blue skies. Those whose voiceless waters promised him endless summer evenings and his star floating

* ERIC FELDERMAN, *born in 1944 in New York City, graduated from Columbia College in 1965 and received his M.A. from Cornell in 1966. He is currently a Ph.D. candidate at the State University of New York (Buffalo). The Dummy's Soliloquy (1965) is a collection of poems; a second book is now complete.*

brightly down landing soft as a child's glider on the wet grass. Glory and gentleness co-orbit strangely in my song.

The best I can hope for is emptiness. But they promised me. Dead sun twitches its broken wings in invisible spaces. But they. Again.

The acuteness of depression revived him. The slight perfume of nostalgia revived him. He got up and walked to the canvas, his fingers wanting to make at least this failure articulate. He got up and stared at the canvas. A blue line there? A third zincyellow orbit? He didn't care. A smile? A grimace? Sharper incisors? I don't care. I want to paint that I can't paint. You pr . . . to paint that I hate painting. The lobster turned like the sun when water whispered to a boil.

He sketched instead.

The renaissance Jew?

Walking to the toilet, he thought sometimes I think my paintings stink and I feel rotten because I'll never be a good painter sometimes I think *painting* stinks and I feel rotten because I can never be a good painter now I think painting stinks but even if painting didn't stink *I* would stink is that worse?

The light switch snapped his picture in the mirror. He says warily "this is I." It didn't sound right. Maybe "this is me." Life sounds that way. No, living sounds that way. Without retrospect, without effect. I. With no past or future. With no windscapes rushing by. I am glass waterflies aimless darting not in or over water. He becomes dizzy focusing and gives blurred thanks for the blur that follows. "Yeeaaaaaaaaaaaah!" Cockroach! wiggled past his smile. His scream shocks him. Like cartoon marines ripped up by cartoon bullets. He scrambles with the toilet paper will the bug get away into the medicine chest tune in next week he tries to joke. Beeeooooow. He slams down tissue on the glass. and tenses panting, will the ropes hold?, smiling at the newsreel cameras. He warily lifts the paper, looking for the funny corpse, revolving it slowly, like a sore head, slowly, like a clock without smiles.

"Yaaaaaaaaaaaaah!" Like a tank its nozzled head and slippery tentacles reared over the tissue. He lost his grip screeching down the mountainside he saw the cockroach rising into the bathtub. Coward! He straightened out his smile and called a strategy meeting. Quick, the waterglass. Scalpel. The fragrant gush of winter-water completed his power. The little monster wriggled up the tub. BloplashBloplash. And it lost hold dropped backwards, back-side down it made tiny thrashes. Give my regards to the Lord of Hosts. But the little pecker righted itself and wobbled up the tile again. BloplashBloplashBloplash. It shot down in a rush of water side and center toward the drain braked backside in a puddle thrashed. Ha, Ha, try and try again, I'll fix you you little bastard. The shiny devil righted up curved forward quick greasy legs drooping feelers. Heroic endurance. BloplashBloplashBloplash-Bloplash poured the whole cupful over him skidded down the drain in what must've been tidal wave. HaHaHa HeeHeeHee. Little brown bug, don't I crush thee! He surveyed the battlefield soggy towels under the sink, urine and grime on the toilet rim.

Tentative feelers quibbled in the drain. Then up. The bug is back. This isn't Germany yet. What've I done to deserve this. He watches the monster scramble up the wall. For 300,000,000 years, they're older than man, two feet long I can see them bathing in primeval savannahs. He watches the monster scramble up the wall. Resistant to radiation—after the bomb they will live in our houses, they will live in our corpses, bathing in our corpses in the tubs where we will die hiding from the fires. He watched the monster scramble up the wall. Did you ever see a cockroach smile? Maybe their faces are too small. It would be horrible anyway. They are stronger than man. The monster heading for its crack. Quick! Jittering toward the medicine chest. Quck! No time water. Qck! No time paper. Qk! Slanted between tile and chest down grimey wall. Your finger it'll get away. He watched the monster scramble . . . A sudden squash I see my middle-finger on the bug squashed.

His coward banged against his ribs. He opened the faucet full-blast stuck his hand underneath eeeeeeyow it's the hot, he looks at it boiled red and disinfected. "Forgive me, God," his coward whispered through his ribs. It wasn't guilt for the bug. I don't want forgiveness. "Disinfect me, God." He wanted to run outside into the cold night. He wanted to take dexedrine. "Scrape the carbon off my brain. I want my points to fire." He didn't drink, he had a picture in his brain of a brain labeled in a medical bottle

filled with vodka. He walks into the kitchen and *sits* down on the
floor against the dirtstreaked refrigerator to disguise his kneeling.
It was disgusting—an atheist wanting to be disinfected. He used
to promise the nothing sky that he would believe in you God if
you let the Dodgers win the pennant. That was already after sky
was imaginary and weightless. He looks across the kitchen at a
dirty milk bottle he had bought in a fit of nostalgia. Oh Lord
were you testing me with the roach? I want to go outside will you
kill me will a sign fall on my head? It would have been mean to test
me with a roach because I will die anyway if I don't kill the roach
they will get into my hamburgers and I will get hepatitis and pass
away in the night like that frog I ran over in the car and saw it all
crushed and popeyed on the dirt road. But that was different I
like frogs I didn't mean to kill the frog. I was sick for a day afterwards like a little boy. Oh God, why are you such a bastard I
wouldn't do things like this to you. I didn't mean that, God, but it
doesn't matter I might as well talk he knows everything anyway
if he does exist probably. I might as well talk because if God is so
mean I couldn't trust him anyway no matter what he said even if
he disinfected me a sign might fall on my head and I might pass
away like a bat in the night poor little bat that nobody loves or
remembers women lock their doors and windows they're afraid it
will get into their hair. I didn't mean it. No, me atheist! Stop! I
didn't mean to really! Stop it! Stop!

Black stood. And pulled himself up into the bedroom like the
descent of man.

He propped his rented bones on the wooden floor. His stomach
is full of loose change—nervousness. Details. Brainwebs I catch
the flies with I catch the stars with. Poor prince I am deafdumb-
andblindandparaplegic in a rented castle with magical spiders for
my whispering advisers only my grief is my own and I keep it
locked in the safe with my valuables. Mail me home in a timecap-
sule to my father. In my condom and sunglasses I have traveled
across America. I am lost in a rocket with Pain and Pleasure and
Mygrief—four forgotten astronauts playing hideandseek aging
slowly with their phony clock I am the lost Magellan praying
eternity will disappear up its rich asshole. Please understand me. I
must walk up and down this little room until my father the king

becomes night in a charmed bat for a moment above the hurrying curtains, winks. I'll brush my teeth and fall in love. Till then I must hide like an abortion in my rented safe and remember again and again how I can do nothing when the vanishing bat blips faintly through the radared distance and behind tiny eyes the universe is pain and dying.

The room was white around him. He was a surgeon. He put his head on the mattress. He rested his head in the bungled intestines of his dead patient. I could amputate my legs and my arms. I could amputate my belly and my heart my islands of magellan and my brain. I could amputate myself. He amputated himself and his dreams rose to the ceiling like cigarette smoke in a landsend graveyard in early september. Down the cliff breakers rattled past rocks like pebbles piddling off a dark window tangloing out among kelp's hydraheads, rainwhite, or a sizzling skillet nextdoor, rear and undertow, rear and undertow, fate or ambush, his dream slept back under the drizzle, his squinting brain dreampt too under a drizzle noting murder left blood on a chessboard.

Deep under sleep the king of heart's last trump tatooed a sentence on him for killing time. Condemned to solitary confinement. They nailed shut his doors and scribbled "moron" above his stickler. He squatted in the closet and gave birth to a pin-up magazine which he cried over like his very own honeybaby, and then he ate it up snidely like a cat.

Waking, his bladder had distended his wand. If I put it in her hat, out comes a bunny. Only an hour had passed. Time has changed. To revive his reticular ammunition he desired to apply icecold compresses to his cerebellum. Unable to get up inspite of the distention he thought latin was like bathing in olive oil it was antedeluvian he meant antebellum it was like speaking into in between a lady's legs that does it he got up walked to the pissoir still feeling slowwitted but also salubriously slowly muscled he waited in the mirror for a bus finally his prick loosened down piss how ingenious the tubes listening to the efficient flush he walked forward the closet reliably like a husband passing the time thinking will nude swimming revolutionize america thinking will tv poison me with radiation above the coats and dirty sheets was his plaster of paris statue bust of Galatea he referred to it with shy jocularity he took it down and rested it on the big table it had a sharp borgian nose I may be prejudiced but it was worthy of Cellini it was white as the desert whether egyptian or vanilla cold and ambivilent she had white northern breasts but slyly pointed like a balinese on which he had put a green bra he had stolen from Jane as a keepsake it was a portrait of Jane.

There was some love in it, no? don't say there wasn't he zipped down his fly and let his pants drop he stroked himself with Jane's hand faithful in my fashion he looked at her plastered face the bra was necessary clothes were her nakedness nakedness implied her clothes the possibility of refusal the smile beneath lipstick the eyes beneath blue shadow the nails beneath plastic claws the pearl necklace that clothed was her power, in bed was her slave necklace he would bend her back backwards till it cracked petitely like knuckles and she would moan like a movie stroke mentioned the coxswain he liked her because she was bald under her hair tied back into a wig and all the whorish expensive things she zippered and tugged onto herself who would guess that her mother looked like Sidney Greenstreet or her father was Nathan Hale he must have been a cat toasting away his life after every meal for his country he liked her because walking through the street her thin energetic thighs rhythmically split her tight dresses but always knowing how broken back she would cling to him in bed and her cunt was so skinny he could rape her again and again it was better than love no sooner were those words spoken than he dropped his hand knowing to come now is adding suicide to injury he pulled up his pants and walked across the room and slammed up the window and looked up above the buildings into the night and looked so hard he broke the sky's thin ice and fell into the deep cold stars. "Oh father," he said.

You gave me life and I let you die. If what I wish comes true, I must have wanted to kill you although I didn't know you and I was so small. How can I make it up to you. Take my art, it will make you immortal you will like that and you will be happy with me. Wind, and trees down the block.—You are deluded. Art is illusion. The illusion of continuity.—No. No. Then life too is illusion. The illusion of continuity. Windy clouds, and down the block the river through black trees. I'm trying to be rational:

Console yourself, no matter what you do everything turns out for
the worst. How can I. Love is too important to be left to the
lovers. Why can't I say would it were I my love flies up my heart
remains my deeds remain down the block are felt the palisades
politics is too important to be left to the politicians the end of
ideology means men no longer feel compelled to rationalize their
crimes my father's last smile is dying comatose on a yellow ra-
tioned, snapshot.

My cock is cold as a sausage
Your cunt is sticky as gravey.
We'll never fuck in the field again
and find our snowred baby. Never. Even saying never he talked
to an invisible love who hid anyway behind the waves he walked
into outward.—and I would be dead then. dead as . . . dead forever. If they would just let me get up in a thousand years for a
few minutes—if they would just, every few thousand years, let
me get up and look around again. "And maybe have a salami sandwich?"—I would be so hungry then. I would enjoy it so much. If
I could just get up and look around, and see if the sea is still blue,
if birds are as green as they used to be, I want to know if the sun
is still the color of your kisses.

The blue waves blooming as they die.

Do you remember those blue days, love?
—dripping flowers blown through our hair.

the drifting moon turns my bones to chalk—
do you remember those blue days?

That will never be—my cock in your cunt your tongue in my
mouth. He hated running circles around himself boredom to love
to sadnessfearingloveloss to horror to guilt to selfpity to nobility
to love to sadness take your pick you never laugh when you're by
yourself this is your life should I kill myself? maybe I should go
to sleep. I haven't finished my work. Please.

In bed. The old gypsy bites the counterfeit moon and rings it
on the counter I crooned a tune last june the bride and tomb and
something blue are rowing home by the light of the tune I
crooned last june when the counterfeit gypsy bit his tongue i

stared up blind on moonshine to save last june i thank whoever put tin moons on my eyes when they rolled me back into the dreamcold morgue.

Tell me mirror on the wall is I be a coward? The mirror is out of order this is a recorded announcement announcing that the mirror is out of order and this is a recorded announcement announcing that the m . . . Oh give me my kazzoo me my washboard on give me banjo and violin case with the penis wrapped up neat inside is my secret weapon. Tell me true scoobydoo is I be your loveydovey handydandy courageous and witty fucking machine tell me I won't take no for an answer tell me.

She's going to tour the world on a banana boat.

It is at such times in the breaking of nations when special reports are interrupting the commercials on my TV set that I wish my synapses could sparkplug quicker so I could think quicker though at the moment here stinking on the hall tile floor I can't think what I want to think quicker.

Once was a pig who lived in a poke he didn't know what to do.

There's nothing to do except things.

Name me things to do to do things name me name me do things please pretty please.

You can shit in your pants or take a chance. I'll take a chance.

You can twiddle your cock or peddle your rocks. I'll peddle my rocks.

You can scream till you're blue or save for a screw. I'll save for a screw. Now what's there to do?

Name my thingssywingsy things to do to do things name me name me please things name me things to do please please.

There's nothing to do except things.

O.K. you motherfucker I'll break your ass now come'on.

There's nothing to do except things.

Pretty pleasyweasy name me name me things to do please please please.

Black lay stiffly back. He is a corpse. Tax collectors pry the wedding ring off his finger. All the whores are mourning in their black nylon stockings.

The elevator doors clattered open, and dusty light pointed

across the hall. Heeltaps coming. The shutter closed. Kick against him, tripping noise, eeek noise, softhard falling feminine lovely thud on him, she fell on him. He rolled over. She, negro!

"Excuse me," said Black, "I was just lying here."

"Oh," she said.

"Do you know what time it is?" he said.

"No," she said.

"Oh," he said.

"Is it cold outside?" he said.

"Yes," she said.

"Oh," he said.

"Why were you lying on the floor?" she said.

"I don't know. Why are you lying on the floor?" he said.

"I've hurt my ankle," she said.

"I'm sorry. Can I help you?" he said.

"No. I'll be alright. I'll just lie here for a little while," she said.

"Don't mind me," he said.

"That's O.K." she said.

"I'll lie here also," he said.

"Yes. Go right ahead," she said.

They lay there for a while. Black thought he was falling in love again.

"What do you think of the civil rights bill?" he said.

"It's O.K." she said.

"Yes," he said.

Then they lay there again for a little while.

"Are you sure you're alright?" he said.

"Yes, I'm alright," she said.

"Are you sure?" he said.

"Yes. My ankle feels better," she said.

"Ankles are tricky," he said.

The hall is cold and dark. In which we are lying is very nice.

"Do you want a drink?" he said.

"No thanks," she said.

"No. Have a drink," he said. He took out the bottle of scotch he had stolen.

"I can't drink it lying down," she said.

"It's better lying down. Try it," he said.

"I'll try," she said.

"O.K." he said. He handed her the scotch.

"I got it at the party," he said.

"You're gurgling," he said.

"Excuse me," she said.

"No, I like it. That's why it's better lying down," he said.

"I see," she said.

"Do you love me?" he said.

"You're gurgling," he said.

"Excuse me?" she said.

"Forget it," he said.

Then they lay there again. Black listened to her gurgling. It sounded like a bird.

Wind, I permit your squalid ecstasies. Tenderly, sun, your illusory voyage. Earth, your lonely solar gyres till oceans mirage epitaphs and you come nameless home to eyeless abstract space with me.

Earth, your lonely solar gyres
till oceans mirage epitaphs
and you come nameless home to eyeless abstract space with me.

"Don't go to the party," he said.

"I came all the way," she said.

"Don't go." he said.

"The scotch was the only good thing there," he said.

"Please," he said.

"Where'll we go?" she said.

"Thankyou," he said. "For a walk?"

"O.K."

Night flattened out the city till it was real as a movie. They walked a safe gauntlet of star chamber alleys haunted by picturesque rapists and snipers moaning swansongs as the neighborhood slowly succumbed to automation and taxicabs. They were very wet and they were very jolly, they went back and forth across the river all night on a trolly.

"It's a beautiful night," said Black.

"Yes," she said.

Walking toward Riverside Drive. He peeked at her. Her

breasts are a genius! Met eyes. He looked ahead, walking. Does she see I'm looking funny. Always think I look pitying funny at negroes like their black skin is a harelip. But I love her big plum-luscious lips her black curving face. He must give her weapons against him. They reached the river.

He started north. She hesitated.

"Which way?" he said. fiftyfifty chance.

"That way," she pointed downtown.

"That way," he pointed uptown.

"Why?" she asked.

"I live at 111th street."

"Ho-ho."

"I want you to see my etchings."

"I thought we were going for a walk," she smiled.

"Yes. Cross my heart and hope to die. But I really have some very nice etchings I want you to see."

"Are you a painter or something?" she asked.

"Yes."

They're walking uptown.

"What kind of painting?"

"Great painting," he said.

Beyond the barbed frantic trees the high black cascading sky. The petitions I didn't sign, the pickets I didn't join. Must do my part. Keep the conversation spiritual and political. Wonder if her thighs are hot even though it's cold her hands are probably cold I would feel them on my I would feel how hot her thighs are with my cold hands. God, there are few things in the world that mean very much to me but this I promise I promise I will not get an erection. Think of the sky. Think how black the sky is. Then think of the river. Think how black the river is. Then think of the night. Think how black the night is.

"The party would have stunk anyway," he said.

"You probably don't like parties."

"Sometimes I like them." He shivered, speaking fast. "But usually I can expect to reach that same kind of terrifying point when I get irritable because I think the subtitles are missing. Then all the ushers start war-dancing around me screaming I'm smoking and I'm dropping candy wrappers and I'm in the kiddie section.

and I don't have a ticket for the loge and I don't have a ticket. But not all parties are as bad as that."

Down the drive a big red bus was farting through the night like a madman.

"Someone must be taking that bus to Havana. Let's take the bus," said Black.

"It's only few more blocks."

"It's cheaper for me this way. See that old lady by the bus stop who's trying to hide her purse from us and's trying to swallow all her Klu-Klux-Klan dues books. When it stops for her we'll grab on to the back and think nostalgic thoughts all the way to 111th street."

They ran across the street.

"Hey, take off your heels," he said. In the middle of the street she took off her shoes, leaning against him. The high black windy sky.

"Hey, hold on with both hands," he said, the bus accelerating with a roar. Paternalism? Cowardice? The fast black night.

Oh fuck the exhaust it's supposed to be cool it's hot smog.

"I didn't remember the exhaust," he yelled through the road and heat and smoke. But she was laughing. He laughed. He leaned backwards chasing the moon through accelerating branches. Cold now that we're moving.

Her eyes before naively suspicious now looking into the wind she leaning out on one hand.

"Hey, you're beautiful," he shouted through the roar and wind.

"What? I can't hear you."

"You're beautiful" he shouted louder.

"I can't hear you," she shouted back laughing. He leaned out laughing on one hand too because it was so fast night was so cold the buildings so toledo bone of gleaming kiss her wanting to through the wind laughing. Lost hold foot can't catch help that's the way it happens help that's the helphelp way it happens he thought help falling plumplusciouslips that's help the . . . eyes, she lurching back grabbed his belt he rocking forward grabbed her waist swung right branches gleaming off bus windows letting go swung side to side leg to leg saved silent through the night they rode.

At 111th street they stepped down. Black bowed ceremoniously, knelt, looked up at her. He lifted her foot tenderly and rested it on top of his head.

"You saved my life, sahib," he said. He rose to attention.

It is a very evil bad thing I do but I must kiss her because I am overcome with gratitude anyway she saved my life. No, if I saved her life then I could kiss her, stop.

"Don't misunderstand, Sahib," he said and he kissed her gentlemanly as he was able about ¾ of an inch above and to the right of her softhard lovely is it orange lips unable to quite kiss her lips or her cheeks stop he kissed her.

"I *hope* I understand," she said and she kissed him right on the lips right over the lips right in the lips she bit his mustache she kissed his freak show adam's apple.

"You're gurgling," she said.

Let's go upstairs and lie down, no. "Let's go upstairs and see my etchings," he said, no. Just let's go upstairs, oh well. They went upstairs.

"I wish I had old family heirlooms to desecrate," he said. "I wish I had medals from the czar to melt down to make you golden slippers. I wish there was someone I could betray for you."

Do I? He was walking into the kitchen to get some cheese to add to the wine and candles. Don't let emotions interfere with passion. Leave the cheese out. Too much of a plot. It was—don't dilute sex with emotion. That can't be true. Nice guys don't win. In baseball.

They sat on Black's mattress looking through the silent dark except for nerves and now and then a car and across the street a disgruntled pianist.

"Talking can't be worth anything," he said.

"You've got to do something," she said.

"Yes. But good talk must be at least as rare as poetry. If it takes a good poet a year to write 30 minutes, how much of what's said is worth remembering? Worth remembering? Worth saying. Mostly silence, and friendly noises, angry noises."

"Then why are you talking?"

"I'm willing to stop," he said smiling in the dark and stopped.

White eyes, white teeth, across the room. She can only be as noble as a savage to me. It is the violence I lovingly observe holding her up by the scruff of her neck helpless I like her black in my black room silent, on the mattress the dead chaperone.

Strategy, I am speechless with lust. Are the condoms in my wallet? Squeeze loftly starry the pig stick.

"Oh," he said. He sidled unconvincingly with many a squeak across the mattress misunderstood and wishing to make conversation.

Then they sat that way thigh to thigh in the veryweary dark. Dear darling, having very nice time wish you were here it is so dark you cannot see your right hand even when it is right in front of your left face god forgive me.

Honey, you is sweeter than the fruit of the jumble, baby he thought slying over kissing her neck like a mouse dammit. Then they just lay there kissing her neck for a while.

Then he caressed her arm and they just lay there caressing her arm for a while. Then he caressed her thighs as far down toward the knee as he could, and they just lay there caressing her thighs as far down toward the knee as he could for a while. Then mostly because of an orderly parliamentary he with all deliberate speed caressed her breasts, and they just lay there for a while because of parlorgentry seizure caressing her breasts for a while like Julius Seizeher, thinking of his slapstick.

Then he slid his hand rather awkwardly cross chest carry I could drown that way is her bra white opposites is what gets me probably black girlie magazine garters on white girls ergo. Keep smiling, can't quite get the zipper down, kiss her, don't let emotion bust the cookie jar.

She sat up. Why didn't I pay the candle bills with more light it would have gone better. Eh, tough, well, shit, sourer than the toots of the bungle.

She sat up and she zipped down in the dark that was all her dress. She stood up and she dropped off in the dark that was all her dress. Black sprung up three ring circus opened his shirt unbuttoned his pants kicked off his shoes and kissed right place at the right time just as she rolled off her bikini panties as gentlemanly as he was able about ¾ of an inch above and to the left of her warmsmelling plumwet silent cunt at first sight.

He grabbed her they sped around the bedroom his wicked metronome beat her time.

In my mind I must tell you we appear to me beautiful lying down your black thighs veed up and open. They leaned down into the bed springs squeeling off into sparrowcupids out into nighttime out into classically bribed with quarters and harpsads the open window out the black open night. Oh my condom. Kiss her. my pants.

Honey, would I fuck you if I didn't mean it he kissed her "excuse me" he said went fishing for his condom like he was going to the toilet excuse me here I am naked it's peculiar not in the right pocket not in the left the ceiling peeling rummaging behind me in the dark is a dark lady waiting to be laid it's saturday. wee early morning someplace behind me in the dark ambassadors are trading cities playing footsie under the marble table my wallet on the table my fucktool's limping with philosophy go back do your duty not to reason why.

"Darling," he whispered creaking back into bed with a babyproof fangle in his hand.

Blacked out airraid they wriggled civil in their bombshelter. He was the mad doctor proudly sticking her with his hydrophobic needle.

"I love you," she whispered. Don't spoil it his armpit whispered. She cozed warm and sad under his chin face against his chest knees drawn up a rollypolly fetus. Black felt slimy with a fetus in his arms. Black disgusts himself. Look, this is a stage she's got to pass through, be nice. All the world's a stage some people like puns and some people don't.

She licked his heart. It's too much sheets cold white under them night through the window cold and wet with seaflowers. Black's heart bloomed like a wet sheet in the sunset his heart was warmed. Black's heart got warmer and warmer he kissed her on the forehead Black's penis got littler and littler. Till it was very little indeed. She hugged Black desperately. Christ, come.

It must be sex isn't sexy. In the street you think cunt all day in bed all you think is Shakespeare. Can't even see her tit or ass, got to feel for them, or jut up on my knuckles for the view, you can see seven states from this here lookout point well known to be famous from the rockies to the smokies holy gee. Fucking blind, that's the worst of it, I might as well be Homer it's all in the mind. It's fucking blues that's what.

Fuck is a one way street, next's the bladder, 'tween piss and shit said the fathers, ha ha can't fuck in latin twat is the mother of us all yielding piss 'n shit is us. The genital phallacy. Stop. I have confidence in you, Black, agent X, do your stuff.

He kissed close her mouth. Cruel in order to be kind? If I fuck you black and blue forgive me because I know what I do. He closed his eyes and bit her nipples and she was wearing fishnet servant stockings shining. bellydancers' rhinestone in her naval a mascara birthmark on her cheek he bit her black thighs babyblue held back, a swift genuflection to automation rolled on the soul-catcher, knelt briefly, rough ease plunged in her smooth must have been lovelywet dammit cunt. jolted together swallowing her hair. Then slow.

Be nice, let her come. He was in a rowboat and the moon rocked up and down like children going to sleep. His arms held tight and motionless behind her back and he jolted in her groin slowly. Instinct. Even rabbits. In the dark he fucked Annie again, he fucked Leila and Nora. I layed Annie in the grass. She was the first so I loved her. Leila had a pretty ass. Nora used to sing and smile. Jane had the tightest cunt of all her skinny legs around me now. Smelling rain through the black girl's hair. I liked it that way the spent sun blacking her smile when I slanted my face. I saw a sign above Jane's cunt, it said: Abandon all hope, ye who enter here. Black girl's pagan warm liquid cunt's best. My night prow cuts ahead.

I'm just an old cod fish with hooks in my heart, ate up the fishergirls in slick magazine rubber fishing pants, he banged her pelvis harder, girl faces ecstatically flat against the glass dying. He strangled her like water black she was and haremspangle moon glint swaying he grabbed her in and pumped her out his legs tightening his fish throbbing red white blue flagpole to the tip. Be nice. He rubbed her he scratched her he bit her he kissed her he licked her he twiddled her tit he jiggled cliopatra he pinched her ass he cleaned her bellybutton there are limits. Come he yelled down the alley. An uppercunt? I'd break my balloon, ah be nice. He lay quiet it was raining under the tracks a skeleton played the harmonium. Intimations of postcoitus.

"What's your name?" she asked sad looking up at him.

And that was to be the best sopoetic sad and nameless. He said, "Frank." The dogtag. Drafted cuntfodder. Now the trench.

"And yours?" he asked leaning up running his hand down between her sweating breasts.

"Cora," she said and clutched up happy close against him her switches thrown muscles already starting shaking.

Now quick or you'll miss the wave you can see it out there the big blue one above the others coming in. Swim out to meet it. It too fast? He bopped the mermaid ripped her jewels invoking leila nora annie jane surf against him fucked her fins to wriggling legs smoothing her water warm against him black stroke out his bat spreading black out under the sea lifting the planet on his shadow her legs split out his muscles wrapped around his stick the camera stopped he and sweet sea against a stop on all angels on slowly blinding aching timeless pin, the muscles ripped the deep wave caved he broke her black unwinding to the beach.

Wind came to the world he lay cooling in his private darkness on the first land. Distant lonely lightning fizzled down her thighs. The world faded back on photopaper dripping up from the greypink chemical sea. His pompous ass itched.

Cock shrunk? Pregnant then. No time for sentiment. Business first. He brushed a kiss, felt down, tugged out, sat up off the bed pulled off the slimy rubber, wiped on the sheet, iced water? but turned back to her. He lay back next to the black fleshthing next to him, held her black sleep-suffocated hive of hornet thoughts, held her big hard explorerphoto breast, slowly dissolving squabbling loving intriguing families through the ceiling floors above him, the moon disappearing high above within its octopus ink night, his brain dissolved like candy in a bowl of water.

"I love you," suddenly Cora said. Black held her closer, I cannot tell a lie. He held her closer, should I prepare a lecture? Gilgamesh, Plato? St. Paul, de la Cruz, Don Juan, Petronius? Freud, or Brecht, or the blue girl, or Jenny. He held her closer, it could have been bluegirl beside me sad looking up 'I love you' I would have held her closer, it could have been Jenny. Pavlov? Night's nice anyway, cold. Be nice. He trickled his hand down between her breezecool breasts.

He lay quiet it was raining under the tracks a skeleton played the harmonium. Borning, fucking, dying is what we do. And in between we think of them. He was in a rowboat and the moon rocked up and down like children going to sleep.

"I love you," he said.

AARON FOGEL*

❧

Gardens
gardens Gardens,
Toads

You play stickball with a stick and a pink Pennsie Pinkie, not with a bat and hard ball. The stick is often the thin body of a beheaded mop, and tape spirals its hand-hold. The ball is soft. Look at your fingernails and you'll know something of its color. It can travel quite far if met solidly (and slickly) by the wood. The game is somewhat silly and contrived, according to Enac. I, too, dislike it.

I played it only once within the past few years, though my childhood is full of stickball. Enac played too that day (he said he liked it then), and Ekaj, the crippled lion, Perez, and Araom with his twisted hazel eyes, and Leba, who is nineteen and looks sixteen, Shooshara, who smiled, Arba, who played only a few minutes and got tired (that evened out the teams), and Aivlyse, a mother duck. . . . I think. These things are important . . . because they are useful.

"The weather report says it's going to rain," says Arba.

". . . rain? So what, so we'll play as much as we can and then we'll stop," Ekaj answers. He takes off his shirt, and combs his hair with a broken comb whose fangs fall out one or two with each stroke. Ugly fat, elephants pushing.

* AARON FOGEL, *born in New York City in 1947, received his B.A. from Columbia College, where he edited the* Columbia Review, *and he is presently studying at Clare College, Cambridge. His stories have appeared in* Art and Literature *and other magazines.*

We put our stuff down on the lawn, and the radio. The radio is static, static over Mozart, static over the news, static over the weather report.

We choose up sides. Perez flips Ekaj. Who wins? Ekaj.

Ekaj chooses me, Perez chooses Enac, Ekaj chooses Aivlyse, Perez chooses Arba, Ekaj chooses Leba, Perez chooses Shooshara, little Araom is left, they flip, Perez gets him. Araom is hurt at being last, he does not feel well, he pulses. The same thing may be said for all of us.

We want to see which side is up first, so Ekaj seizes the stick, holding on upside down, and struggles handerunderhanderunderhand with Perez until Perez's hand rounds roundbottom.

Who, then, is first to pitch, who first to get on base?

Ekaj of the dark navel pitches first, thrusting the Pinkie over the mossrock plate. As when a Cyclops lifts and hurls the immense boulder into the sea to crush his enemy, invoking the greybeard god to grant him vengeance, but misses, because the Fates have shouted "No!" so throws Ekaj, practicing. Finally he gets used to the distance and pitches well.

Enac comes to stick first, giggles a little, and apologizes when he strikes out.

Then Araom (who can hardly hold the thick stick) slams shut his eyes, spins round at each pitch. Black. He misses twice.

Two outs. Perez then, of the tranquil moustache, seizes the low end of the stick, raises it high, and with a congenial laugh says: Something! Cyclops hurls. Ekaj throws. Perez, mocking the ball's speed, gathers his strength.

Perez slams the ball, slick, and, the sound comes and goes, came and went, the ball dissipates, doesn't come near me (thanks), reappears, Aivlyse quacks after it with laughter as it rolls fast. Perez reaches me easily at first, then rounds second (a split tree), lopes over to third and gets home long before Aivlyse can throw the ball.

"You mean it's my turn now?" Arba says. She has been sitting against a tree, and as she speaks she stands up slowly, shrugging one shoulder.

"How do I hold the stick?"

Perez shows her patiently she holds it misses the first pitch he shows her again tells her "keep your eye on the ball" the second pitch approaches low she stoops swings hits so that the ball rolls left she drops the stick says "should I run?" she runs to first I move aside Ekaj battles after the ball bends for it a long time he throws it to me I fumble it falls on the grass bounces I gather it up fold it in my arms pull it toward my groin to secure it.

"I never knew I could do it," she laughs, gasps.

Shooshara sticks next. She strikes out.

Three outs. We come home as they go out into the field. There are five of them. Perez tells Araom, "You play the outfield," a plain of high grass where no balls will come. The boy lifts the lids of his eyes when told where to go, and presses together his jaws. He walks out there and stands in the pulsing sun. The earth is bright and hot, the earth is shade, the earth is bright and hot, the earth is shade, his eyes sting from within, from without, and he stands in the high grass. He stands so long that he begins to feel as though he is upside down: the earth is a shell, on the inside crawls the moving life, while I stand fastened outside, shoved deep away, deeper away into space than even the high grass. . . .

Araom reminds me of myself. His presence infuriates me.

I am up first. Perez throws the ball. I don't swing. I haven't played for years. I was never good as a child. I hold onto the stick. I feel the cloth tape under my hands. I determine to watch the ball and get a hit. It comes. I watch. I swing. I feel the stick resound against my palm. I drop the stick. I begin to run. The ball goes foul. I come back. I pick up the stick again. It comes low. I swing solid. The ball goes straight. It goes toward Arba on second. She sees it. She winces. She puts up her hands. She folds her head towards a shoulder. The shoulder rises. The ball hits her hands. I am running. She seizes her hand. She hisses. Perez picks up the ball. She keeps hissing.

"You okay, Arba?"

"Well, I don't know," she says, laughing, a laugh. "I hurt my finger. You know I never knew that ball was so hard." Shooshara smiles. Arba laughs, "No no no no no I mmean bebebecause it's going so fast. Ofvvv course itsits nothing, I I mean, you shouldn't worry about it or anything, of course, I'll I'll I'll I'll I'll I'll I'll just sit down for a while by the tree. But don't don't worry, you know I mean I'll I'll live," laughs. She walks back to the shade where the stuff and the radio are, she turns on the radio.

Static, tatic, atic, tic, ic, c. Statictaticaticticicc.

Perez calls to Araom to come and take Arba's place on second. The boy looks up, and turns around as though to find something he has dropped. He spreads his hands over his eyes to wipe away the wet, and then runs towards second.

Ekaj softly Leba tells that it is her turn. I find her mysteriously beautiful, with the "dark sexuality of a frightened girl." She stiffly walks to the plate and picks the stick, up. Her shoulders hunch. She holds the stick at the wrong end. Ekaj tells her. She laughs embarrassed, "O I'm such an idiot I don't know what's the matter with me," and she mutters to herself, "stupid!" She hits her thigh. She stands front to Perez. Ekaj tells her to stand facing the plate. She does. She holds the stick, chokes far up. Perez pushes the ball very slow, very straight. She steps one foot back, pulls the stick to herself, and swings with elbows severely bent. Perez says, "Now, you see, bunny, you don't bend your elbows like that. You see you have to keep them straight. And keep your eye on the ball, because otherwise how could you hit it?" laughs. He stands on the pitcher's stone and traverses a mock swing without a stick. "Keep your eye on the ball. Okay. You ready?" She nods her head and looks about distractedly. Her brows fast together, her face knits up. She mutters. He pitches the ball slow and straight again. She swings and misses completely. Her eyes leap about in the hollows between fielders. Two strikes. "That's better," Perez says. "By next time you'll be able to hit it." She puts down the stick. Her back unhunches. She doesn't look around, and walk stiffly back to the tree, sitting down next Arba. They do not talk.

Ekaj takes up the stick.

And now here friends is the moment we've all been waiting for!

Yes it's Ekaj coming to the plate. Perez looks at him tranquilly. Wonder what goes on in his mind at a moment like this, fans? He winds up. Swing and amiss. Ekaj flexing his shoulders, bends down and picks up the ball, throws it back. Look at that arm, ladies and gentlemen! Around stickball we call him the Lion. Perez winds up again, 1 and 0, he throws, it's a fast ball, Ekaj swings, he makes contact! The crowd is going static, and there goes the ball, high up, over their heads and out in the grass. Araom runs after it, but he won't get it home in time. Araom rounds third and rushes top speed home, what running! It's Ekaj round second now, trotting home casually into the arms of his teammates. And the score is two runs for Ekaj's team to one run for Perez's team, with one out in the second half of the first inning.

Ekaj hits the ball. I leap and run as fast as I can. There are times when you put on speed. You feel the strength going all to your legs and you push as though the ground isn't helping you, jutting each leg ahead before you know you've moved the other. I put on that kind of speed now until I realize at about ten feet from the plate that I'm running too fast. As I pass the plate I slip slightly and coast to the ground hands first.

Perez watches me.

"God," he laughs, "you don't have to run like a bunny rabbit. It's only a game."

I rest on the ground, bend my head, hold open my mouth so that my hysterical . . . rapid . . . breathing is less . . . evident. . . . I smile, I laugh, I say, "I enjoy hhh running."

And I recuperate my breath as Aivlyse strikes out. My turn again. I swing empty, twice. Three outs.

II. Whether it is then necessary for us to go out into the field?

Obj. 1: It seems that it is not necessary for us to go out into the field. For, as is sometimes said, "each person should labor only in his own field," meaning the field in which he works best. And Ekaj's team did excellently at the plate. The plate may also be called a field. Hence it is not necessary to go out into the field.

Obj. 2: Further, it is not necessary to do anything. For each act is determined by will, not necessity. Hence it is not necessary to go out into the field.

On the contrary, Philoctetes says, "but what I must look for in wrongs to come," implying that if we do not go into the field, the tide of Fate will turn against us.

I reply that it is necessary to go out into the field. When one plays a game, one must do what is customary in that game. So it is said, "stick to the rules."

Reply obj. 1: Ekaj's team has also done excellently in the field. For the opponents have only attained one run, due, we must assume, to excellent fielding. For what other cause could there be?

Also, the plate may not, strictly speaking, be called a field.

Reply obj. 2: It is necessary to do anything. For if one does nothing, one ceases to exist. Further, will can only be expressed in acts. So, it is necessary to do.

How Many Acts?

"You stink!"

Ekaj begins pitching again after we find our proper places. Enac strikes out, shrugs his shoulders loudly, and decides to be catcher. Araom is up and spins out again. Then Perez is up. He hits the ball straight and hard, just to the left of Ekaj. Ekaj lunges for it and falls. The ball walks off into the grass as everyone rolls toward Ekaj. Who stands up, Elbow bleeding.

"You a'right?"

Ekaj mocks, grunts. "It's nothing, yeah, just go wash it off into the fountain, that's all," he says. Arba follows him with a blue cloth.

We stand around, throw around the ball, hit a bit, but can't play because there is no way. Ekaj returns. "I'm sorry I broke up your game, kids." "Don't be silly, that's ridiculous." "Yeah, we're going to kill you for falling."

Ekaj cannot play. Arba says, "I can play now if you need a player." We say okay. I pitch. It is not easy. Shooshara strikes out. We're up again.

As we walk back to the plate, and they to the field, it starts dripping.

"Looks like rain."

I hold out my palms. I look up into the sky and open my mouth. Yellow.

They reverse direction and begin coming in. The pour clusters, red black green gray white blue yellow white brown red orange yellow blue violet purple pink red white yellow blue red brown

brown red white/yellow/red/blue/green/pink///pink/blue/red/
brown red white green gray white, we run.

". . . rain?" says Ekaj. "This is a flood. What we need is an
ark."

The rain rings some of the blood on his arm. We dry off in the
ping-pong room, and start a few matches.

Note. It is necessary to mention that the following lines were extracted
directly, without quotation marks from Marianne Moore's poem,
"Poetry":

> I, too, dislike it.
> These things are important . . . because they are useful.
> elephants pushing
> The same thing may be said for all of us.
> holding on upside down

In addition, the title of the story was suggested by a line from that
same poem: "imaginary gardens with real toads in them," (itself in
quotes).

The line, "How Many Acts?" is from Gertrude Stein's *Four Saints
in Three Acts*, though the question mark is mine.

❦

Vietnam

1.

After a haircut, feeling the cold wind closer to my scalp.

From the barber chair a series of repeated diminishing reflections
In the opposite mirrors that should technically be infinite
But end at seventy or so.

In the chair next mine, an officer of the college NROTC
Is talking about stocks with the Jewish Barber who owns the shop.
The barber cuts hairs from the officer's nostrils
And the officer turns his words toward Vietnam.
The barber says that the Russians will help the Viet Cong.
"From where?"
"From Vladivostok," the barber says with his accent.

"But we throw up a blockade. What'll they do then?" the officer
    laughs.
The barber walks away from the chair to get lather, and says,
"They came by sea."
His fingers full of white lather.
"But we put up a blockade, right around it.
What can they do about it?"
"The Russians are going to help them with their navy."
The barber is behind the officer, studying his hair sculpture in the
    mirror.
"But we throw down a blockade. They can't get through it," the
    officer insists.
The barber continues to say that, "The Russians will help
The Chinese, no? They'll send in troops."
The officer finally gets his point across while the barber is vacuum-
    ing his head
"Yes, but we throw a blockade and what can they do about it?"
"So . . . then they'll come through China."
The officer laughs. "Through China? Ha!
China and Russia aren't friendly enough. We'll live to see
The day when Russia asks us for help. We'll live to see the day."
The barber sweeps him with a hand broom. The officer say,
"You and I will live to see the day."

    2.

All over America today poets are looking up from their
Newspapers, holding their fingers near their ears,
Listening, smiling, saying, "Vietnam . . . the name has a nice
    sound."

A photographer friend of mine said, showing me a photograph
Of Negroes beaten in Selma, "Isn't that a great photograph?
What a strong shot. Look at that white cross. Look at this grey
        up here.
Look how sadly this woman is kneeling."
The old paintress writes
"There is no ecstasy like an ecstasy of compassion"
As she composes her book on school integration in New York.
She later writes, "And then, of course, I thought, if
Death were to be triumphant, what colors should be used
To be the most triumphant?" She chose blue and red.
I would use elephant grey. The elephant is big and has a hard hide,
The elephant forgets, the elephant is a gentle creature,
Who loves water. World Book says,
"Like most other animals the elephant dies
Wherever he happens to be at the time."

"The only thing is," he said, "the terrible thing is, I want to help
These people and I can't."
"Yes, that's the terrible thing."

"Art," she continued, "is a state of being.
For instance, one time Picasso was, we were drawing together in
        the park.
Which we sometimes did, and I drew some trees and foliage.
And he said, O Sarah, that looks like a tomato. 'Permit me.'
And he sat down and drew a tomato in my leaves.
Art should properly be the tear-gas of the heart.
It should make the feelings run out of their houses
To do battle in the streets. One time I saw two people
By the sea. It suddenly struck me how beautiful they were,
And, you see, I had this state of being, so that I wanted to cry out,
'You are as beautiful as
Two Egyptian statues!' "

In John Jay Cafeteria, reopened now for those
Among us who had been boycotting it
To get union elections—

Now that the boycott is over, I ate there two nights ago,
Sat near a young fellow in NROTC who spoke of the walks in
        space,
Assuring a pale, high-voiced man of thirty,
"The Russians are terrible photographers. We've got much better
Photos of the moon. We'll win."
He laughed happily. Then he described the techniques and history
        of the war
In Vietnam, and said of gas,
"Actually, it's more humane than bullets."

   3.

I too love my baby food.
The click of swallowing. I eat sweet celeries
That crackle, I laugh, and when my belly
Is touched by Judaism or by Carol's
It grows warm and I am inclined to smile
I know that there is goodness and peace
In my world in our time but I do not
Even think anything like that sentence
But simply listen with a kind of concentration
On being to the hysteric chirps of birds
In a college morning nesting in the stone library
Above the columns as I walk over the red bricks.

Anna read to her small son the story "Vietnam."

"The red sky at twilight is covered with a blue cover,
Becomes violet, burns itself out
Against the finiteness of its own time.
A smell of burning gasoline comes from the sky
And with it a healthy looking man whose eyes betray
To us that he is in nirvana. He comes in a red
Car and wears white robes that overcome the fine night.

"Among the Viet Cong there are 431,543 kotis of lotus Buddhas.

"He sings, 'The Buddha-field filled with rice-paddies.' "
All over New York this fine spring

A host of white rice and brown rice-paddies
Of yellow rice and cardinal red rice-paddies
Came down.
　　　"When the citizens of Vietnam woke up
That morning they could find no rice and no rice paddies
Anywhere in their lovely land and they wondered,
'What has . . . ?' "

Anna noticed that her son had fallen asleep.
He was drooling on her dress.
She carried him to cot and went to an afternoon movie.

　　4.

"The U. S. Government will not tolerate
This attempt to destroy our destroyers."

STATE DEPT CITES DISTINCTION BETWEEN OVERT AGGRESSION AND RETALIATORY RAIDS

The poet takes his toke and gives a sermon
On the marvelous experiences to be had from LSD.
"Hot Green Leaves! Burning Bush! Brushed Cheeks!
What Heat! What Light!"

　　5.

Ray and his friend were discussing Vietnam at a party.
Ray said that we had not given the Buddhists free elections.
His friend said, "Frankly, I'm not interested in freedom.
We're defending our own interests." "What interests have we
Got there? It's strategically unimportant," Joan argued.
The friend thought.
"Well, economically, for one thing. There are a lot of rice-
　　paddies."

Exiting from that trionfi party
Where the team of play and silence triumphed
Over the team of dance and concentration
I heard two "Bastard!"'s.

Across the street, two wives stood in the half open doors of their
    opposite houses.
Their husbands screamed at each other on the lawn of one.
In the other house the old wife wept, "Stop it. Stop it."
But her husband pushed the other over the porch
Railing head first into the snow.
A few seconds later they began punching each other and fell onto
    the snowy ground, jaws shaking.
I ran across the street and broke it up.
They lay on the ground for a few seconds. Then one got up.
An old man came out with a rake. He was dressed in tweed
And said to the man lying still on the snow
Who had not punched first
Who had been the one to fall head first into the snow,

"George, get back in your house."
His rake made him appear a vulture
Reminded me of a political cartoon I had seen
Portraying Boss Tweed and cronies as vultures,
With the inscription, "Let us Prey."

George said, "This is my land and I'll stay here
If I want to." He lay on his back in the snow,
Snow as cold as statuary,
Which had lengths of green and purple vegetation running
    through it
It was lovely suburb, frame houses
Surrounded by a belt of cemeteries
Clean doorsteps and the young wife said
"Sylvia, for ten years this has been going on,
The same story. If you wanted something,
Why didn't you ask for it?"

NORMAN FRUCHTER*

❦

An Act of Comic Revenge

Mary McCarthy's *The Group* is an act of comic revenge, directed not against eight Vassar girls of the class of '33, but against the shallow and mechanistic progressivism of the thirties. Miss McCarthy's girls have left Vassar in a flux of loosely ordered concepts and notions knitting into a characteristically "progressive" ideology, which contains attitudes towards not only problems of politics and economic organization, but also home furnishings, child-rearing, the management of marriage, and, of course, sex. After Dottie Renfrew gets seduced, then humiliated by her fitting for a "pessary," and almost destroyed by her seducer's failure to receive her and her equipment, Miss McCarthy shifts to Kay Strong, who becomes Mrs. Harald Petersen with a mind stocked with consumer research tidbits and a ravening desire to achieve more than her fellow group members. Two chapters later, Helena Davison surprises Kay's husband, Harald, kissing Nora Schmittlap Blake, wife of a left-wing fund-raiser, and we enter Norine's world of Marxist jargon and unending cultural cross-reference. Each girl's entrance sends up another thirties clay pigeon; we dissect scientific child-rearing with Priss Hartshone Crocket and psychoanalysis and psychotherapy with Polly An-

---

* NORMAN FRUCHTER, *born in Philadelphia in 1937, took his A.B. at Rutgers and later studied in England on a Fulbright fellowship. As a writer he has published one novel,* Coat upon a Stick *(1963), and essays on politics and literature, particularly in* Studies on the Left. *As a film-maker, he co-authored the short feature,* The Troublemakers *(1966).*

drews. *The Group* begins with Kay Strong's marriage, with all the girls gathered to celebrate, and ends, eight years later, with Kay's funeral, and the same girls gathered to mourn; the intervening chapters attempt both a narrative of the group's career and emotional progress, and a comic encounter between each girl's progressive notions and the particular thirties' fashion or institution she chooses to work within. The intention is to take on both the ethos and prevailing ideology of a historic period, and a clearly defined group of characters, and to produce comedy from the inhumanities of the ideology and the limitations of the charaters. The attempt fails, badly, and for several reasons.

In most comic novels, the humor comes from the action, or interaction, of characters we *understand* and yet find ludicrous. The action is revealed through a normal third-person narrative, with occasional digressions into the thought processes of the unfortunately comic character. But since none of the characters in *The Group* exist on a level complex enough to make them understandably comic characters, in the tradition of Tom Jones or Mr. Micawber, there is no comic action. Instead, there is only the dry humor that occurs as we laugh *at* the exposure of each girl's inadequateness; instead of scenes of hilarity, *The Group* presents a mixture of dialogue and perception which captures each girl's shallowness in moments of satiric and sniggering condescension. That condescension is one of the keys to the book's failure, since Miss McCarthy evades any analysis of the two girls she treats most sympathetically (Helena and Lakey) and turns the section dealing with Polly Andrews, the most "normal" member of the group, into a fairy tale and women's magazine parody. Similarly, though sex is one of the book's preoccupations, Miss McCarthy manages only an ironic and clinical description of all the girls' unsuccessful sex. Polly, safely within her fairy-tale world, enjoys warm, "successful" sex, but her experiences are never related.

Miss McCarthy uses what seems to be a conventional third-person narrative to expose her girls, thus saddling herself with the most cumbersome method for detailing thought and response—the he-thought, she-thought device. She surmounts this awkwardness by using a differentiated narrative which changes for each girl, and utilizes the girl's slang, dialogue tics, and favorite expressions within the narrative. The attempt is towards a double exposure, as each girl is partially revealed by the narrative and then more revealed once we realize that the narrative is meant to read as if each girl were speaking, in the third person, about herself. Unfortunately, the attempt does not succeed. Miss McCarthy employs a judicious, balanced prose, which progresses with the careful pace of the essay. Neither the pace, nor the balance, changes as the characters, and hence the narrative organization, change; Miss McCarthy cannot really differentiate her wry, analytic prose for the rhythms of the different characters, and so all the stylized narrative amounts to is the use of some slang and some speech idiosyncrasies.

This inability to create comic action or to differentiate her prose for each character really stems from Miss McCarthy's basic inability to create character. Her acute intelligence, which has produced, among numerous other fine critical essays, the most perceptive treatment of William Burroughs' *Naked Lunch* I have read, manages only character dissection within her fiction. A character is carefully defined along a programmatic line of some psychologic or psychologic-social construct, and then the requisite number of physical facts, personal habits, ideas, slogans, and tics are pasted on. When the character is sufficiently layered with fact, he is set within a scene (usually a dialogue where some argument or clash develops) and exposed. Unfortunately the exposure reveals nothing that we have not already understood in the logic of factual accumulation, except Miss McCarthy's cool pleasure at dissection.

The inability to create character stems from an imaginative sterility that no amount of intelligence can fertilize. Miss McCarthy's earlier novels dealt with thinly disguised contemporaries; beneath the wealth of surface observation and behavioral detail (usually malicious) was the same lack of any creative conception of what the character under the microscope eye of the prose was really about, almost as if one of Miss McCarthy's ordering assumptions about fiction is that if you ridicule a character enough, you somehow make him real. The same wry, astringent, analytic and non-sensual perception which dominates the earlier novels triumphs in *The Group*, although Miss McCarthy's attempt at individualized narratives ought to produce tones other than her characteristic skepticism. One of the lesser ironies of *The Group* is the construction of an elaborate form which attempts to eclipse Miss McCarthy's usual perception and only succeeds in reinforcing it.

Lukacs might attempt to analyze the causes for Miss McCarthy's creative failure by examining both the value structures (especially the repudiations of most of the positions she took up in the thirties) which are defined in all her books, and the political and ideological positions she currently holds—a judgment of creative sterility through ideological default. I think that both the attempt and the conclusion are not particularly useful; biographers, finally, can concern themselves with the ultimate relations between the life and the work, and the general judgment on most of the ideologues of the thirties is so obvious that it is useless. It seems more useful to examine why Miss McCarthy has failed to achieve the comic novel she hoped for, and to locate that failure within her own perception; the final causes for the inability to respond to one's own experience with the qualities necessary to create vital fictional characters will always escape analysis. It is sufficient to point out that Miss McCarthy has never been able to deal with those areas of human consciousness not concerned with already generalized ideas, and has confined her analysis of emotions to the lower range of feeling. Polly's experience of anxiety in *The Group* is an example of the cold reductiveness Miss McCarthy takes for humor, just as the number of climactic incidents which occur off-stage (Kay's suicide, Lakey's lesbianism, Jim and Polly's love-making) is a key indication of Miss McCarthy's failure to handle any significant and deeply felt emotion experienced by characters she is not prepared to ridicule.

A final note, on the object catalogs, attacked by most critics. *The Group* is choked with objects, which are described, priced, grouped together, and used to explicate the values and choices each character exercises. For me the objects became, perversely, the most consistent and original achievement of the book, for Miss McCarthy succeeds in focusing and using her objects to define both her characters and the particular environments they choose to move within. But perverse, finally, because in most novels, comic or not, the character's inner organization determines how he lives with and uses the objects that surround him; in Miss McCarthy's novel, the characters, lacking any convincing inner organization, are defined by the objects they choose. The result is a style so heavily naturalistic, so limited by what can be labeled and identified, that no real comedy is possible. The final irony of Miss McCarthys' book is that she set out to expose the mechanistic assumptions of the thirties, but could manage only a naturalist prose style and a series of equally mechanist assumptions about her characters. Instead of the humor which should stem from all the human improbabilities confounding inhuman, though progressive, notions about economics, sex, and child-rearing, *The Group* emits only Miss McCarthy's characteristic dry chuckle.

KENNETH GANGEMI*

❦

Olt

Robert Olt felt the pain again when he bent down to pick up a cracker from the floor. He put a hand to his belly, wondering what the pain was, and tossed the cracker into a paper bag marked "Ducks." He walked over to his bureau and picked up a slip of paper:

> Man is the species *sapiens*
> of the genus *Homo*
> of the family *Hominidae*
> of the sub-order *Anthropoidea*
> of the order *Primates*
> of the sub-class *Eutheria*
> of the class *Mammalia*
> of the sub-phylum *Craniata*
> of the phylum *Chordata*
> of the sub-kingdom *Metazoa*
> of the animal kingdom.

Also on top of his bureau was a clipped advertisement that offered, for one dollar, a list of two hundred uses for sawdust, newspapers, and tin cans. There was a book about dinosaurs, a folder describing giant binoculars, a Japanese camera, a letter from a friend, a map of the city, a bear's tooth, and a list of forty-two differences between sunrises and sunsets.

The bear's tooth reminded him of his trip to the zoo the day

* KENNETH GANGEMI, *born in 1937 in Scarsdale, New York, graduated from Rensselaer Polytechnic Institute and later worked as an engineer. After a hitch in the army, he turned to writing. His stories have appeared in* Art and Literature *and* Transatlantic Review.

before. He remembered the alarm at four o'clock in the morning, coffee in the all-night cafeteria, and the deserted streetcar. He had presented his Zoological Society card at the gates and been admitted just as the first rays of sun were striking the treetops. A white pigeon had flown up from the shadows and flashed into the sunlight. Robert Olt remembered the morning when he had crawled out of a sleeping bag and watched a magnificent sunrise while standing naked on the rim of the Grand Canyon.

The veterinarian had hurried by, off to treat cases of barn itch, big head, lumpy jaw, black scab, breast blisters, blue bag, scabby nose, and ox warbles. Once Olt had watched him take semen from a bull rhinoceros and inseminate a female. He had watched him operate on a hippopotamus, deliver a baby giraffe, and extract a bear's tooth.

Olt had made friends with some of the keepers, and they permitted him to enter the cages. The flying squirrels had glided down to his shoulders, landing with soft *thumps* on his sweater. He had played with the ocelot cubs, and tossed fish-chunks to the dripping otters.

During the winter he had watched the macaques turned out to play in the snow. He had watched the keepers take buckets of neat's-foot oil and long-handled brushes and oil the elephants. They had told him that one of the performing elephants, in order to avoid punishment for mistakes, secretly practiced her act at night.

Olt had seen a bighorn ram mount a small female, forcing her to her knees. He had walked through the Australian collection and seen the kangaroo, boobook, bandicoot, cockatoo, kookaburra, numbat, nardoo, wallaby, wallaroo, and jackeroo. He had gazed with admiration at the furry, black-and-orange scrotum of the Bengal tiger and had wanted to swap.

Robert Olt stopped thinking about the zoo, put on a jacket, and left his room. He was going to visit a girl who lived nearby. It was a warm day, and after he had walked two blocks he took off his jacket and carried it over his shoulder. He saw the market ahead and decided to buy her some peaches.

A bakery and a flower shop adjoined the market. Olt walked into the bakery and sniffed the warm, sweet odors. When his sense of smell became used to the bakery he walked next door to the flower shop and sniffed the flowers. Inside the market he looked into the eye of a fish and saw the image of a straining fisherman. At the fruit counter he looked at a shiny plum and saw the image of a sweating Mexican fruitpicker.

Olt suddenly felt the pain in his belly again and paid for two pounds of peaches and left the market. He thought about his friend as he walked towards her apartment. She had told him about the time when she was fifteen, with stickers in her socks, and dead leaves on the back of her coat, walking alone out of a woods. He knew about her summer job in the department store, where she had gone to work in the mornings without a bra and had come home at night wearing a new one. He knew about the time she had hitchhiked across the country on three dollars.

Once she had been pregnant and looking for an abortion. She had heard that women with German measles could obtain legal abortions, so she found a sick little boy and tried to catch his German measles. She couldn't catch them, but luckily she met the little boy's doctor, and he consented to help her.

When he arrived at her apartment she had just taken a bath. She was lying on the bed, her robe half-open, playing with her Siamese kitten on her bare belly. She smelled of soap. Olt remembered that for a few months, after she had returned from Europe, she had only shaved her right armpit, keeping the left full of silky brown hair.

She thanked him for the peaches and gave him a list of some old college friends she had recently seen. After every name she had written either *growth* or *degeneration*. The list read:

> *degeneration*
> *degeneration*
> *growth*
> *degeneration*
> *degeneration*
> *growth*
> *degeneration*
> *degeneration*
> *degeneration*

degeneration
degeneration

He told her the joke about the woman who wanted to seduce the Pope. She told him about two nightmares: driving through an endless suburb in a station wagon filled with children and collies; and being tossed, naked and bound, into a white-slaver's van. They talked for a few minutes about the possibilities of a tropical garden, the men in the French resistance, the relative decline of the United States, the inefficiency of learning in a classroom, and the handful of people who achieve the good life. They talked for a few minutes more about her plans to spend the summer in Denmark, and then he left.

Twenty minutes later Robert Olt bought a newspaper and walked into a cafeteria. At the counter he overheard an old man insist that the *Titanic*, instead of sinking to the ocean floor, had reached equilibrium at a great depth and was still suspended there, slowly revolving in the gloom. He heard a Negro laborer in muddy workshoes order French fries to take out. Olt paid for a cup of black coffee and walked over to a good table by the window.

Three high school girls were sitting at the next table. One girl was looking through the new yearbook, and the crackle of the heavy pages reminded him of the special *smell* of a yearbook. There was a new fad: in front of each girl, purposely displayed, was a packet of birth-control pills.

He picked up the newspaper and began to read. The United Nations was considering the establishment of an international holiday; it would occur on the vernal equinox, the day when all places on earth have equal day and night. Chemists in the perfume industry had succeeded in synthesizing mate-attracting odors that operated below the conscious olfactory range. The planet Venus would be easily visible at midday with the naked eye.

A naturalist reported that the California condor and the whooping crane were now definitely extinct. A political advertisement attacked public libraries as "socialized books." An art gallery was showing a collection of thirty-two framed and mounted death warrants. Another gallery was showing a collection of nudes: aged female derelicts, in calendar-girl poses.

A new one-act play was reviewed. The play was a conversation among seven characters: an infant, a schoolboy, a young man, three other men aged thirty, forty-five, and sixty-five, and a senile old man of eighty, all with the same fingerprints.

Construction had started on the African superhighways. A surgeon had been accused of grafting his wife's navel onto her buttock. The body of a suicide had been discovered in a cheap hotel: no identification was found, just a geological time chart and a map of the stars. A man had been arrested during High Mass at St. Patrick's Cathedral for urinating on the altar.

An editorial-page poem was about a rehabilitated man working with a rebuilt bulldozer in a reclaimed desert. The Internal Revenue Service announced that there were 15,000 millionaires in California. A college fraternity had been suspended because three of its members had shaved a girl's bush. A man from Skagway, Alaska, had murdered a man from Mazatlán, Mexico, after an argument over the duration of twilight.

The Psychiatric Society was to view a documentary film on high school orgies. Police were looking for a man, dressed as an exhumed corpse, who was hiding in cemeteries and sneaking up on people. A columnist wrote about the New Prostitution. Three wirephotos showed Eskimos on motorcycles, Pygmies on waterskis, and the funeral of Henry Luce. Seventy-five tons of apples had been dumped in the Columbia River.

A filler said that in the last 100,000 years 68 billion humans had been born and had died. African antelopes were being introduced into New Mexico to fill "unoccupied ecological niches." The Coast Guard had reported over eighty inhabited sea grottos on the Pacific coast. Russia was building the biggest roller coaster in the world.

The sports section had photographs of skiers. Robert Olt suddenly remembered skiing on a sunny spring afternoon and a girl lying in the snow, her knees bent, thighs still spread, vapor rising from her wet pussy into the cold air. She had tossed tiny snowballs at his steaming cock. They had laughed about chapped nipples, and snow-lobsters, and her bush turning white every winter like a snowshoe rabbit.

He turned to the classified ads and read the "Help Wanted—Men" section. No men were wanted to rebind books, build fountains, paint streetcars, erect junglegyms, or make rowboats.

Olt folded the newspaper and gazed out the window at the passing people. The sidewalks were crowded. He saw two policemen hustle a man into a paddy wagon and felt uneasy, as though his place was also inside the paddy wagon. He saw an old man stagger by with two broken suitcases tied with string. He saw a midget bitten by a Pekingese, a man carrying a sign that said "Keep the Pope off the Moon," and a Negro boy with a violin case.

Olt left the cafeteria and started walking towards the park. He passed a school where ninth-grade girls in white gym uniforms were playing volleyball outside. He stopped to watch them for a few minutes, thinking of the hot, crowded locker room afterwards. He remembered the time he and two other schoolboys had looked through a roof window and watched thirty naked girls taking showers.

Near the park a street-corner preacher had attracted a small crowd. Olt stopped to listen.

"Do any of you people," asked the preacher, "know the difference between God and Santa Claus?"

Everyone was silent. Then a drunk tittered and said, "There is no God!" and everyone laughed.

Robert Olt entered the park and paused to look into a baby carriage. He saw a sleeping baby lying on top of a woman lying on top of an old woman lying on top of a half-decayed corpse on top of a brown skeleton on a tan skeleton on a gray skeleton on a great number of white skeletons, gradually crumbling into a column of white dust.

At the first bench he sat down and took off his shoes and socks. He tucked them under the bench and walked over the freshly cut grass to the pond. The summer before he had watched them drain the pond; they had scooped out all the trash fish, and then restocked with bass and bluegills. He sat down on the grass. Two boys were doing something on the other side, and a minute later he watched a toy sailboat, loaded with three hamsters, cross the rippled pond.

Robert Olt smiled and lay back on the warm grass. He felt the sun on his body and imagined himself basking naked on a sunny island with hundreds of seals. He tried to picture the faces of the drugstore and grocery clerks in all his old neighborhoods; wondered if it was possible to run across a pond that was packed with floating bodies; thought of some things he had *not* learned from people he had *not* known.

He imagined earth as it appeared from the other side of the Milky Way; hundreds of naked children running and laughing along a sunny beach; River Street on a summer evening after a thundershower; Dostoevski and H. G. Wells discussing the evolution of the teachings of Jesus Christ; a naked girl sitting with spread legs at the edge of the surf; a chipmunk peeking out of the eyehole of his bleached skull.

After a few minutes Olt remembered that he had to go to the library and got up and started walking towards the children's playground. He passed an old woman scattering a black powder over the flowerbeds. When he got to the playground he climbed up on the junglegym and sat on the top bar and watched the children playing on the swings and seesaws. A little girl in the sandbox looked up at him and smiled, and he smiled back.

Olt saw a Greek gardener reading an Athens postcard and remembered an old dream. He had dreamed of finding himself in a laughing group of eight men and eight women, quite young, still in their twenties. They had been wearing old European costumes and speaking languages he did not understand. One of the girls had smiled at him. She had introduced herself as the girlfriend of a Danish student, and had told him that they were his sixteen great-great-grandparents.

Robert Olt smiled again at the little girl in the sandbox. Then he felt the pain in his belly and decided to go to the library. He climbed down from the junglegym, walked back to the bench, put on his shoes and socks, and left the park.

When he arrived at the library he took out a slip of paper. He had written a list of things to look up:

glaciers
American Bison Society
interrogation techniques
advice on dealing with blind people
egret hunters
Japanese relocation
appendicitis symptoms

He looked over at the prim librarian. She was the type that had a very hairy body. She undoubtedly used electricity, razors, or chemicals to combat the unfashionable hair, and he imagined her running naked in the wilds, leaping over logs, with her hairy arms, hairy thighs, hairy back, hairy breasts, and hairy belly.

In the reference room Olt leafed through volume twenty of the encyclopedia—*Sarsaparilla* to *Sorcery*—and read the article on *sedition.* He read about the men who opposed the Louisiana Purchase. He read why there wasn't a heavier immigration to the Amazon basin.

Olt found an article entitled "Disasters of the World." Six pages of disasters were listed, classified as marine disasters, airplane accidents, conflagrations and explosions, earthquakes and volcanoes, and hurricanes, tornadoes, and typhoons.

He read why Theodore Roosevelt never created a Lake Tahoe National Park. He read about the naturalist who walked northward with the spring from the Gulf of Mexico to the Canadian border. He looked up *appendicitis* and quickly decided to go to the clinic after reading the part about reverse peristalsis and fecal vomiting.

Before he left, he stopped in to see the famous mural in the children's library. The mural covered an entire wall: Gulliver, Robin Hood, Ferdinand the Bull, Rumpelstiltskin, Babar, the Headless Horseman, Mowgli, the Jabberwock, the ticking crocodile, Glinda, the Tar Baby, Huckleberry Finn, the Seven Dwarfs, the Roc, Winnie-the-Pooh, Long John Silver, Johnny Appleseed, the Bandersnatch, the Forty Thieves, the Goose Girl, the Blue Ox in the Blue Snow, the Cheshire Cat, trolls, castles, the Enchanted Forest, the Emerald City.

That night, as he lay in his hospital bed, Robert Olt thought about the doctor who was going to remove his appendix the next morning. The doctor's face was dominated by overdeveloped snarling muscles. Every time he spoke the snarling muscles triggered and drew his lips back from his teeth. Olt envied the doctor's hands. They knew the feel of goiters and wrinkled skin, and Olt had always wanted to fondle an old woman's goiter.

Earlier in the evening he had read a pamphlet about a soldier who had been shattered by a land mine at El Alamein and had undergone 410 operations in nine years; and he had sat in a big group of bathrobed people and watched an old Charlie Chaplin film.

The lights were turned out in the ward. Robert Olt yawned and moved his legs between the clean hospital sheets. He smiled, thinking of the young nurse who had shaved his belly, and soon fell asleep.

MICHAEL L. GLENN*

❦

The Room

1

I am sitting at my desk. The window is to my right. Through it I can see the street and the apartment house across the street. When my shades are up I can see the top floor of the building, but when they are half-down as they are now I can only see the bottom two storeys and half of the third one. I haven't yet met any of the people across the street. I haven't yet been out of my room, not since I entered it, not since I paid the old lady her rent for a month in advance and moved in with my groceries. One large rectangle of glass forms the lower half of the window, but the upper half, the half covered by the torn yellow shade, is composed of six smaller rectangles of dirty glass. There is a crack in the very top frame, to the right. But since the shades are halfway down I can't see the crack now. And it is just as good that way. I'm sure I would feel a draught on my neck from the crack if I could see it, but now, that I cannot see it, I am sure that there is no draught in the room.

It is cold. It is almost December. When I came here with my groceries, the landlady made a joke about Thanksgiving, and I laughed. But I had no turkey. I don't celebrate holidays. Every day is like the one before it to me. But that is beside the point. What matters is that it is cold. Perhaps there is no heat. If the old landlady thinks I shall put up with no heat during the coldest

* MICHAEL L. GLENN, *born in New York City in 1938 and raised in Atlanta, earned his A.B. at Princeton, his M.A. in comparative literature at Harvard, and his M.D. at Columbia Physicians and Surgeons. He is currently taking his residency at New York State Psychiatric Institute. He has finished one novel and started a second and a third.*

months of the year, she is wrong. When I see her I shall speak to her, I shall tell her that it is cold in my room, I shall not laugh at her jokes unless she promises to warm my room. I must make a note of that. But, of course, she will probably say the heat is already on and that it must be a crack in one of my windows that is causing my room to be cold. What will I say to her then? What could I answer without affirming that, indeed, there is a crack in the uppermost right pane of the window, the one which is covered by shades now. I had best not mention it at all. If I ask her to fix the window she will become angry. She will stalk about my room waving her arms around. I do not want that. I shall say nothing to her, then. I shall pretend I do not see her if she comes. I shall lock the door. But all this is beside the point. I was talking about the room.

My bed is on my left. It is unmade, as usual. My small stack of clothing is on the floor behind me. My books are on the bed, and some are on the floor beside it in a nice pile. My apartment has only two rooms, or rather only two sections to its one room. My desk, bed, books, window, and clothing are here. The toilet and sink are in the other part, and a mirror which I bought myself from the five-and-dime store when I came is over the sink; my stove and small ice-box are there, too.

That doesn't seem to say it right. When I say stove, I can see it by craning my neck. It is my stove. In the ten days I have been here, I have grown to know it. My stove, with its four burners, round black holes, covered over with a circle of grimy metal on which I lay my coffeepot and frying pan, the circle resembling a star, a starfish whose innards are missing, but which I put over the flame anyway, because I need something on which to rest my coffeepot. But there is more to the stove than that. I am forgetting the pilot flame, burning with its blue flame like an eternal light. Last night, or the night before, I'm not sure, I watched it from my desk-chair for an hour, the blue flame, wavering slightly in the draught that must have come through the crack in the window. And then there are the stove's great white sides, there is the oven door, its dull handle spattered with the grease from something I cooked above it. There are the black legs, short and squat, on which the stove rests like some heavy bird. There are the knobs that control everything, little white knobs for turning gas on and off, which I played with at first for a while pretending they were teats until the smell of gas made me sick. One can't forget the knobs. And there is the kettle on the stove, which I brought from the other house, the one I lived at before I came here, a light-weight kettle with a piercing whistle, it holds exactly five and a-third cups of water, it is always polished, it is round. The kettle is not like the knobs, though. The knobs are uneven and hard, but the kettle is somewhat plump. The kettle is my friend. I can't say the same for the knobs. Yes, that is what I mean when I say stove. Four feet high, heavy, cube-shaped. It looks like a dwarf beside my ice-box. The ice-box and the stove looking like my Mutt and Jeff, my food and sustenance, quiet servants, masters, it doesn't matter which, how can a stove matter, it's always a stove, even if it's a friendly one.

Where was I? Oh yes, the room, the stove, the desk, the window, next door. Next door they are singing. They have been singing for ten days, ever since I got here. I banged on the walls, but it was no use. They must think it's amusing. It must give them pleasure, like it gave Murray pleasure when he sang his old songs, I can still hear him singing his old songs, the songs next door make me remember, I've been remembering a lot lately, things come back, all the things I'd forgotten, all the things I wanted to forget, all the things I couldn't forget, like Murray's song, like the dog, whose dog, Murray's dog, was it Murray's dog, I don't know whose dog it was, what dog, I can't start remembering the dog now, not the dog, nor the hole, the small black hole, small and oily, I can remember it now, but I should forget it, I can't be sure about that anyway, it's best to forget it, I can't forget it now, not the hole nor the dog nor the song nor the face.

I'm not to blame for any of it. I wouldn't hurt anyone, not even the old landlady, not even the people next door. If they get angry I'm sorry, but it isn't my fault, none of this is my fault, not the dog, not anything, I'm not to blame, and if I remember it's not my fault either, I can't help that.

The glass was sweating as much as he was. He took a deep breath, wiped his forehead with his sleeve, looked at the table. But the beads of sweat on his glass stayed. He didn't wipe them off. One of them began to trickle down the glass, leaving a clear stripe as it rolled, moving down, around the curve of the glass, around the bulge, and then, more quickly once it passed the bulge, rolling to the base, stopping, a pearl of water at the thick base of the glass, then, weakly, making contact with the wooden table, soaking into the grain, disappearing except to leave a dark spot, like a stain, and all the time he was looking right there, right at the base of the glass, watching the drop disappear, and not saying a word all the time.

I have to stop thinking of that. It wasn't my fault. Later, I can talk about it later. But now I have to think of other things, like the room, like the noises, like myself. For instance, I am growing bald. I can put my hand to my head, and pull out a few strands whenever I wish. At a comparatively young age, I am growing bald. My nose is running too. I think I must have caught a cold from the draught in this room. And I have a pimple on my chest which, in the past day or two, has been growing. It doesn't itch, doesn't hurt, but I can feel it. I know it will grow bigger, and when it grows big enough I shall squeeze it, pop the head between my fingers. That will amuse me. Purgation, I shall call it. Then I shall wash my hands.

I am losing the skein. The song reminded me of something, of someone. Not Murray, because I have resolved to forget about Murray for a while, but about someone else, about *her*, yes, about her. It's strange. It's strange for one to treasure one image above all others, and to feel sorrow over it. But I feel it deeply. I can see her image, I can remember her story, I can see her face. Ah, Valla, woman of my youth, love.

I must control myself. If I am going to think about her I must use discretion. Too many sentimentalists are running about as it is. My passion was not like that. Valla, what would you say if you could see me now? Would you laugh, or sing? I think you would. Then it is just as well that I left you, that you left me, that it ended between us, all because of, because of what, of a black circle, of a small circle, of a laugh perhaps. Valla, shall I tell about it now or not? Shall I think about it?

First I'll raise the shades, so I can look out while I think, so I can see the people walking around. Valla, would you like it here in this room?

It was at least ten years ago, maybe more, I'm not sure. Time doesn't matter that much anyway when it's behind you. I was young at the time. I was lonely, too. My father had remarried after my mother's death, and I felt I was no longer welcome at the house. Besides, I had finished college, and I wanted to be out in the world on my own. For almost two years I had lived by myself in an apartment like this one, off a main street in a rather large town. I made a living by teaching English in a public school, but I hated the work. At the end of the term I handed in my resignation. With the little money I had saved I planned to keep myself in bread and coffee for a few months while I decided what to do. I had the intention to write.

(This is not the story of Valla, I'm telling the story of Murray. I don't like that story at all. It sounds just like all the other stories I ever heard, and I know the ending already. It is very sad. I have to tell the right story. I'll start again, anywhere, the middle perhaps.)

I met Valla by accident one night.

No, that really isn't so. I waited a long time to see Valla, I used to watch her walk down the street, I was too timid to talk to her, it was only by following her to her house, without her knowing it, that I found her last name, on the mailbox, and, by looking up the last name in the phone book and checking it against the address which I knew, that I found out her first name, Valla, which stayed on my lips from then on. Even then I did not speak to her. When she walked past me, my lips formed the syllables, Valla, but I made no sound. Some evenings I watched her house to see if she had a boy-friend, lover or suitor, but she had none of these. One morning I followed her to work, and found out she was a librarian. From that day, I made it a point to go into the library once a day. It was inevitable that she should begin to notice me. I waited for the right moment to speak to her. I knew that once I had spoken the delicious period of waiting was over, and I would have either made contact or lost it. There could be no second tries, I felt.

How many times did I rehearse each gesture, each accent of my speech. How many nights did I spend, my head tightly in my pillow, thinking of the words I should say. Then, finally, one sunny autumn day when the trees outside the library window were in full color, I spoke to her, I made my move. And she answered. She smiled. I saw her lips quiver. I was beside myself, in ecstasy.

That was how it began. Yet it seems I have told it too quickly. Each moment of expectancy, of fear, of hope, each moment of longing should be re-lived. After all, it is the only love of my life. I'll have to tell it again, go over it and try to explain.

No good. It was doomed to failure. Even Murray could not bring me back to my senses after it all happened. And it was I who left her, not she who left me, regardless of what I say later or said before, because now, telling the story, I remember clearly, I know how it all happened, I know I left her, because I was too delicate for her, for anyone, was then, and am now, because I had to leave her, the only love I ever had, the only woman who ever loved me, all because of what I could not help seeing, could not help hearing, all because of my own self, because I have been and shall always be that way.

I am that way now. I am solitary, egocentric. I know it. It's like a cloud in my brain.

The walls of my room are blue. From the yellow ceiling hangs a large bulb at the end of a slim metal chain. There is no lampshade. If my back were not to the lamp, there would probably be a lot of glare. My bed, as usual, is unmade. By my hand is a clay ashtray, orange, with three butts of varying sizes dumped in it. The ashtray stands on three legs. Its inside is almost pink, but the rim has been blackened from having many cigarettes tapped in it. It resembles an open mouth.

The shades are up. I can see all the way to the top of the building across from mine. Most of the blinds are drawn. I expected that. People in this neighborhood keep their shades down, especially after dark. Now, even though it is not dark, most of the blinds are drawn. It gets me mad. I have always peered into windows. There's nothing wrong with it. I just like to watch people, from a distance, see what they're doing.

Some old woman is out walking. Her head is bent into the wind. She looks like a nail someone hit with a hammer. Dressed all in black, the way European women are always dressed, she looks like she's going to someone's funeral. She's going to the corner now, heading for the store to get some eggs and butter.

There's that dog again. He's following the woman. When I first came here, he barked at me, showing his yellow teeth. Now I hate him. I see him a lot from the window, and whenever he sees me he lifts his big black head and howls. During the day he lies on his owner's porch. I don't know what he does at night. Perhaps the next time I go out, if I go out for food, if I get hungry, I shall try to make friends with him. I know how how to do it. A few days ago, a little girl called to him, and he came over. She stood quite still and extended one hand towards that monster. He crept closer and thrust his wet nose against the girl's hand. She still did not move. Then she began to speak some kind of baby talk, and the dog listened. Within a few seconds the girl was patting his head. He was conquered. It's disgusting. Evidently it's very easy to make friends with that animal if one wants to. Now I do not think I want to, not that animal, not with his head

tilted at a slight angle from the line of the rest of his body, his eyes looking upward, his tongue lolling out, his black fur matted together at his neck, glistening,

no, not at all, not that dog. Look at him following the old woman, padding along behind her. It would be funny if he ate her, but I doubt that would happen.

They are still singing. Where was I? I was telling part of a story from my youth, what kind of story, what kind of youth, negligible, insignificant, poignant only to me. It's true, about being poignant, all my stories are poignant to me, I get tears in my eyes over any of these stories, I can't help it, they're my stories, to me they're beautiful.

II

If I am to tell stories, I shall have to apply some order to the process. I shall have to tell them from beginning to end, or from end to beginning, for that is how stories are told. It is ridiculous to try being different. After all there are rules in everything.

I shall warm up first. This is a short story which actually happened. It will serve as the introduction to the longer, more poignant story I shall tell later, the story I can't get out of my mind even now. It is called THE EGGS.

Once, several days ago, a man, I, was hungry. It was late in the evening, after dinner, and nearly into the early morning. What was there to eat? The man went to his cabinet, took out his frying pan, and took some butter from its place on the third shelf in the icebox. He put a large pat of the butter in the pan, which he then placed on his stove. The heat went as high as it would go, and a blue flame darted from the pilot to the burner and spread out fan-shape beneath the pan. The man, I, went next to the top shelf of the ice-box, and returned with a small carton of eggs, half-empty. Ah, even now as I tell the story, I can still feel the man's excitement, my excitement of several days ago. An egg. A beautiful, smooth egg held in one's hand. Can there be anything more lovely? Can there be anything which gives greater pleasure?

The butter was crackling in the pan, sending small yellow-brown bubbles above its hot surface. With a quick and dextrous motion, the man cracked the egg on the side of his frying pan, and, with one hand, spread the segments of shell apart so that the egg could drop, unencumbered, into the pan. It fell perfectly into the hot butter. The plump yolk was exactly centered in the pool of albumen, like a yellow flower in a pond. The egg began to cook. The albumen began changing from a jelly-like mass to a white ring, like a lacy collar around the yolk.

The man discarded the egg-shell into a brown paper bag at the foot of the sink. Then he reached gravely into the carton again. He chose a fine, smooth, brown-shelled egg and repeated the same ritual. Once transported to the stove, the egg soon dropped gracefully into the pan beside its brother. Both were cooking, together. It was a spectacle to behold and admire.

The man let the butter fry the edges of the eggs, and once or twice he tilted the whole pan so that the butter could trickle inwards in the direction of the yolks. When a brief few seconds had passed, he grasped a spatula in one hand and held the pan with his other. The eggs seemed done on one side. With a skillful, rapid movement, he flipped the eggs over to their other sides. Oh how they sizzled! The yolks held firm.

Ten seconds more, and he turned off the flame, lifted the pan from the stove, and deposited the eggs on a plate which was lying on the table. What a lovely sight they made, the two eggs. Like two eyes, two breasts, two hands: two eggs. With salt and pepper, and a dash of paprika the eggs were prepared further. When all seemed done, he raised his fork to his lips in a prayer of thanks. Then he lowered the fork to the plate. Soon, the eggs were gone. The first egg was eaten alone, by itself, plain. The second was dispatched in company of a modest chunk of black bread and butter.

Oh! How good it was. How lovely! How rich and creamy was the yolk, and how crisp were the edges fried in butter! The bread sopped up the remaining yolk. The plate was spotless. The meal was done.

For a brief moment, an all-important moment, the man felt as if life had a goal, a purpose, a sense to it. If only because he had eaten such eggs and might, the next day, eat two others like them, if only because of this, he was ready to go through the dark night until the next day came. There was true hope, in the shape and taste of an egg.

An egg exists to please. It does not ask to be pampered. It does not ask to be fed, to be dressed, to be considered, to be complimented. Its entire purpose in life is to be eaten and to be enjoyed. An egg is an instrument of love, there's no denying it. The egg loves whoever eats it; whoever eats it, loves the egg. There is no whining, no false promises, no placating. In short, this noble man reflected that, given a choice between a woman and an egg, only a fool would not choose the latter.

Having thought this, the man, fatigued by now from the intensity of his experience, wiped his lips and, with a last sigh of pleasure, walked into his bedroom. There he slowly undressed and went to sleep. His dreams were happy, and his sleep was unbroken.

That is one of my favorite stories. I tell it because I like it. In that short story are embodied the simple principles by which I now live my life.

Great pleasures are to be had among everyday things, if one looks for them. In the form of an egg, in the warmth of a bath, in the smoothness of clean bed-linen can be found perfect joy. The only complications in such a life come from without, such as the incessant singing noise from next door or the incredibly ugly face of my landlady. But more of that later.

Now that I have hinted at my secrets, I am free to tell my longest story. I have been remembering bits of it, more and more, during these last ten days. A scent, a color, a face, is enough to set it all off.

The moon lit up the last window to the right. It was dark, but vague outlines were visible. A silver-colored hand moved over the window-frame on its way to the arm of the sofa. And suddenly, framed by the shining glass, a face appeared.

The sun is going down in the West, and the sky is very blue. Soon it will be dark. I can already see lights behind some of the shades across the street. For some reason the singing has stopped. They seem to be listening to me next door, wondering what I am doing. Now they are laughing. Yes, and now they are going on. One of them has put a record on the phonograph at its loudest volume, and they are all singing with it, following the leader,

like a summer in Italy. She had been sitting in the chair a long time. Now she rose from it, stretched her hands over her head, leaned back. Her fingers loosened her hair from its tresses. Dark hair fell over her bare shoulders. She wanted to play a record. ("Piacere?") When it was playing, she began to dance, and her body undulated like a ten-cent hula doll. ("Lei?") Somewhere behind me the two chambermaids peeked from the half-open door, the dark one with hair tangled on her legs and the blonde, the tall blonde, who wanted to be a movie star. When she came towards me I, not knowing anyone was watching, reached out my hands towards her hips. I was accepting her invitation. We didn't speak for a few moments. We danced, and she was humming the song's melody. But then one of the chambermaids, the short dark-haired one or the tall blonde, giggled, and I turned around to see who it was. The girls ran away. When I looked back at *her*, she was laughing, too, and the record was no longer playing. The room was quiet. There was noise coming from the outside, though. Now I was blushing. ("Ebbene, cara, come si chiama?") And then I knew I had transgressed, stumbled into a situation I couldn't control. ("Wanda," she said.) The floorboards seemed to groan as she passed over them. A wave of the hand was for me. She opened the door of room number six and closed it behind her. A thin sliver of face still peeked from behind it as it closed, and I could see the expression in the one eye visible, an expression of disdain, mockery, contempt, I could feel it all the way into the parlor where I stood, not knowing what to do, by the phonograph which had stopped playing, while those two chamber-harpies clanged dishes together in the kitchen.

Why am I thinking of that? Have I then retained my memory, am I going to be taunted by scenes like that for the rest of the day, of the night, do I have to re-live all my old mistakes, the ones I couldn't help doing, the ones I was ignorant of when I did them, the ones I now understand, am I to be taunted by memory, when memory should be pleasureful and not tormenting, with the result that I am deceived by my own self, the self I wish I could forget, which I cannot forget?

Where was I? Before, before they had put on the records, when the sun was still above the top of the apartment building across from my window whereas now it is below it so that there is no glare, but the sky is getting redder and redder all the time as if there were a fire somewhere. I was trying to tell about myself, in an orderly way, starting the farthest back, with Valla, but Valla wasn't the farthest back, that was Murray, although Murray was both before and after Valla, and Wanda was before only, or was it after, I'm not sure, all these things happened so long ago, so far ago, how can I be sure of them, how can I be sure of anything, I, who only know that I am in a room outside of which on the right is a street and on the left is another room where they sit, the ones who keep on singing, and that I am at my desk, and that if I turn my head a hundred-thirty-five degrees to the left I shall be able to see the blue flame of the pilot on my stove, this is what I know, and at times I even question this, and, if I cannot be sure of the flame in the room, how can I be sure about the stories, be sure if they are so, or if the sequence is really as I think? For I may think today that Wanda came before Valla, and tomorrow that Valla came before Wanda, and yesterday it may have been that Valla and Wanda were the same person, and that is just as plausible as it is not, so how can I know, and how can I be sure? So why not take it as it comes, memory, and let the scenes follow what they will, because it's all me, I know that, it couldn't be not-me, because there is only me here in this room, and if there is also any face or any scene, then that face or scene must in some way be me, too, or else I would have to believe in spontaneous creation and worms coming out of rotten milk and things like that, which everyone knows cannot be, even I, I who am, who am in this room, who must choose now and go on, I cannot get stuck, I must go on. I started with Valla, I see her again, Valla the librarian, Valla the dark-haired girl whom I followed one day from her job, after I had spoken to her, the day we talked together, as we walked through the fallen leaves.

"My name is Valla."

I told her mine. We were on a residential street that led from the main road to a district of our town where librarians, students, and unemployed artists lived. The houses on the street were set back from the sidewalk by their lawns, and trees stood between houses and in the front yards like domestic gods. A man raking leaves waved to us as we passed. The smoke from his fire of dry leaves filled the air about us with a strong, autumnal scent. Two children were on his front porch, playing a game with some sticks. They, too, waved at us, imitating their father in the way they moved the fingers of their right hands from the tip of their foreheads just below the hair-line, upwards, frontwards, and to the right in a precise arc, while their forearms, which had thus far been bent, straightened themselves out, until their fingers and hands were extended out towards us at the end of completely extended right arms. All this was accompanied by a large smile from each child, as it had been from the father. I smiled back, feeling very much a part of the day, the weather, the street, the people.

"They're cute, aren't they?" Valla said, waving to them.

"Yes," I said.

I had followed her out the library door that day. I walked behind her at first, but then I caught up to her. She seemed to recognize me. I fidgeted a moment, and then asked her if she'd mind if I walked a little way with her. She said it would be all right. And now we were walking together.

"I've seen you quite a bit at the library," Valla said. "You come in there often."

When she spoke, her lips formed the syllables of each word. Yet she did not speak slowly. Or, even if she did speak slowly, I was nevertheless entranced by the beauty of her voice and did not mind having to wait for the entire sentence. In fact I enjoyed prolonging the pleasure of each word. At the word, "you," her whole face centered about her puckered mouth, her eyes seemed rounder and brighter, and the sound of her voice seemed to hover in the air like a small ring of smoke. The slight down on her upper lip made this motion all the more charming by encircling her lips above with a darker band, while a dark spot just below her lower lip seemed to be a natural counterweight to it. Spot, down, shadow, and hue: all made her mouth a thrilling object. I was enchanted.

"I live to the right," she said.

We both turned down a very small street, almost an alley. The houses here were no longer suburban-type; rather, they were older and more crowded buildings. I kept step with her. She couldn't know how happy I was. In the short time we had been walking, I had told her about my family, about the job I had just abandoned in the hopes of doing something better, and about the year I had spent in Italy and France. This last bit impressed her. She had never been out of her home-state. Her mouth formed an incredulous "O" when I described Paris to her.

"And you have really been there!" she said. "That's wonderful. I wish so much I could go."

"Yes. And it's everything it's supposed to be."

She shook her head. "I don't think I'll ever be able to get there."

I assured her that she would, especially since everyone was getting a chance to see Europe these days. I laughed when she laughed, I turned when she turned, I believed all my waiting had not been in vain. I did not, of course, tell her how long I had watched her from the opposite side of the street when she went walking, how I had hid behind iron gates when she passed so as to sniff her perfume, how I had waited outside her house at night watching for visitors, how I had constructed fantasies in my mind at all hours of the day, fantasies in which I would conquer her and find in her everything I had always wished to find. No, I told her nothing of that. It would have frightened her away, I'm sure of that. It would have frightened anyone away, all the tricks and games I played, all my thoughts, my observations, my obsessions, no one could really understand them but myself, and that is why I kept them from her, tried my best to portray myself to her as I knew she would want me to be, she, a lovely and lonely girl, undoubtedly given to fantasies herself, but hers of a totally different order from mine, and those fantasies, hers, being the ones I had to satisfy. I had to portray myself as the loving and gentle creature of her dreams, I had to hide every part of myself that was incongruous with that picture, I had to lie, to laugh at foolish things, to pretend, to tell her about places I had been, about places I had never been, I had to support her breathless wishes, and all because I liked her, because I had myself grown attached to the myth, to the dream, to the fanciful image that creeps every so often in youth into one's mind, threatening to blind one to the realities of the world, I had to satisfy my own dream (or disprove it) in satisfying her own. It was a sordid business. And I am happy now that it has ended. I can only go so far, in spite of what my dreams may require. After all, so far and so much, and past that no further. I say all this by way of explanation, not that I feel badly about it, for I do not, I am happy about it, but because I simply could not go further with it, it had to end, that black circle, her sensual mouth, her lips, dark and oily with cosmetics, I could only accept so much, what attracts one is usually the repulsive, and it was that way with me, I offer no excuses, I am just explaining now, about how we went walking the first day I spoke to her, when she thought I had never thought of her until I spoke, "by accident," in the library, as I was returning a book of Napoleon's *Memoirs,* and attracted her attention, when in reality, as I knew and did not say, I had planned the moment carefully for weeks, planned it even to her reactions, even to following her out of the library that day and asking to walk beside her, yes, all of it, every action, every word, was planned, as it had to be, everything was planned, and she thought it was all sudden and spontaneous, because, you see, she *had* to think it was sudden and spontaneous, that was her dream, her myth, and it was that to which I played, sordidly, treacherously, in grandiose, hypocritical fashion.

"You know, I've often wondered who you were," Valla said. "I see you almost every day at the library."

"I see you, too. You know," I said, "I was hoping we'd have a chance to speak. And then, today, all of a sudden, everything just happened." (Here I smiled.)

"Yes," she said. "It's so funny things happen that way." (And her mouth, on the last word, "way," opened wide so I could see her teeth and gums and even the wiggly uvula far down inside.)

At this point an old man, bald and doddering, walked past us. He used a cane to support himself. For an instant he raised his eyes, as if reflecting on our identity. Then, he lowered them again to the ground, where his feet, shod in a pair of dirty, torn, badly scuffed shoes, slid one after the other through the leaves which littered the sidewalk that day like confetti after a parade. Was he humming a song? I cannot remember. Let us say that he was.

Valla nodded at him. She smiled just as she had smiled at the man raking leaves. All friendliness and cheer on the surface. "Nice old man," she whispered to me as he passed. I said nothing, although I did smile. She took a deep breath and commented on the smoky smell, and on how winter was around the corner.

It was growing dark. People who had already come home from work were in their houses, and the lights were on in almost every house we passed. I had never before realized how romantic, how poignant was the twilight. The sinking sun made the sky redder and redder, and the clouds began to be filled with colors. Shadows got longer. The air seemed more fragrant.

I walked Valla home and left her at the door. It was understood that we would do the same thing the next day, meeting at the library return-desk and then walking out together when the clock on the wall directly over her amber-varnished desk stretched its hands as far apart as possible, signifying that it was six and time for the lights to be turned out and for everyone to go home. We would walk out together, not separately as we had done that first day, for from that first day on the contact had been made, and it was only a matter of time as to how far the relationship would develop, if it did not end.

After she closed the door that night, I remained outside it for a while, thinking how I had spoken to her at last. I recalled the many evenings spent watching the door from a doorway further down across the street, knowing that behind the door was my Valla, knowing that she was even then telling her mother how she had met a gentleman coming home from work that day, someone she had often seen in the library before, and her mother, suspicious, saying, What does he look like, Is he rich, Just what do you know about him, Are you going to see him again, while she, Valla, bustled about, taking off her coat and hanging it in the closet, going to her room where whatever mail she had received that day was carefully laid on the fold of her bed beneath the pillow, washing her face with warm water, wiping it with her red towel, the one with a deep-hued carnation in the lower corner, returning to the kitchen-dining room where her mother was ready to ask her more questions while they both prepared the dinner they would eat later, together, sitting one on one side of a small wooden table and the other facing her from the other side, with only the kitchen light on in the whole house because they saved money that way, while outside it grew darker and darker and the stars came out and the moon grew from a shy silver to a rich golden color, and the street that ran right and left from the small walkway to the door was quiet, because it was night, and even I, who had stood for a while outside the door, thinking, even I had gone home to my own rooms, gone away from their street, gone away from their talk, yet knowing they were still talking of me, knowing she was still thinking of me, just as she, Valla, was on my own mind as I prepared my dinner and planned the steps I should "spontaneously" take the following day so that she would begin to like me, trust me, confide in me, even love me. And so, that night, each of us went to bed, thinking (she later told me this was definitely the case, as I had expected) of the other and wondering what the next, the following days would bring.

It is getting dark in my room now, and the story is going nicely. I have stopped because something is happening outside my window. The young married woman who lives on the second floor has come out on her porch to take in the few things she hung on her line this afternoon. She is a thin woman, unattractive except for her legs, which she usually covers with sheer black stockings. They probably excite her husband. Right now, she is attempting to take down some stockings, two pair, from the short clothesline she has rigged up on the balcony-porch where she undoubtedly suns herself during the summer. She stretches up, her arms are reaching high over her head. This pulls her black sweater up, so that there is a narrow strip of bare skin just above her waist. I can see her belly. Her small, high teats are even smaller and tighter as she reaches up. She doesn't know I'm here. Now she reaches down into the straw basket she has carried out and puts the stockings in it. She is going to take in a few pairs of silk panties next. I watch her. She stretches again, and again I can see her midriff, again I can almost feel the tautness of her breasts and the willowy quality of her legs as she stands on tiptoes. Her face is plain, but I don't mind. These are the pleasures of life. These are my rights and privileges, to watch what goes on in the world outside my windows.

Oh. She has just noticed me. She looks angry. She has just pulled her sweater down over her bare belly, indignantly; who does she think she is, who does she think I am, where is she going? She is going indoors. That's the end of the laundry. What if she tells her husband? No, she wouldn't tell him. Perhaps she would. But what could he do, nothing, he couldn't bother me at all, and if he came up here fuming I wouldn't let him in.

Perhaps the husband is next door now, singing, with the others. Perhaps the woman wasn't really taking in clothes, but just enticing me, making me stare at her, and at the same time giving a signal to her husband who was watching her from the next-door window, waiting, until he too could give the signal for everyone to start singing louder, to start banging on the walls, just as they are doing now, so that I can hardly think, so that I almost forget about my own stories which they have interrupted. Now I shall go on. I shall forget the woman with the small, high teats and the bare midriff and the willowy legs, she's gone into the house anyway, I won't even look through the window for a while, if that will be possible. If she or her husband or the people next door want to make trouble, let them, let them bang their fists against the wall, let them shout and sing, but I won't apologize, I won't stop, after all I'm perfectly within my rights, I know that, just as I was within my rights with Valla, and with Murray, yes, even with Murray.

Now the dog from across the street is looking up at me through my window. I see him. What is he doing there now, staring at me as if he knew something I didn't want known. I never thought dogs had good sight, but he can always find me at my window, and he stares, that big terror of a dog.

And now the dog is lying in the street, right in the middle of the street, where the cars pass. He does this often. In a few minutes he will be rolling over from side to side, flexing his hairy paws, flapping his pink tongue from right to left as he rolls. He will snap at flies. He will feel secure on his back. He may even wag his tail. But he does not know that in a few minutes he will still be on his back, unable to move, his spine crushed without mercy into the hard pavement of the street. A car makes a dreadful mash of any animal. And from mine, I can look through the window, over the steering wheel, though the window, and see him looking up at me. I wonder if he belongs to the woman who was taking in her wash, whose husband is probably next door, banging on my wall while the others are singing. I shall shut them all out. I shall close my window. I already know how to get up from my desk, it is easy, and with my right hand I can pull the shade all the way down, steadily, just by tugging on the small circle of string tied to the dangling shade-cord, tugging with my finger in the small hole of white cord almost black from the dirt of this apartment which the old landlady has not cleaned in months. And then the shades will be drawn, and I will be untouchable, safe in my dark corner.

LOUISE GLÜCK*

❦

The Racer's Widow

The elements have merged into solicitude.
Spasms of violets rise above the mud
And weed, and soon the birds and ancients
Will be starting to arrive, bereaving points
South. But never mind. It is not painful to discuss
His death. I have been primed for this,
For separation, for so long. But still his face assaults
Me, I can hear that car careen again, the crowd coagulate on
        asphalt
In my sleep. And watching him, I feel my legs like snow
That let him finally let him go
As he lies draining there. And see
How even he did not get to keep that lovely body.

* LOUISE GLÜCK, *born in New York City in 1943, grew up on Long Island and attended Columbia University's School of General Studies. Her poetry has appeared in* Mademoiselle, The New Yorker, Poetry, Salmagundi, Tri-Quarterly, *and other magazines and her first collection will appear in 1968.*

❧

Pictures of the People in the War

Later I'll pull down the shade
And let this fluid draw life out of the paper.

Telling how. Except instead
Of showing you equipment I would first off share
My vision of the thing: the angle of that head
Submerged in fixer there, the bare
Soul in its set, you see; it's done with speed
And lighting but my point is that one never
Gets so close to anyone within experience. I took
These pictures of the people in the war
About a year ago—their hands were opening to me like
Language; tanks and dwellings meanwhile misty in the rear.

❧

Grandmother in the Garden

The grass below the willow
Of my daughter's wash is curled

With earthworms, and the world
Is measured into row on row
Of unspiced houses, painted to seem real.
The drugged Long Island summer sun drains
Pattern from those empty sleeves, beyond my grandson
Squealing in his pen. I have survived my life.
The yellow daylight lines the oak leaf
And the wire vines melt with the unchanged changes
Of the baby. My children have their husbands' hands
My husband's framed, propped bald as a baby on their pianos,
My tremendous man. I close my eyes. And all the clothes
I have thrown out come back to me, the banners
Of my daughters' slips . . . they drift; I see the sheer
Summer cottons drift, equivalent to air.

❧

Solstice

June's edge. The sun
Turns kind. Birds wallow in the sob of pure air,
Crated from the coast . . . Unreal. Un-
real. I see the cure

Dissolving on the screen. Outside, dozing
In its sty, the neighbors' offspring
Sucks its stuffed monster, given
Time. And now the end begins:

Packaged words; he purrs his need again.
The rest is empty. Stoned, stone-

blind she totters to the lock
Through webs of diapers. It is Christmas on the clock,

A year's precise,
Terrible ascent, climaxed in ice.

❦

Firstborn

The weeks go by. I shelve them,
They are all the same, like peeled soup cans . . .
Beans sour in their pot. I watch the lone onion
Floating like Ophelia, caked with grease:
You listless, fidget with the spoon.
What now? You miss my care? Your yard ripens
To a ward of roses like a year ago, when staff nuns
Wheeled me down the aisle . . .
You couldn't look. I saw
Converted love, your son
Drooling under glass, starving . . .

We are eating well.
Today me meatman turns his trained knife
On veal, your favorite. I pay with my life.

STEVEN GUARINO*

❧

The Perimeter Walker

I am the perimeter keeper. It is very important to keep
a difference. no one knows this. I have to eat bread to
stay alive. I am the only one who isn't doing something
and now they've told me I am doing something too.
   I am being given my sovereignty. It is all unfortunately **true**.

   Life is boundless. My life is stunted like a tree.
The packages of wire come out here and I pile them.
I have a german friend who owns a motorcycle. It is
all true. He is allowed here; inbetween I in a sense wait.

       they are trying to get me a job at the
World's Fair, in which case I will have to give it up.
It is a very suspicious case, but I am going to look into it.
If it is a very good offer I will have to leave the forests.
Some things must be sacrificed. I can write a new man
instructions by mail.

What I do is unwind the wire. They say you can do that
as well at the World's Fair and besides get payed for it,
as much as a night watchman. But I know it is a futile chase out
there, and as yet, the forests are mine. The oil drum stands in the
middle of the forest, MY THINGS! my twigs! I want everything
but the wire to snap or be left alone.

* STEVEN GUARINO, *born in Staten Island, New York, in 1941, grad-*
uated from Brooklyn College and then served two years in the Navy.
He has written but not published many poems and stories, as well as
a few novels, a section of one appearing in Spero. *More recently, he*
has abandoned writing to become a Hindu monk.

II

Listen to me and you listen to One. All this (what?)
I'll lose in favor of money and action at the World's Fair.

III

Last night I went out in the dark and told the black birds on the
branch that it was for them I was leaving. A likely story.

IV

"You are alive for need like everyone else. If you go it will be
for the same brightlights reason, please don't leave your disgusting honey drippings on our branches.
Go somewhere true—make a destiny bend."

V

Was just out looking at my forests. To hell with them—I mean
the World's Fair. My forests are people too. Someone had shattered one of the cement drinking fountains—some sprite with a
sledge hammer.

VI

Tomorrow I have to go. I'm preparing a white shirt. If the
offer is marvelous I'll have to take it.

(Tonight, a man in a black and white checked jacket following
me twice. How can I leave this world for the world of men in
black and white jackets?)

It took the perimeter walker a full day to recover from the
interview. The forests were tolerant of him the first night; he
returned through like a rude young man. He lay back on one of
the rocks and sang old popular songs at the moon, and stretched
not a foot of wire.

The keeper had it. Plain. Sometimes no food, no angels. Most time
just oneself, and that was the main attraction; he would blast himself into the World's Fair; rather than gruel in the morning he
would rush to work in a fancy suit. The profoundest crag in the

forest bespoke it was all the same: "You touch us every night with your moccasined feet, why not touch the world? The Wire keeper was feigning in his obedience to one or the other—where? —in space staring at a wide solitude under the bright gray bridge —chance, gamble, "throw your die our way," advised the rushing river, *that was the way to talk*. With ten thousands of feet of wire waiting to be stretched.

> Mushroom, river, and innocence
> "I buy it, I buy it all. I have so little money.
> But I'll buy your bag. But come to me and flatter my worries
> I am a simple creature who needs stroking.
> This is one entrance. The moon is full."

> "Seek me out the hidden wellspring of love
> I trickle from ledge to ledge in sparkling drops
> You cannot find it at the World's Fair, they sell it in

none of the outdoor fruit markets, it's not in the mandolin—have you noticed the emptiness in even the most romantic moments, when the mandoliner is bent forward—it is as if you were all flat. Except the most human. We present you with entity—with the stipulation that you stay. Play in our valley, we produce spirits from the trees, popup shows for elves.

Where can you do better?—but the price!"

> "Who's afraid of Nasty's fangs? I."

*

The Keeper's First Interview:

Entered nonsmiling in a brown suit, tho the pants were unpressed. The highbrowed, hudo headed Keeper into the room for the interview. Poor Keeper. There are no jobs in the city for you. Refer yourself to the inner life, he did—it was as if he put his finger lightly to a spinning wheel.

Woman in an orange dress, orange telephone. "What have you been doing," she, a shut up owl in her face, two eyes dim slits behind her glasses.

"I have been wirekeeping." *That?*—she looked up quickly. She took his shoe size and neck size in case he got the job.

"And in case you get the job what is your favorite color?"

"Red."

"And in case you don't?"

"Blue."

"Thank you Mr. Keeper and thank you for coming. If you don't hear from us you'll know you didn't get granted a second interview. That will be pretty clear won't it?" "Thank you," he exited to the outer room where he does not linger. *Home*, keeper, he signaled his imaginary land. Alas how thin and see-through bare the city had made him, how pale and wasted—the forest turned the other way, making the slim difference whereby they did not admit him—he felt the air was too cold and went straight to his hut. There was nothing to eat inside but stale rice. He didn't have any job at all, they had put him nowhere, there was no such thing. He turned on the short wave radio and a girl sang wringing her hands "Oh life is a wringing worry

> a sorry hurry,
> a meal of sorrow-oats
> life is a morning and a day

They wanted to lift him whole out of the forest. One who had an amused sympathy for the wire keeper pointed out the senselessness of the task. "Wire keep yes possibly in your old age, that's not something you should be thinking of now, now is your time for having a good time, working! living!" His father who drove a fire truck in the region stopped by one day and both sat on empty wire barrels while young Keeper got his advice. He felt his head leaning towards his father.

"I can tell by looking at you. You're out here because—" Dealing with wire so much, the Keeper's hands were incredibly toughened and scratched like wood, he stared down. Somethings he couldn't communicate; in the advice-giving the incommunicable became the embarrassment—but the father wouldn't buy it, it seemed too sleek and obscure (like an eskimo's black artifact stuck in the ice)—and it became the See Through To Infinity—and by that time the father rolled off his wire barrel, but wouldn't buy it or be helped to his feet; he drew on his silver fire badge and black-red raincoat and left the keeper saying "it's better each time I visit."

Alone the keeper pondered on the amusement and the waste. He has intended to live his life on the verge of the human extreme, on the border to metaphysical paradise, the first on line if anything happened. Now the thought frightened him as something he'd better abandon. The infinite gesture, like a hand absentmindedly indicating space—seemed hopelessly vapid to him, why do it? Why stand like a wizard alone in the middle of a bareshack? And still there was time—the tries of the cyclist, his father's infrequent but persistent visits, the eyes of the woman on the subway last night—and, the thought he was beginning to add to all of theirs—I can still keep my sovereignty and forests, how could I be refused them whenever I want them?

Keeper wandered the realms with amusement in his marrow. The rocks and crags he had seen before, the trees were at the peak of winterend. It was a spring morning only colder. Where streams would've run were frozen waterfalls, beards of ice: down the highways he trod acre after acre, separating almost unconsciously, his wire. The only building on his property was a stone ruin.

"Keeper of the rocks, why do you scratch us with your wire,
we know the difference,
we know the difference is being kept,
we've been here since prehistoric
we know you're the favorite athlete for this age, but—
why do you never race against another?"

Keeper wandered the realms debating realities, debating possibilities.

A faded newspaper page struck its attention to his foot. He picked it up, standing along the highway where it swoops nearer the river—he held the paper to the light of day, shadowy gray soldiers were landing on a beach, 2 buddhist leaders posed eternal at a conference demanding a withdrawal of troops.

Wars, climaxes go off in a world off Keeper's head. *"Not my world? The time I live in? I live in which time then? the 1960s? —where are they?"*

All this (what?) he'll lose.

Keeper You Should Be Somewhere Else

A racer like you, eyes overshadowed with the glint of barbed wire, sits outside after no-lunch, *can't leave, for all your reasons and mine*, am at the bright river WIRE COILED ACROSS THE CHEST like viva zapata notorious hideaway of passes and coves— long live the wire itself, no more than that. Long live the sharp piercing hands, the exquisite cage-pain.

"I am myself again after the interview with my father. I am watching a crown of smoke go angelic over a candle, in the dark, room, alone, gently walked out on the century"—before the un- locked tomb of an Egyptian god, before the treasures, nothing to take, stand carefully lest the air dissolve to dust. Lest the illusions mix in the pack . . . after one drink . . . the dagger appears in the side of the boot . . . the mummy has been restored to life and stalks the neighborhood in a black overcoat and watchcap. The bundle of wire sits in the corner of the room, like a classical guitar. Beside the candle there is a lightbulb burning, and a ciga- rette ash growing between the fingers. Beside the steam radiators there is nothing else. Except a truck in the distance, a part of the night. Yellow lights appear in the lights of the houses in town, the major lights light the sky—the forest is elliptical, and smaller than he had thought, it is bound on one side by the river, on the other side, the highway. The bridge soars above the forest into the water and sky. The little house is in a pothole. The oildrum stands in the middle. The bridge roads weave cloverleafs and if a car ever once got on them he would slope and slope under the stained feeble lights,

clear red smudge is evening sky, the moon like a wooden moon

between the trees painted by Henri Rousseau. The Keeper sits
   outside

on the bench, his hands on his blue-trousered knees, his official's

cap on straight, smoking under the moon, and an assyrian cat

lingers on four creamy paws by the open door of the empty
   room.

there is a cherry ripe puff of smoke

and a piece of wood—a branch scraping in the clear breeze.

the Keeper looks like he's waiting for a locomotive.

Sunday he was back at the eternal grind. Turning around until Sundown, what the chaste know as A Dance To Bullets Shot At The Feet.

Wire keeper dreaming of young girls, when gray replaced yellow on the water, sovereign walks on the top of the wall overlooking the grounds where the American Revolutionary War was fought, the beginning of Upstate New York; at the end of his walk is always the last standing wooden Water Wheel. Nowhere else is there such a Water Wheel. No initials are carved in it, no one wonders how many people know of it, it is located way down at the bottom by the edge of the water and takes its turn from a spring in the rocks. It is a persistently ungrave sight, old wheel clacking slowly with its fresh water-burden, dumping it into the Hudson like it was rare ore. No there's no sense in leaving such sights as this,
and there's no possibility of trying to bring anyone down there. How could they find the path?

*

But a long-time friend from a park in Detroit, another wire keeper—came out to see him.
It had been going bad with this friend.

> *But I am myself,*
> *that's good*

They walked Keep's path: "This path goes one way or another."—But the friend was despairing of the task: "As of course you are too. Wire talk, wire talk, shop talk," he kept saying it, desperately,

> *No there is much more*
> *to go*
> thought Keep as they were about
to cross the road into the woods.

"I'm sick of it" said Keep's old time friend—he wore an army jacket, he was tough and scared at the prospects—you saw that in his face, when they met he was grimacing with his teeth in a way Keeper had already passed through. *If he's got that grimace he's scared.*

The friend liked the trees and the river, sun glinted and shone for him, trees did their bare limbs against the sky, for him. Keeper became hardly aware it was his own path.

The friend found another. Is that enough? It helps through a day. Keeper felt it was beating your fist against the stone, it was healing, you laughed with pain.

"Yes I *want* desperation." said the friend and he went off, with a rough handshake. "But stay with me, there is something between us, over us, not friendship."—both found another and they parted to solitudes, with a handshake.

ROBERT HEAD*

❦

Sancticity

To Mary Newell

ACKNOWLEDGMENTS: *The scene with the dog and the crocodile is not original with me. It's an old story. It was passed on to me by John "Whitey" Patterson, Bo'sun.*
I am indebted to Richard Levy, Director. The play is part his.

Players
BLACKOUT
MARASCHINO
ZERO

Costumes
Prison uniform cut.
BLACKOUT *Gold velvet.*
MARASCHINO *Bloodred velvet.*
ZERO *Burnt sienna velvet.*
Chamois modern dance shoes.

Scene: The open stage. A pool of light. The stage is bare. MARA-
SCHINO *and* ZERO *are downstage speaking to the audience.* BLACK-
OUT, *upstage in the darkness, taps his foot in measured rhythm.*

ZERO (*Dead pan*) The last time I was in Santos, me and my watch
  partner had some time off so we decided to take a little trip

* ROBERT HEAD, *born in Memphis, Tennessee in 1942, grew up in the
South and currently lives in New Orleans. His play* Sancticity *(1963)
has been performed at Tulane and Oberlin and in Minneapolis. He
has worked at various trades in several countries, most recently in
New Orleans as an apprentice printer.*

168

up into the interior. So we got our gear together: sun helmets and maps and mosquito repellant and binoculars and .357 combat magnums, and hired a guide with a canoe. We're getting ready to let go and the guide puts this little dog in the canoe, and I say, "Man, we can't take that little dog up into the interior with all those bad skeders and vipers and crocodiles and head-hunters and piranha fish." And the guide, he says, "It's a nice. . . ." Take it, Maraschino, you're the guide.

MARASCHINO It's a nice little dog and it only eats hay.

ZERO So we put a bale of hay in the canoe for the little dog. On up the river we run up against some rapids and the canoe tips over a little bit and the little dog falls overboard.

MARASCHINO Dog overboard.

ZERO And the piranha fish ate all the skin and hair and meat off that poor little dog. We fished out the skeleton and dried off the bones and put it in the bottom of the canoe.

MARASCHINO My poor little dog, we can't take him on up river with all those vipers and crocodiles in the shape he's in now.

ZERO So we paddled over to this island and put him on the beach and left him the bale of hay.

MARASCHINO It was so pitiful to see that poor little dog eating the hay and as fast as he'd eat it it'd fall out of his ribs.

ZERO So we paddled on up river and we come upon this cave just like it said on the map. And I get my paraphernalia and a book of poetry and go in the cave and there is this rocking chair so I sit myself down and read my book of poetry.

MARASCHINO And you fell asleep and the book of poetry slid off on the floor. And then this crocodile comes crawling along and starts reading the book of poetry and he falls asleep.

ZERO And I woke up with this eight-foot crocodile asleep on my feet with my book of poetry under his snout. The fourth tooth of his lower jaw fit into a pit in the upper jaw. So I got out my binoculars and turned them around backwards. He was so small. I picked him up with my tweezers and put him in a match box.

BLACKOUT The four-bar introduction is over.

(BLACKOUT *weaves, dead slow toward center stage*)

MARASCHINO The voice breaks silence.

ZERO The master of ceremonies is coming on.

MARASCHINO This guy can play. He undid some bad cats.
I'll never forget the way he held his knife. The switchblade
crucifix.
He was something else. He was otherwise.
Someone from another star. So bright before his fall.
A gold-toothed bloodhound, sun in his eyes, a frozen smile,
and old gold clothes.
The end. The snake's hips.
Dread the passage of Jesus, for he does not return.

(BLACKOUT *the feature attraction*, MARASCHINO *bows like a
gentleman*)

BLACKOUT (*to the audience*) The speech has nothing to do with
anything.
This is how it goes.

(*He taps his foot three times and pivots toward* ZERO)

Take it, Zero, you're the judge.

ZERO Hang on. Let me go get some dignity.

(*He disappears*)

MARASCHINO Kangaroo court.

BLACKOUT Child's play.

(ZERO *reappears, dressed in dignity, a once-black blanket*)

MARASCHINO You call a two-bit prison blanket "dignity?"

ZERO Another word out of you and you get six months for contempt of court. This is a black velvet robe.

MARASCHINO Yes, your Honor.

ZERO, MARASCHINO *and* BLACKOUT *face* ZERO. *He pantomimes a gavel
with his hand and imagines a police record.*) Blackout (*description of player, e.g.,* Negro male, 35, 170-175 pounds, six
feet, black hair, black eyes, dark complexion, an arrow piercing a heart tattoo at base of left thumb)
Wanted on charges of felonious assault, burglary, narcotics,
transporting firearms, unlawful flight.

Blackout is being hunted by the FBI. They label him dangerous.

An incorrigible criminal described as a "loner" and a nomad. A deceptively mild appearance masks a vicious nature. Blackout will shoot it out with the police. Subject has stated he will not be taken alive. Desperate, facing a long rap, and armed with a sawed-off shotgun, rifles and pistols, Blackout is considered extremely dangerous.

BLACKOUT Do that "unlawful flight" bit again.
It's some pretty. Only angels fly.
ZERO Mr. Blackout, you are not an angel.
BLACKOUT It cost you a mint to clip my wings.
ZERO In the light of your record, the court cannot in good conscience do otherwise than impose the maximum penalty of life imprisonment at hard labor, Sundays and holidays excepted.
BLACKOUT Make little ones out of big ones, that's the voice.
This yardbird ain't ever gonna hit the ground.
ZERO Mr. Maraschino, in view of your co-operation with the police, the court has recommended clemency. I hereby sentence you to a term of two years in the State Penitentiary.

(BLACKOUT *and* MARASCHINO *mimic kangaroos.*
ZERO *takes off the blanket and holds it up in front of him.*
BLACKOUT *and* MARASCHINO *jump behind it*)

Those two kangaroos were so scared they jumped into each other's pouch.

(BLACKOUT *and* MARASCHINO *walk out from behind the blanket*)

MARASCHINO Allow me, your Honor.

(MARASCHINO *takes the blanket and tosses it into the darkness.*
ZERO *claps in silence*)

BLACKOUT Now let's do ourselves.
ZERO Three zebras in a cage in Galilee.
MARASCHINO Emote.

(Naturalistic acting from here through ZERO's *"He got free, he died."*

Let the Audience believe in what is happening)

BLACKOUT Maraschino, Baby, how come I got life and you got a deuce?

MARASCHINO The judge, he said you was a habitual criminal.

He said you was considered extremely dangerous.

BLACKOUT I thank you.

MARASCHINO You're welcome.

BLACKOUT And you?

MARASCHINO Dunno.

BLACKOUT I know. And that's why I'm gonna take you for an easy ride.

You thought I'd made my last score. You wrong.

I got one more to go.

MARASCHINO Who let the razors out?

BLACKOUT I got busted on the way.

It had to be a snitch job.

MARASCHINO Blackout, I'm sorry.

BLACKOUT Wrong number. Hang up.

"I'm sorry" don't cut no ice with me.

You are singing off key.

Crabs ain't no good if you cook them dead.

You got to boil them alive.

ZERO Canaries sing real pretty with their tongues slit.

MARASCHINO Somebody's gonna throw you out of the airplane.

ZERO Crazy.

BLACKOUT Let's get it over with.

Turn around so you don't have to look at me.

MARASCHINO Help!

BLACKOUT Yourself.

MARASCHINO Looks like I'm going home in a burlap sack and a yellow pine box.

ZERO Die hard.

BLACKOUT And one fine day you'll get all dug up.

No Potter's Field for you.

And they'll put away as nice as nice.

An ebony coffin trimmed in silver.
A twelve-cylinder, jet-black Cadillac, niggered to heaven and
    waxed white.
Red velvet and shredded roses.
A nine-day wake, and money close your eyes.
MARASCHINO *To the ceiling.* Hello Beautiful.

(BLACKOUT *advances on him*)

Hang loose. Don't get blood in your eyes.
BLACKOUT Come on, Baby, cut the stalling.
    Let's go rock-a-bye.
MARASCHINO My girl, I got to leave her something.
ZERO Now ain't that love.
BLACKOUT Alright. You got one minute.
MARASCHINO (*He reaches in his crotch. Out comes a golden pocket
watch*)
    Give her the time, with bells.
    It's all I have . . .
    besides my wings,
    and you can't get cash for them.
    All you have to do is tell her my name,
    and she'll know what to do.
BLACKOUT No sweat. She's a purebred, she'll join you.
MARASCHINO (*Mary: the* a *is long*)
    She's an Irish nightingale.
    A oncer with the flame hair,
    so red, it looks about to catch fire.
    Her name is Mary, but me, I call her Mary Jane.
    I changed her name.
    She give me lockjaw. No chairs in *her* room. Dream bait.
    O to step off the carpet with her.
        Eagle on the dollar gonna rise and fly
        When you take it home to Mary.
BLACKOUT Please stop. It's too beautiful.
MARASCHINO That's all she wrote.
ZERO Dear John.
MARASCHINO (*He hands the watch to* ZERO) Eyeball the second
hand.

ZERO It's hardly moving. This watch don't work. This some kind of joke?

MARASCHINO No joke. It works alright.

That there's the best timekeeper in the Delta.

That's my Mary Warner watch. Mary Warner gave it to me.

It's set right. It's taking it on the slow bell.

It takes a month for the hour hand to go all the way around.

BLACKOUT Yeah.

MARASCHINO My ticker goes to Mary.

Maybe somebody she'll learn to tell the time by it.

ZERO I thank you.

MARASCHINO Don't go thanking me. Anybody can play the role.

You thank the holy angels.

ZERO It ain't safe to fool with the angels. I ain't trucking with them.

MARASCHINO You'll get yours. They play for keeps.

BLACKOUT Maraschino, this is it.

MARASCHINO No, Blackout, no.

BLACKOUT You're a stool pigeon.

MARASCHINO No, no, I'm not a stoolie. Blackout, Blackout, don't.

(*He starts to run for it.* ZERO *pinions him*)

No!

ZERO The squealer's mark.

MARASCHINO I love you!

BLACKOUT I love you too.

(*He strangles* MARASCHINO. ZERO *lets him go. He falls face down*)

ZERO He got free, he died.

(*Pause*)

BLACKOUT The masquerade is over.

(MARASCHINO *rises up and bows.* ZERO *claps in silence*)

ZERO The dead man dances.

BLACKOUT And I have a confession to make.

MARASCHINO I'll go get the sin-hound.

(*He disappears*)

ZERO (*To the audience*)
Gentlemen, members of the parole board,
I ask you, was that good enough for you?
It was some fine? I thank you.
But we made enough noise to wake up the dead?
Okay. I'll see what I can do.
We wouldn't want to wake up the dead, would we?

(*He whispers in* BLACKOUT'S *ear and points to the audience*)

BLACKOUT Hey, MARASCHINO, play this next one kind of quiet.
(MARASCHINO *reappears adorned in deep black velvet vest-
ment*)

MARASCHINO (*To* ZERO) Son, you do the confessional box.

Down on your prayer-bones.
ZERO Yes, Father.

(*He gets down on his hands and knees.* MARASCHINO *sits on his
back.*
BLACKOUT *kneels*)

BLACKOUT Bless me, Father, for I have sinned.
It has been six weeks since my last confession.
During the past six weeks I missed Mass six times.
I committed a sin against purity.
MARASCHINO With yourself or with somebody else?
BLACKOUT With number one.
MARASCHINO Whenever you have an impure thought look upon
a statue of the Blessed Virgin Mary.
BLACKOUT Yes, Father.
MARASCHINO Anything else, my son?
BLACKOUT In my mind I broke the fifth commandment.
In my mind I killed my partner Maraschino.
He was a nightingale, no better than he should be,
but I didn't do it because he sang.
He showed me he was almost ready.
Everything was jake.

That blue-eyed boy was flying right.

He was the white hope and I kilt him, just playing mind you, trying to bring on the Holy Ghost.

MARASCHINO The Man won't show until you offer Him a corpse.

BLACKOUT Yes, Father.

MARASCHINO For your penance say:

BLACKOUT Our Father which art in heaven, lead us not into temptation.

MARASCHINO And make a perfect act of contrition based upon a perfect love of God.

BLACKOUT Yes, father.

MARASCHINO God bless you. Go in peace and pray for me.

(MARASCHINO *disappears.* ZERO *and* BLACKOUT *stand up.* MARASCHINO *reappears defrocked*)

BLACKOUT Where you been?

MARASCHINO Looking for the priest. I couldn't find him nowhere.

BLACKOUT He was just in here while you were looking for him.

MARASCHINO No kidding? What'd he say?

BLACKOUT That first I got to put you on the shake.

MARASCHINO Is that right.

BLACKOUT We'll do the Houston job.

The one where you was the gay beautician.

MARASCHINO That cute little thing.

(ZERO *gets down on his hands and knees.* BLACKOUT *sits on his back.*

MARASCHINO *goes behind* BLACKOUT *and pantomimes a hairdresser, affected femininity*)

Ma'am, you surely have a healthy head of hair.

And what beautiful bracelets. Are they real gold?

BLACKOUT (*Affected femininity*) They surely are, Honey, and my ring's a real diamond. Two carats. I finally talked my husband into buying it for me. He's loaded.

MARASCHINO Ma'am, that sure is interesting.

(BLACKOUT *snaps his fingers to end the scene.*)

BLACKOUT (*To the audience*) The same night. I'm the pistol.

MARASCHINO (*He folds his handkerchief into a bra the way school-children do*)
You wore a 15 denier, seamless, sheer stocking on your face like a nun wears a veil.

BLACKOUT Zero, you're the music man.
Maraschino's such a music lover, he can play the mark.

MARASCHINO There's always someone got to play the music.

ZERO The setup man?

BLACKOUT. . . . is out of sight.

(MARASCHINO *puts on the bra.* BLACKOUT *pinions* MARASCHINO *from behind*)

ZERO Ma'am, it's a pity your husband's out.
We could pick up on the family jewels.

BLACKOUT Ma'am, you sure have some fine high-class features.

MARASCHINO (*Affected femininity*) I thank you.

ZERO Now, Ma'am, you just tell us where the stash is at and we'll be real nice to you.

(MARASCHINO *shakes his head "no"*)

BLACKOUT Maybe the lady would like a smoke.

MARASCHINO Please. It'd calm my nerves.

ZERO You can say that again.

(*He imagines a cigarette and match out of his sock.*
Lights it and places it in MARASCHINO'S *lips.* MARASCHINO *inhales*)

Now, Lady, for the last time, where's the stash at?

(MARASCHINO *shakes his head "no."* BLACKOUT *nods to* ZERO)

Ma'am, I'm obliged to take that cigarette back from you.

(*He takes the cigarette from* MARASCHINO.
He holds MARASCHINO'S *hand and applies the cigarette to the finger tips.*
MARASCHINO *screams. There is no sound.*
ZERO *puts out the cigarette on the floor. A scream is heard*)

What was that?

MARASCHINO (*Dead pan*) B flat.

ZERO No kidding, what was that?

MARASCHINO That was something else.

BLACKOUT In a blues scale you can't play on no piano.

MARASCHINO The pillpad for the Zulu epileptics, it's right next
door.

The sun's going down . . .

BLACKOUT The sun goes down in blood.

MARASCHINO. . . . and just like nightingales, they sing at dusk.
No serenade for squares. They worry those tones.
Such blue notes you never heard.

BLACKOUT And everytime they have a wing-ding
it butchers their little gray cells
just a little bit more.

MARASCHINO (*He grimaces in pain*) That's alright.

ZERO (*To the audience*) I beg your pardon? It wasn't the epileptics screaming?

It was the new prisoner? Members of the parole board . . .

BLACKOUT Pardon denied again.

ZERO Hush.

(*To the audience*)

Members of the parole board,
on behalf of the guards please accept our most sincere apolo-
gies.
You may be sure his screaming won't disturb you again to-
night.
It was a mistake.
The gag must have slipped off his mouth when they punched
him in the face.
Carelessness.
Pardon? Oh yes. You just now passed another law:
Prisoners must first be securely gagged before they are house-
broken.
But, Gentlemen, that's going to cut your style.
Think of all the trinkets and delicious refreshments you pour
down their throats.

Can't do it with a gag on.

Oh, I see, their screaming woke up the warden twice last night.

I'm very sorry.

Perhaps you could soundproof the fish tank.

No? It cost too much. Too high for you. I see.

Well I'll pass the word along for everybody to try not to scream next time.

Gentlemen, perhaps we could do a refrigerator-room scene for you.

BLACKOUT (*He puts his hands behind his back.* ZERO *pantomimes a blackjack with his handkerchief*) Coney Island.

The roaches give me the blue third with a pretty yellow sock full of laundry soap.

A pretty red iodine bulls-eye painted on the kidney.

MARASCHINO Artistic yet. (*He takes out his handkerchief and approaches* BLACKOUT *from behind*)

BLACKOUT Puke a pint of claret and there ain't a mark on you.

Agony in red. Drowned by a John.

(MARASCHINO *puts his handkerchief over* BLACKOUT'S *mouth.* ZERO *draws back to hit* BLACKOUT *in the kidney. Slow motion. The pantomime breaks at apex of swing*)

ZERO (*To the audience*) Pardon?

You made the refrigerator scene earlier this evening and you'd rather watch something else.

Okay. It's three days later and the boy's got his strength back.

He can stand up all by himself.

RLACKOUT So the roaches hauled me out of the goldfish bowl and took me in to see this here lady nutpick.

I didn't know what for at first.

I wasn't lonesome.

Let's go, Maraschino, you're it.

You're Dickless Tracy, the . . . uh . . . what you call it?

MARASCHINO Sociology lady.

BLACKOUT That's right, the sociology lady.

(MARASCHINO *ties his handkerchief around his head like a scarf*)

ZERO Brass knuckles knock knock on the door.

MARASCHINO (*He adjusts his imaginary girdle. Affected femininity*)
Come in, Gentlemen. Your eke-names please? (*He records
what* BLACKOUT *and* ZERO *say in his imaginary notebook*)

BLACKOUT Blackout.

ZERO Zero.

MARASCHINO Now, uh, Mr. Blackout, I just want to ask you a few
questions, so don't be nervous.

BLACKOUT Who's nervous?

MARASCHINO Did your mother drink?

BLACKOUT No.

MARASCHINO Did your father stay out late at night?

BLACKOUT No.

MARASCHINO Did your sister. . . .

BLACKOUT Lady, this is weird. I don't figure your racket.
Blackmail?
You don't look the type.
You never can tell.

MARASCHINO Son, I'm trying to rehabilitate you.

BLACKOUT You see, Miss Fairy Lady, I'm from the planet Kryp-
ton.
Like Superman.
I ain't got no earthly people.

(ZERO *laughs much too loud*)

MARASCHINO Son, I'll repeat myself, I'm trying to rehabilitate you.

BLACKOUT Lady, you ain't ever gonna slipper me.
I'm evil money.

MARASCHINO It says here on your rap sheet that you did two years
in Leavenworth for draftdodging.

BLACKOUT Well, you see, Lady, it was like this.
Here you go.
Zero, you're the draftboard man.

ZERO I'm a thief. I have my pride. I won't play no draftboard
man.

BLACKOUT It makes no never mind.

ZERO A draftboard man gets more to scoff.
I ain't fat enough to do no draftboard man.

BLACKOUT Well stick out your gut and look dumb.

Righto. Let's go.

Mr. Draftboard Man, how much money I get in this outfit of yours?

ZERO Ninety dollars per month.

BLACKOUT Ninety dollars a month.

I can top that in one night hustling.

Well, how much loot I get for each guy I knock off?

ZERO Son, we don't pay you by the number of natives you kill.

We pay you by the month.

BLACKOUT Honeyface, that's nowhere.

I collected two thousand bucks a head working for this outfit in the Kansas City Tenderloin. Ta-ta.

(ZERO *resumes his previous position and claps*)

Mama don't 'low no hand-playing here.

MARASCHINO Now, Son, you know you don't join the army to make money killing people. You join the army to defend your flag.

BLACKOUT Horse apples.

MARASCHINO Oh!

BLACKOUT Pardon my French, Ma'am, I mean road apples.

MARASCHINO Oh!

BLACKOUT (*He bares his teeth*) You see these teeth?

MARASCHINO What gorgeous gold teeth you have.

BLACHOUT Lady, what you call these kind of teeth?

MARASCHINO Well, Son, the wisemen and the doctors and the scholars, they call them canine teeth, incisors.

BLACKOUT Well, Lady, I don't know about that. Me, I call them dog teeth.

MARASCHINO I see.

BLACKOUT Now, Lady, what are these teeth *for?*

MARASCHINO Carnivorousness.

BLACKOUT Come again.

MARASCHINO Carnivorousness. Eating flesh.

BLACKOUT That's right, Lady, you're on the ball.

There was this red-headed girl with freckles.

The freckles turned into red ants.

The red ants devoured her.

MARASCHINO Ugh! that's pretty.

BLACKOUT Now, Lady, some other lady, I might rub her back,
but you. . . .

MARASCHINO Oh. (*He faints*)

ZERO You done it now.

BLACKOUT Yeah.

(*He snaps his fingers to end the scene.* MARASCHINO *does not
move*)

Maraschino?

(ZERO *kneels and takes off the scarf.*)

MARASCHINO (*whisper*) Call me a doctor.

ZERO Okay. You're a doctor.

MARASCHINO (*rises up*)

(*To a member of the audience*)

Sir? Oh, I beg your pardon. We most humbly apologize.
We didn't know your wife was a sociology lady.
(*To the audience*)
Gentlemen, members of the parole board, the party's over.
I realize you're under the impression
that you invited us here to perform for you tonight.
But it's like the rich gentleman who found the whore. Who
found who?
Gentlemen, members of the parole board,
I'll tell y'all why we invited you here tonight:
It's all part of a monstrous plan.

(*He introduces the scene with the appropriate gestures.*
MARASCHINO *pantomimes a queen. She dances around* BLACK-
OUT)

BLACKOUT Baby, you're coming on strong. What's on your mind?

MARASCHINO Some work, Dad. You been in here a long time. It'll
calm you down.

(*The pantomime goes comic; the audience laughs;* MARASCHINO
faints)

ZERO (*To the audience*) Miss Maraschino's sensitive to laughter, very very. You hurt her feelings.

(BLACKOUT *carries* MARASCHINO *upstage into the darkness*)

Gentlemen, members of the parole board,

this is not the movies; two of us are live actors.

If anybody wants to leave, you better go now while the going's good . . .

before somebody locks the doors.

I'm on your side. You can trust me.

Blackout's up to no good. I know.

Remember what the good priest said.

I'm giving you fair warning:

y'all stay any longer and somebody's gonna get it in the neck.

There's nothing I can do. It's up to you.

Another five minutes and you'll all be cold-blooded murderers.

(*Pause*)

And when the roaches get here. . . .

BLACKOUT (*Comes downstage into the light. He pantomimes a pistol with his hand*) Okay, okay, what's going on here? This is the law.

Somebody's dead back there. Who made him happy?

ZERO Not me. I'm on their side.

(*He points at the audience*)

It was Blackout, sir.

BLACKOUT Blackout? Don't gimmie that.

We executed Blackout a year ago.

(*He turns the pistol on the audience*)

You're all busted.

(*Lights out*)

There's no such thing as an accident.

MARASCHINO Accidents do happen.

BLACKOUT They found my body yesterday.

MARASCHINO They're showing movies in the catacombs.

BLACKOUT I'm a crime wave.

MARASCHINO And crime is on the rise.

BLACKOUT I'm the third rail.

MARASCHINO That nobody can touch and nobody can bribe.

BLACKOUT I'm a flying coral snake marked with red.

MARASCHINO Disguised as a mimic king snake marked with red.

BLACKOUT The snake has two legs.

MARASCHINO A coral snake can sure tiptoe.

BLACKOUT I'm a *Centruroides* scorpion out to score.

MARASCHINO It's just like strychnine.

BLACKOUT And I don't do the Dutch act when I'm surrounded by a ring of fire.

MARASCHINO Nothing's left of the insect but an empty shell.

BLACKOUT I'm a common visitor to your room.

MARASCHINO And death is not uncommon.

BLACKOUT Just close your eyes, that's all you have to do.

MARASCHINO And now you know where you are going to.

BLACKOUT The gas you smell is coming from the sky.

MARASCHINO It's time for one of us to say good-by.

(*Lights on.* ZERO *is caught in the act of climbing back on stage*)

BLACKOUT The priest, he said to me:
The Man won't show until you offer Him a corpse.

(MARASCHINO *shakes his head "no"*)

The priest said so.

MARASCHINO It wasn't me.

ZERO Now listen here. Priest or no priest, I do not like the magic show.

BLACKOUT Zero, on your left arm, do you have a little tiny scar?

ZERO I do. A smallpocks thing, you know.

BLACKOUT And do you believe in smallpocks?

ZERO Well I guess I do, the docs, they said it was for real.

BLACKOUT And what would you do if you all of a sudden stopped believing in smallpocks?

ZERO I wouldn't get no more shots.

BLACKOUT And then what happens to you?

ZERO I get smallpocks.

BLACKOUT And take a fall.

MARASCHINO One becomes a ghost in playing a ghost.

BLACKOUT No sweat. It's just a little nothing game. Play it out.
I ain't gonna put you on ice.
The cat putting on the magic show is only gonna do the gestures.
His lunch-hooks won't hardly touch your neck.
Now whether you pull a shuteye
or whether you walk forever in a wooden overcoat,
it all depends on the night people.

(*He gestures in the direction of the audience*)

MARASCHINO Yes.

ZERO Or No.

BLACKOUT God only knows.

ZERO First cut out.

BLACKOUT No cut out.

ZERO Count me out.

BLACKOUT (*Plainchant. Pentatonic mode*)
Eeny, meeny, miny, mo,
Catch a nigger by the toe,
If he hollers let him go,
Eeny, meeny, miny, mo.

I'm out.

ZERO You numbers man.

MARASCHINO Fair chance.

BLACKOUT
Eeny, meeny, miny, mo,
Catch a nigger by the toe,
If he hollers let him go,
Eeny, meeny, miny, mo.

Zero's out.
Maraschino, you're It.

MARASCHINO You wordshark.

ZERO No chance.

MARASCHINO It can't be helped,

ZERO This jungle science.
MARASCHINO It's all there is,
ZERO This fever in the South.
BLACKOUT Well just between the four of us. . . .
MARASCHINO The noose is hanging.
ZERO The sky-juice is falling.
MARASCHINO The god-box is playing.
ZERO One more tune before you go.
BLACKOUT A one, a two, a three, celebrate.
MARASCHINO (*He screams*) Death light.

    (BLACKOUT *and* MARASCHINO *freeze*)

ZERO (*To the audience*) For God's sake clap. All together on the
beat. Follow me.

    (ZERO *leads the audience in clapping.*
    BLACKOUT *and* MARASCHINO *go into a formal variation of the
Afro-american ring-shout: a counterclockwise circle; never
crossing their legs; shuffle, clap, and shout in three separate
rhythms. Crescendo from here through* BLACKOUT'S *"The
snake dies hard!"*)

BLACKOUT I've gone the route. My shoes are shined.
    I'm gone and rid of myself.
    I'm twirling the keys to a brand-new Cadillac.
    You can go for a ride in it if you want to.
    It's payday.
    The day the eagle screams.
ZERO (*To the audience*) The car is yours.
    This man bought it for you.
    Don't ever hock it.
MARASCHINO Peace be unto you.
BLACKOUT And unto you peace.
MARASCHINO That makes two of us.
BLACKOUT What more do we need?
MARASCHINO No hassle. The 'goric's cooked.
BLACKOUT Now or never.
MARASCHINO All or nothing.

BLACKOUT Extra quiet.

MARASCHINO No fuss.

BLACKOUT I schooled you.

MARASCHINO You schooled me.

ZERO The ghosts of the gas chambers are still at large.

> (*He joins the ring-shout.* BLACKOUT *and* ZERO *circle* MARA-
> SCHINO)

BLACKOUT The ghost walks.

MARASCHINO Lay me out in Lavender. I'm just right.

BLACKOUT And do you have a glow-on?

MARASCHINO Indeed I do. I get a rise out of you.

BLACKOUT Now's the time. I'm gonna elevate you.

MARASCHINO And there ain't nobody gonna hold me down.

BLACKOUT You gonna get to take the first solo.

ZERO And wake up with the angels looking at you.

MARASCHINO It's gonna be fast and it's gonna be clean.

BLACKOUT You're stepping on the roaches.

ZERO You're going out of bounds.

BLACKOUT You're going over the speed-limit.

ZERO You're breaking the sound-barrier.

BLACKOUT You're passing time!

MARASCHINO I'll always be twenty years old.

BLACKOUT Come with me, and I'll give you, for ever so long, a
snakeskin glow.

MARASCHINO The snake stands straight up!

ZERO The snake looks good!

BLACKOUT The snake dies hard!

> (*Full stop.* ZERO *signals the audience to stop clapping*)

MARASCHINO Solo.

ZERO Jing-jang.

BLACKOUT Sprout wings.

ZERO Go over the wall.

BLACKOUT And coming to nothing.

MARASCHINO Amen.

> (*Sustained and flowing movement, slow as slow, from here
> on out.*

MARASCHINO *sleepwalks toward* BLACKOUT.
He has a smile. And glittering, lidless eyes. He genuflects.
BLACKOUT *puts his hand near* MARASCHINO'S *neck.*
MARASCHINO *drops in his tracks.*
ZERO *rolls* MARASCHINO, *dearly beloved, over on his back.*
He has a smile. And glittering, lidless eyes.
ZERO *kisses him.*
BLACKOUT *stands at ease. His eyes are closed. He has a smile.*
ZERO *recedes into the darkness. He kneels. His eyes in mourn-
ing.*
Enter three GUARDS. *They have on .38's)*

BLACKOUT The angels have come.

(BLACKOUT *leads off. The* GUARDS *follow at a funeral pace.*
MARASCHINO *glitters in a pool of light.*
The last GUARD *disappears. The* VOICE *breaks silence)*

VOICE Go, thou art blest.

Lights out

MICHAEL HELLER*

❦

Fragment

'the hidden harmony is better. . . . '
                    —*Heraclitus*

laughed

        thought of the coins
        beside

the wrinkled kleenex

               is the shoe?
how 'this age'
    will bear it   to be
                excluded   the hand

against
your knowledge: her
secrets, what

she looked like   your eye

says everyone at once

excludes design of
spontaneity
            that

* MICHAEL HELLER, *born in New York City in 1937, took an engineering degree at Rensselaer Polytechnic Institute. He has published poems in* Paris Review, For Now, El Corno Emplumado, *and other magazines, and he is currently working on a novel.*

before us stretch

the young girls'

> neither firm
> nor soft

perfection

DICK HIGGINS*

❧

Intermedia

Much of the best work being produced today seems to fall between media. This is no accident. The concept of the separation between media arose in the Renaissance. The idea that a painting is made of paint on canvas or that a sculpture should not be painted seems characteristic of the kind of social thought—categorizing and dividing society into nobility with its various subdivisions, untitled gentry, artisans, serfs and landless workers—which we call the feudal conception of the Great Chain of Being. This essentially mechanistic approach continued to be relevant throughout the first two industrial revolutions, just concluded, and into the present era of automation, which constitutes, in fact, a third industrial revolution.

However, the social problems that characterize our time, as opposed to the political ones, no longer allow a compartmentalized approach. We are approaching the dawn of a classless society, to which separation into rigid categories is absolutely irrelevant. This shift does not relate more to East than West or vice-versa. Castro works in the cane fields. New York's Mayor Lindsay walks to work during the subway strike. The millionaires eat their lunches at Horn and Hardart's. This sort of populism is a growing tendency rather than a shrinking one.

* DICK HIGGINS, *born of American parents in 1938 in Jesus Pieces, Cambridge, England, has a B.A. from Columbia University's School of General Studies. Enormously productive in various media, he has composed music, created mixed-means theater pieces, made films, published plays, written polemical articles, produced a book of criticism,* Postface *(1964), and founded the publishing house Something Else Press.*

We sense this in viewing art which seems to belong unnecessarily rigidly to one or another form. We view paintings. What are they, after all? Expensive, handmade objects, intended to ornament the walls of the rich or, through their (or their government's) munificence, to be shared with the large numbers of people and give them a sense of grandeur. But they do not allow of any sense of dialogue.

Pop art? How could it play a part in the art of the future? It is bland. It is pure. It uses elements of common life without comment, and so, by accepting the misery of this life and its aridity so mutely, it condones them. Pop and Op are both dead, however, because they confine themselves, through the media which they employ, to the older functions of art, of decorating and suggesting grandeur, whatever their detailed content or their artists' intentions. None of the ingenious theories of the Mr. Ivan Geldoway combine can prevent them from being colossally boring and irrelevant. Milord runs his Mad Avenue gallery, in which he displays his pretty wares. He is protected by a handful of rude footmen who seem to feel that this is the way Life will always be. At his beck and call is Sir Fretful Callous, a moderately well-informed high priest, who apparently despises the Flame he is supposed to tend and therefore prefers anything which titillates him. However, Milord needs his services, since he, poor thing, hasn't the time or the energy to contribute more than his name and perhaps his dollars; getting information and finding out what's going on are simply toooooo exhausting. So, well protected and advised, he goes blissfully through the streets in proper Louis XIV style.

This scene is not just characteristic of the painting world as an institution, however. It is absolutely natural to (and inevitable in) the concept of the pure medium, the painting or precious object of any kind. That is the way such objects are marketed since that is the world to which they belong and to which they relate. The sense of "I am the state," however, will shortly be replaced by "After me the deluge," and, in fact, if the High Art world were better informed, it would realize that the deluge has already begun.

Who knows when it began? There is no reason for us to go into history in any detail. Part of the reason that Duchamp's objects are fascinating while Picasso's voice is fading is that the Duchamp pieces are truly between media, between sculpture and something else, while Picasso is readily classifiable as a painted ornament. Similarly, by invading the land between collage and photography, the German John Heartfield produced what are probably the greatest graphics of our century, surely the most powerful political art that has been done to date.

The ready-made or found object, in a sense an intermedium since it was not intended to conform to the pure medium, usually suggests this, and therefore suggests a location in the field between the general area of art media and those of life media. However, at this time, the locations of this sort are relatively unexplored, as compared with media between the arts. I cannot, for example, name work which has consciously been placed in the intermedium between painting and shoes. The closest thing would seem to be the sculpture of Claes Oldenburg, which falls between sculpture and hamburgers or Eskimo Pies, yet it is not the sources of these images which his sculpture resembles so much as the images themselves. An Oldenburg Eskimo Pie may look something like an Eskimo Pie, yet it is neither edible nor cold. There is still a great deal to be done in this direction in the way of opening up aesthetically rewarding possibilities.

In the middle 1950s many painters began to realize the fundamental irrelevance of Abstract Expressionism, which was the dominant mode at the time. Such painters as Allan Kaprow and Robert Rauschenberg in the United States and Wolf Vostell in Germany turned to collage or, in the latter's case, dé-collage in the sense of making work by adding or removing, replacing and substituting or altering components of a visual work. They began to include increasingly incongruous objects in their work. Rauschenberg called his constructions "combines" and went so far as to place a stuffed goat—spattered with paint and with a rubber tire around its neck—onto one. Kaprow, more philosophical and restless, meditated on the relationship of the spectator and the work. He put mirrors into his things so the spectator could feel included in them. That wasn't physical enough, so he made enveloping collages which surrounded the spectator. These he called "environments." Finally, in the spring of 1958, he began to include live people as part of the collage, and this he called a "happening."

The proscenium theater is the outgrowth of seventeenth-century ideals of social order. Yet there is remarkably little structural difference between the dramas of D'Avenant and those of Edward Albee, certainly nothing comparable to the difference in pump construction or means of mass transportation. It would seem that the technological and social implications of the first two industrial revolutions have been evaded completely. The drama is still mechanistically divided: there are performers, production people, a separate audience and an explicit script. Once started, like Frankenstein's monster, the course of affairs is unalterable, perhaps damned by its inability to reflect its surroundings. With our populistic mentality today, it is difficult to attach importance —other than what we have been taught to attach—to this traditional theater. Nor do minor innovations do more than provide dinner conversation: this theater is round instead of square, in that one the stage revolves, here the play is relatively senseless and whimsical (Pinter is, after all, our modern J. M. Barrie—unless the honor belongs more properly to Beckett). Every year fewer attend the professional Broadway theaters. The shows get sillier and sillier, showing the producers' estimate of our mentality (or is it their own that is revealed?). Even the best of the traditional theater is no longer found on Broadway but at the Judson Memorial Church, some miles away. Yet our theater schools grind out thousands on thousands of performing and production personnel, for whom jobs will simply not exist in twenty years. Can we blame the unions? Or rents and real estate taxes? Of course not. The subsidized productions, sponsored at such museums as New York's Lincoln Center, are not building up a new audience so much as re-cultivating an old one, since the medium of such drama seems weird and artificial in our new social milieu. We need more portability and flexibility, and this the traditional theater cannot provide. It was made for Versailles and for the sedentary Milords, not for motorized life-demons, who travel six hundred miles a week. Versailles no longer speaks very loudly to us, since we think at eighty-five miles an hour.

In the other direction starting from the idea of theater itself, others such as myself declared war on the script as a set of sequential events. Improvisation was no help: performers merely acted in imitation of a script. So I began to work as if time and sequence could be utterly suspended, not by ignoring them (which would simply be illogical) but by systematically replacing them as structural elements with change. Lack of change would cause my pieces to stop. In 1958 I wrote a piece, *Stacked Deck*, in which any event can take place at any time, as long as its cue appears. The cues are produced by colored lights. Since the colored lights could be used wherever they were put and audience reactions were also cuing situations, the performer-audience separation was removed and a happening situation was established, though less visually-oriented in its use of its environment and imagery. At the same time, Al Hansen moved into the area from graphic notation experiments, and Nam June Paik and Benjamin Patterson (both in Germany at the time) moved in from varieties of music in which specifically musical events were frequently replaced by non-musical actions.

Thus the happening developed as an intermedium, an uncharted land that lies between collage, music, and the theater. It is not governed by rules; each work determines its own medium and form according to its needs. The concept itself is better understood by what it is not, rather than what it is. Approaching it, we are pioneers again, and shall continue to be so as long as there's plenty of elbow room and no neighbors around for a few miles. Of course a concept like this is very disturbing to those whose mentality is compartmentalized. *Time, Life*, and the High Priests have been announcing the death of happenings regularly since the movement gained momentum in the late fifties, but this says more about the accuracy of their information than about the liveliness of the movement.

We have noted the intermedia in the theater and in the visual arts, the happening and certain varieties of physical constructions. For reasons of space we cannot take up here the intermedia between other areas. However, I would like to suggest that the use of intermedia is more or less universal throughout the fine arts, since continuity rather than categorization is the hallmark of our new mentality. There are parallels to the happening in music, for example, in the work of such composers as Philip Corner and John Cage, who explore the intermedia between music and philosophy, or Joe Jones, whose self-playing musical instruments fall into the intermedium between music and sculpture. The constructed poems of Emmett Williams and Robert Filliou certainly constitute an intermedium between poetry and sculpture. Is it possible to speak of the use of intermedia as a huge and inclusive movement of which Dada, Futurism, and Surrealism are early phases preceding the huge groundswell that is taking place now? Or is it more reasonable to regard the use of intermedia instead of traditional compartments as an inevitable and irreversible historical innovation, more comparable, for example, to the development of instrumental music than, for example, to the development of Romanticism? [1966]

ARNO KARLEN*

❦

Rain

The dust swirled and eddied over the fields like mist lying low on the sea. It blew into the crevices of the house as it had for weeks, slowly packing under the hot wind, calking even fine cracks in the paint like mortar. Aaron sat in a straight-backed wooden chair on the porch drinking coffee and watching it talcum the wooden railing, his high-ankled shoes. It dusted his splotchy freckles and the red hair on his head and on the backs of his fingers, like red hairy Esau in the desert. He felt sweat roll on his temples, knew the coffee only made him hotter, but kept drinking; he thought of the fine film of dust caking on it and wanted to wipe his forehead, but imagined leaving a track of sterile mud there, and didn't.

"Oh shit," said Mort quietly from the other chair. Aaron knew he would have to look up, but waited. Suddenly he wanted to chew through the cup. The anger trickled away, and finally he tilted back his head, and his pale-blue eyes regarded the sagging elephant-belly of the sky—rich, oppressive clouds like a sponge sopped on a dirty floor, slowly starting to move east with the wind. Once again they would lumber against the mountains that bounded the valley, to feed only the high distant pines.

Aaron looked at his brother-in-law's face—round, beardless, with close-cropped hair, thick glasses, and round little ears. He

* ARNO KARLEN, *born in Philadelphia in 1937, graduated from Antioch College in 1960 and has spent most of his years since then as an editor of* Holiday. *He has published criticism, poetry, translations, journalism, and stories in many magazines; some of the last he collected in* Short Story 2 (1959) *and* White Apples (1961). *He recently finished a novel.*

stared at its porcine blandness till it was as strange and incomprehensible as a pebble polished by the creek. Then, unable to sit and watch the rain deserting, he set his cup down, rose, walked down the two porch steps and began the long walk across the fields toward the stand of cottonwood trees that lined the creek's banks.

Dust blew gently into his nose, his eyes, his ears. It seemed soft, almost insubstantial as it danced in the wind, but blew needle-sharp against his half-shut lids and lay gritty between his teeth. Spitting and squinting, he trod over the dry fractured clods, amid the brittle silvery stubble of the crop . . . *maybe one day more . . . or maybe too late already.* . . . A big rain might drown it all now anyway, widening the cracks in the earth, cutting away what remained of the furrows, washing away the stalks.

He sat in the shade of a cottonwood, knees drawn up and arms clasped about them, watching the creek bed—deep muddy brown at the very center, but shading to tan and finally, at the edges, to a silver-beige powdery crumble. The air was as heavy and hot as on the porch. He sat, sweated, waited; there was nothing to do now but wait . . . *tomorrow . . . next week.* . . . And waiting, he gradually remembered what part of him had been trying to recall all morning, that he had dreamed last night of his stone . . . the wooden stone . . . digging it up and trying to throw it away in vain . . . a search for a missing trash barrel . . . for a trash heap that should have been behind the house but wasn't . . . stumbling with it in his aching arms from room to room. . . .

He had made it when he was fourteen, the summer after his mother died, with minute obsessive care, over a month of nights when the valley was as lush as a melon splitting with its own soft sweetness. He had learned in school about the Kensington stone, the fraudulent Viking runes chiseled, buried, and then "discovered" by a Minnesota farmer. With a child's delight in hoax and a man's dark persistence, he had made a stone of his own—not actually a stone, but a hand-hewn board, carefully charred and cracked on hot ashes, artfully chiseled with sixteen lines of an alphabet invented in variation on a runic model in the encyclopedia. He sculpted, scraped, aged it again with smoke and vegetable juices and diluted inks, and buried it beneath a cottonwood with a promise to himself to let it age there for three years. It had all

been done in inexplicable secrecy, delight, and shame, burying it
at night and touching his earth-caked hand to the down of his
sideburns and upper lip, and imagining the buried angular letters
like little stilts and huts sagging across the wood, and wondering
for a moment, before he caught himself with a twinge of fear,
what they actually said, though their mute mystery was his own
invention.

He came to the spot many times the next four years, to be by
the creek at night. Two years later he came, after a girl with red
hair like his own had kissed but refused to lie with him, and he sat
listening to the water rush and bubble like his loins, thinking . . .
*why wouldn't she? . . . why not? . . . what would it cost
her? . . . why not? . . .* and thinking of the untranslatable
lines, then angrily forgetting their childishness as he swung his
legs over the bank and furiously eased himself in the darkness,
letting his seed spurt into the stream and be carried off by the
water. Another time, drunk and ecstatic, he sprawled on his back
there, laughing aloud at the stars wheeling in vast blurred circles
above the branches, the sod pillowing his head as the earth pil-
lowed his stone, and he laughed in delight at his own grand mys-
terious gabble buried beneath him. And the night before he left
home at eighteen, remembering the stone, wanting at once to
smile and to wince, looking back to the light of the house and
thinking of the new world beginning tomorrow with the bus ride
away. He had never dug it up, thinking, when he thought of it at
all, *I don't want to,* yet at the same time dimly wanting to and
afraid of being ashamed of it, made with the last gasp of his silly
secret childhood and the first breath of the man, ashamed as when
he remembered the night when he sat upon the bank sick with
anger and love, or drunkenly abandoned, or as when he thought
of the strange haunted month when he fabricated the thing.

So he never dug it up, and then he left for Agriculture, met and
married Joanne, returned with her, let her brother buy in for a
third when father died. Now Joanne was with the children in the
city nursing her old mother. Aaron knew the mother wasn't that
sick, it was that Joanne couldn't bear to watch and guess, to hope
and try not to hope, with him, thinking each day . . . *is this
day's dust one too many . . . ruin? . . . will the wind?. . . .* So

now she telephoned each night, and no longer asked because it was painful, though her not asking pained and embittered him more.

Aaron leaned over and broke a clod from the edge of the bank. A few gray-yellow ghosts of grass stuck from it; the sere fuzz of the rootlets felt like a dead thing's fur, and he squeezed the clod so it crumbled and sifted between his fingers in dust and hard little lumps. The clouds moved almost imperceptibly now in the wind, which was slowing down, lazy and tauting. It was even hotter, stiller, than before. A bead of sweat dripped from his chin and made a dark muddy splotch in the dirt. He turned his head to look back across the fields to the distant farmhouse, where he could just make out Mort leaning against the porch rail.

Yes, even if the wind stopped and rain poured down, today might be one day too late. It made him close his eyes and rock his head that even if it were too late, this wouldn't necessarily ruin him. He might just be able to clear himself from the loss with two good years in a row . . . *if they're good . . . two years to mark time . . . two good to pay for one bad . . . it fits . . . it all fits.* . . . Joanne had left but not really deserted him, just fled in weakness he honestly couldn't blame too much . . . *I would if I could.* . . . He was past anger at her, at the weather, at the jagged white stalks and brittled leaves, past worry, and disgustingly not quite at despair . . . *maybe nowhere.* . . .

He did not realize what he was doing until he had well started, rising and wandering among the trees in a circle with aimless exasperation, absently kicking up a clod with his foot, then another, stopping, starting listlessly again, then squatting to push aside earth with his hands. And then, by the time he said to himself what he was about, he was digging in earnest, the soil damming beneath his fingernails, the words in his mind moving in rhythm with his arms . . . *what else do I have to do? . . . pull in the crop? . . . sit on the porch with Mort? . . . sweat ten drops into the empty creek? . . . make mud?* . . .

When he had gone down eight or ten inches, his mouth tightened angrily . . . *how deep? . . . right here?* . . . He alternately kicked, dug with his toe, with a dead branch, with his hands widening and deepening the hole . . . *more toward the tree? . . . farther down? . . . to the left? . . . this WAS the tree . . .* smiling with bitter, giddy anger because this was the only work there was for him, digging up the child's stone.

At last he stopped, squatting and staring bewildered into the empty hole. He had torn a fingernail to the quick. He stood and leaned against the cottonwood sucking and chewing at the fingernail, gazing blankly over the parched furrows. No, he couldn't have forgotten the spot . . . *could I? . . . no . . . here. . . .* Yet it must be that memory had played him false. Or had some other child, over these fifteen years, maybe seen a corner exposed by a heavy rain . . . dug it up . . . puzzled over it . . . carried it secretly home and treasured it as Aaron the child treasured its making . . . stored it in an attic, and maybe finally burned it with his other toys and treasures, denying his other past and untranslatable hordes, as Aaron had abandoned his to its burial place . . . or maybe it had been a transparent fake after all, at first sight, and the boy, or a man if one had found it, laughed and cast it away, maybe into the stream or god-knows where . . . rotted now in ooze at the bottom of a river far away . . . maybe still to be dug up centuries hence . . . at last to be puzzled over and saved. As he thought of the stone he saw it more and more clearly, realized that he knew it as well as his hands or his reflection—the split he had made reaching halfway down from the top on the left side, the rough gouges at the edges, the chisel scrapes on the back, the black patina of smoke and ash, the letters almost really runes. He could, he realized with surprise, almost reproduce the inscription if he had to, for in carving it so long with finicky gleeful care he had graven it in himself. The letters stumbled across in sixteen spindly tilted lines like live little sticks falling and rising again. And once more he involuntarily thought . . . *what did I mean?* For, he now realized, he had meant something that summer after all, something that even then, let alone now, he didn't even know. *Yes,* he thought with wondering, bleak satisfaction, *I meant something I didn't know.* It seemed stupid, crazy, yet also monstrously funny and bitter. He wanted for a moment to run to the house, to the phone, to call Joanne, talk to her, say anything, hear her voice. But the house was far away, and he stood paralyzed with deepening wonder and sadness. He thought of the boy making the stone through the nights in his room by the light of a kerosene lantern, no sound but his father's loud snoring, drunk with concentration, believing that from this childish dedication and sacrifice some grand, miraculous issue would come—a discovery, a world trembling and awed at the silent message, visitors and experts and admirers, and doubters who could prove nothing. And all along, he knew somehow beyond his childish knowledge that not even disaster was final or grand, that ahead was only the day that is maybe too late and maybe not, the missing answer whose very question wasn't sure.

Yet even as he thought this, he felt in possession of deep, unnameable knowledge, and close to tears, why he didn't know. Maybe it was realizing that knowing came only when it didn't matter any more, and all hope was driven out, even the hope of definitive calamity or destruction. The tears were closer and closer to spilling, and he didn't really know why until he let them come. He leaned against the cottonwood and began to cry soundlessly, slowly, with open eyes, and knew now that it was with pity for the boy, such pity and love as he could feel for another person, but never till now for himself. He felt the sobs become harder and deeper, wracking, complete, crying as a child cries; they rose, wilder and wilder, like a runaway animal, rasping and choking with abandon from his chest in a voice he had never heard. He was frightened, but beyond stopping. He let his weeping carry him off, eyes squeezed shut. He sank to his knees in the dust, put his hands over his face and fell forward, forehead to the earth; unable to support himself, he rolled over on his side, choking and braying, teeth bared, sucking in air for his sobs to ride on.

How long it took for the tears to subside and leave him gasping, he didn't know; nor how long before the gasps died down to leave him curled on his side in the dust, hands over his face. He might even have slept, perhaps for minutes, perhaps an hour. It was the clammy coolness of sweat-soaked clothes that finally made him open his eyes and rise to his knees. Stunned, empty, he stayed there for half an hour as the air rapidly cooled and the eddies of dust settled with the dying wind. A huge moist somnolence vibrated over the fields, the house, the entire valley. The air became clear yet eerily substantial, like some pellucid weightless fluid. The points of green that remained in the desiccated fields rallied like a dying man's final frail exuberance; the silver and tan of the earth grew rich and soft. And then suddenly, noiselessly, the earth was speckled with dots of dark brown. A moment later the stippling spread; a moment later grew again, and the ground was half dark; then darker; and darker still. And then the rain came. It poured down in huge drops with the sound of a bird beating madly along the watertop.

Aaron had risen and started to walk before it fell. He strode across the fields toward the house, his face and fingers and clothes streaming muddy rain water. Mort was coming toward him. They drew together where stunted stalks lay battered by the rain and floating in rivulets that sped among the widening crevices between the clods of earth. Mort was shaking his head slightly, with no expression, glancing continually from the earth toward the unslacking sky, not knowing yet whether to give thanks or mourn disaster. He looked to Aaron, but Aaron merely gave one short helpless burst of laughter at his face and passed him, eyes wide open, walking hard . . . *only when it doesn't matter . . . can't matter any more . . . the answer only when there isn't any question* . . . pulling his legs against the suck of the rushing rivulets beneath his feet and of the mud and bits of stubble that caked thicker and thicker on his shoes.

WILLIAM MELVIN KELLEY*

❧

Cry for Me

This is about my Uncle Wallace, who most of you know by
his last name—Bedlow—because that's all they ever put on his
records. I only got one of his albums myself. It has a picture of
him on it, sitting, holding his two guitars, wearing his white dinner jacket, his mouth wide open and his eyes squinted shut. The
name of the album is: *Bedlow—Big Voice Crying in the Wilderness* and I got it in particular because it has the only two songs he
sang that I really like: *Cotton Field Blues* and *John Henry*. Besides that, I don't much like folk songs or folk singers. But I liked
Uncle Wallace all right.

I guess I should tell you about the first time I met Uncle Wallace; this was even before he was folk singing, or maybe before
any of us *knew* it. We just knew he was a relative, my old man's
brother, come North from the South.

That was in June of 1957. We went to Pennsylvania Station
to meet him. He sent us a telegram; there wasn't enough time for
him to write a letter because he told us later he only decided to
come two days before he showed up.

So we went to the station, and the loudspeaker called out his
train from down South. A *whole* bunch of colored people got off
the train, all looking like somebody been keeping it a secret from
them they been free for a hundred years, all bulgy-eyed and con-

* WILLIAM MELVIN KELLEY, *born in New York City in 1937, grad-
uated from Harvard, where he won the Dana Reed Prize for 1960.
He has published three novels,* A Different Drummer (1962) *and*
A Drop of Patience (1965), dem (1967), *and one collection of stories,*
Dancers on the Store (1964). *He lives in New York City and teaches
at the New School.*

fused, carrying suitcases and shopping bags and boxes and little kids.

My old man was craning his neck, looking to find Uncle Wallace. None of us would-a recognized him because when my old man come North twenty years ago he didn't bring but one picture of Uncle Wallace and that was of him when he was about seven. But my old man been back South once and saw Uncle Wallace a man. He would recognize him all right.

But I heard my old man say to my mother, "Don't see him yet."

And then we did see him; we could not-a missed him because he come rumbling out the crowd—the size of a black Grant's Tomb with a white dinner jacket draped over it (he had the jacket even then, having won it in some kind-a contest driving piles, or cutting wood)—and punched my old man square in the chops so he flew back about twenty feet, knocking over this little redcap, and springing all the locks on the four suitcases he was carrying, scattering clothes in all directions like a flock of pigeons in Central Park you tossed a rock at.

My old man is about six-five and two-fifty and works in heavy construction and I ain't never seen anyone hit him, let alone knock him off his feet, and I thought sure he'd go nuts and get mad, but he didn't; he started to laugh, and Uncle Wallace stood over him and said: "How you doing, Little Brother? I see you ain't been keeping up your strength. Use to have more trouble with you when I was six." And he reached out his hand to my old man, who got up, and even though he was on his feet still looked like he was lying down because Uncle Wallace was at least a head taller.

My old man said, "Never could beat you, Wallace. Pa's the only man could." And I remember figuring how to be able to do that, my Grandpa Mance Bedlow must-a been close to eight feet tall and made of some kind of fireproof metal.

Then my old man turned to us and said: "I'd like you to meet my family. This is my wife, Irene." He pointed at my mother. "And this is Mance; we call him Little Brother." He pointed at my brother. "And this is my first born, Carlyle junior." And he pointed at me and I reached up my hand to Uncle Wallace before

I realized he'd probably crush it. He took it, but didn't crush it at all, just squeezed it a little and smiled, looking down at me out of tiny, red eyes in his black-moon face.

So we took Uncle Wallace home to the Bronx.

My old man got him a job with the same construction company he worked for and the foreman, he'd send them both up on the girders and give them enough work for eight men and they'd get it done, and then they'd come home and Uncle Wallace'd watch television until one and then go to sleep. He never seen it before and it knocked him out.

He hadn't seen anything of New York but our house and the building he and my old man was practically putting up single-handed. That's why one Friday night, my old man said: "Carlyle, why don't you take old Wallace downtown and show him the city?"

I really didn't want to go; I mean, that's *nowhere* getting stuck with a man could be your father, but I went.

First I took him to Harlem near where we used to live and we said hello to some of my old friends who was standing in front of a bar, watching the girls swishing by in dresses where you could see everything, either because the dresses was so tight over what they should-a been covering, or because there wasn't no dress covering the other parts. I guess Uncle Wallace liked that pretty much because everybody was colored and where we live in the Bronx, everybody is Italian. So in Harlem, he must-a felt at home.

Then we went to Times Square. I don't think he liked that too much, too big and noisy for him, him being right out of a cotton field. I was about to take him home, but then I said: "Hey, Uncle Wallace, you ever seen a queer?"

He looked down at me. "What's that, Carlyle?"

I was about to laugh because I figured maybe he ain't seen a queer, but I would-a thought *everybody* knew what they was. But then I decided just to explain—I knew how strong he was, but hadn't been knowing him long enough to know how fast he got mad. So I just told him what a queer was.

He looked down at me blank and sort of stupid. "No stuff?"

"I wouldn't lie to you, Uncle Wallace." I took him by the arm. "Come on, I'll show you some queers."

That's why we went to Greenwich Village.

It was comical to see him looking at his first queer, who was as queer as a giraffe sitting on a bird's nest. Uncle Wallace just gaped like he seen a farmer hitch a chipmunk to a plow, then turned to me. "Well, I'll be lynched, Carlyle!"

After that we walked around past the handbag and sandal shops and the coffee houses and dug the queers and some girls in sort of black underwear, and then all of a sudden, he wasn't with me no more. I turned all the way around, a little scared because if he would-a got his-self lost, I'd never see him again. He was halfway back up the block, his head way above everybody else's like he was standing on a box, and a look on his face like he been knocked up side his head with a cast-iron Cadillac. I ran back up to him, but by the time I got to where he been standing, he was most down some steps leading into a cellar coffee shop called *The Lantern.* I called to him but he must-a not heard me over the singing that was coming from inside. He was already at the door and a cross-eyed little blond girl was telling him to put a dollar in the basket she was tending. So I followed him down, paid my dollar and caught up to him. "Hey, Uncle Wallace, what's the matter?"

He put his hand on my shoulder, grabbing it tight so I could hear the bones shift around. "Hush, boy." And then he turned to this little lit-up stage and there was this scrawny yellow Negro sitting on a stool playing the guitar and singing some folk song. He was wearing a green shirt open to his belly button, and a pair of tight black pants. What a queer!

The song he was singing was all about how life is tough—he looked like the toughest day he ever spent was when his boy friend didn't serve him breakfast in bed—and how when you're picking cotton, the sun seems to be as big as the whole sky. The last line was about how he'd pick all the cotton in the world and not plant no more and wouldn't have to work again and how he'd finally win out over the sun. When he finished, everybody snapped their fingers, which is what they do in the Village instead of clap.

Then he said: "And now, ladies and gentlemen, this next piece is another from the collection of Francis Mazer, a song he found during his 1948 trip through the South. A blues called *Wasn't*

That a Man." He struck a chord and started to sing: something about a Negro who swum a flooded, raging river with his two sons and his wife tied on his back. He sang it very fast so all the words ran together.

Uncle Wallace listened through one chorus, his eyes narrowing all the time until they about disappeared, and then he was moving, like a black battleship, and I grabbed his coat so he wouldn't make a fool of his-self in front of all them white folks, but then I just let him go. It was his business if he wanted to act like a nigger, and I couldn't stop him anyway. So I just stood there watching him walk in the dark between the little tables and looming out in the spotlight, burying the yellow Negro in his shadow.

Uncle Wallace reached out and put his hand around the neck of the guitar and the notes choked off. His hand must-a gone around the neck about three times.

The yellow Negro looked up at him, sort of shook. "I beg your pardon?"

"Brother, you better start begging somebody's pardon for what you doing to that song. You sings it all wrong."

Then a bald man in a shirt with the points of the collar all twisted and bent come up and patted Uncle Wallace on the back, hard. "Come on, buddy. Let's move out."

Uncle Wallace about-faced and looked way down at him. "Brother, next time you come up behind me and touch me, you'll find yourself peeping at me out of that guitar."

The bald man took a step back. Uncle Wallace looked at the yellow Negro again. "Now, look-a-here, colored brother, you can't sing my songs that way. You sing them like I made them up or don't sing them at all. And if you *do* sing them your way, then you may just never sing again, ever." He was still holding the neck of the guitar.

"Your songs? You didn't write these songs," the yellow Negro said. "They grew up out of the Rural Southern Negro Culture."

"Go on, nigger! They grew up out-a me. That song you was just singing now, about the man and the river, I wrote that song about my very own Daddy."

A couple people in the audience started to sit up and listen. But that little yellow flit of a Negro didn't believe it. "I tell you, these songs were collected in 1948 by Francis Mazer, and there's no telling how long they've been sung. I heard the original tapes myself."

Uncle Wallace's eyes went blank for a second. Then he said: "What this Francis Mazer look like? He a little old gray-haired man with a game leg?"

That stopped the yellow Negro for a while. "Yessss." He held onto the word like he didn't want to let it out.

"Sure enough, I remember him. He was a mighty sweet old gentleman, told me all he wanted to do was put my songs on a little strip of plastic. I asked him if he meant to write *all* my songs on that small space. He said I got him wrong, that the machine he had with him would make a record of them. And I said for him to go on. I was playing a dance and the folks was happy and I sang from Friday night until the next afternoon, and that little gentleman stood by just putting them spools in his machine and smiling. And when I got done he give me thirty dollars, U.S. currency, and I went out and bought me some new strings and a plow too." Uncle Wallace stopped and shook his head. "Mighty sweet old gentleman. And you say his name was Mazer?"

"This has gone far enough!" The yellow Negro was real ticked off now, sort of cross like a chick. "Arthur, get him out of here." He was talking to the bald man.

Uncle Wallace looked at the bald man too, sort of menacing. Then he looked at the yellow Negro. "I don't want you singing my songs *at all*." Then he just walked away, out of the lights and it was like the sun come up on the yellow Negro all at once.

But the bald man wouldn't let it stop there and said: "Hey, you, mister, wait!" He was talking to Uncle Wallace, who didn't stop because (he told me later) he never in his life got called *Mister* by no white man, so he thought the bald man was talking to someone else.

The bald man run after him and was about to put his hand on his shoulder, but remembered what Uncle Wallace said before and hot-footed it around in front of him and started to talk, backing up. "I'm Arthur Friedlander. I own this place. If you're what you say you are, then I'd like you to sing some songs."

That stopped Uncle Wallace, who told me once he'd sing for

anybody, even a president of a White Citizen's Council, if he got asked. So he came to a halt like a coal truck at a sudden red light and looked down on Mister Friedlander and said: "You want me to sing?"

And Mister Friedlander said: "If you can. Sure, go on."

"But I ain't brung my guitars."

"He'll let you use his. Go on." He reached out sort of timid, like at a real mean dog, and took Uncle Wallace's arm and started to lead him back to the lights.

The yellow Negro, he didn't really want to give up his guitar, but I guess he figured Mister Friedlander would fire him if he didn't, so he left it resting against the stool and stormed off the stage.

Uncle Wallace and Mister Friedlander went up there and Uncle Wallace picked up the guitar and ran his fingers over the strings. It looked like he was holding a ukulele.

Mister Friedlander looked at the audience and said: "*The Lantern* takes pleasure in presenting a new folk singer." He realized he didn't know Uncle Wallace's name and turned around.

"Bedlow," Uncle Wallace said, sort-a shy.

"Bedlow," said Mister Friedlander to the audience.

A couple people giggled and a couple others snapped their fingers, but they was joking. Uncle Wallace whacked the guitar again, and all of a sudden music come out of it. I was surprised because way down deep I thought sure Uncle Wallace was just a fool. He didn't play right off, though, just hit it a couple times and started to talk:

"That song the other fellow was playing, I wrote that when my Daddy died, for his funeral. That was 1947. It's all about how when I was a boy we had a flood down home and where we was living got filled up with water. There was only one safe, high spot in that country—an island in mid-river. But none of us could swim but my Daddy, so he tied me and my brother on his back and my Mama, she hung on and he swum the whole parcel of us over. So everybody remembered that and when he was taken I made a song about it to sing over his trench. . . ." He hit another chord, but still didn't sing yet, just stopped.

"Say," he said, "anybody got another guitar?"

Some folks started mumbling about him being a fake and stalling and a couple of them laughed. I was thinking maybe they was right.

A white boy with a beard come up with a guitar case and opened it and reached over a guitar to Uncle Wallace and so now he had two guitars. I thought he didn't like the yellow Negro's guitar, but he started to get them in the same tune—hitting one and then the other. And when he judged they was all right, he put one on his left knee, with his left hand around the neck like anybody would hold a guitar, and then put the other one on his right knee and grabbed the neck of that one with his right hand. His arms was way out and he looked like he was about to fly away. Then he clamped his fingers down on the strings of them both so hard and so fast they both sounded, not just a little noise, but a loud chord like an organ in church, or two men playing guitars. Then he started to stamp his feet and clamp his fingers and you could hear the blues get going and then he was singing. . . .

Well, not really, because the most you could say about his voice was that it was on key, and it was sure loud! It wasn't deep and hollow, or high and sweet. It didn't even sound like singing. In fact, I don't think anybody ever heard him sing or really listened to him. It wasn't a voice you heard or listened to; it was a voice you swallowed, because it always seemed to upset your stomach. I heard him sing lots of times and it was always the same: not hearing anything, but feeling kind of sick like you been drinking a gallon of wine, and the wine was fighting you inside, grabbing at your belly and twisting it around so you wanted to yell out, but didn't because you was scared the wine might take offense and tear you to pieces. And when he stopped and the grabbing stopped, you'd feel all weak and terrible like maybe you would feel if you gotten a date with a girl you thought might give you some tail and you been thinking about it all day in school and then you went out with her and when you took her home, her folks was out, and so she took you inside and you *did* get some tail and now that it was all over, you wished she'd run inside and not given you anything because then it wouldn't be all over now and you'd still have it to look forward to. But pretty soon he'd start singing again and everything would be like it was before, feeling sick, and wishing you was *still* sick when you didn't feel sick no more.

So that's the way it was that Friday in the Village; that's the way it always was. And the people was always the same. When he got through grabbing at them, no one snapped their fingers; no one ordered anything. The cooks come out the kitchen and the waitresses sat down with the customers. People come down the steps and paid their money and managed to get into a seat before he reached out and caught them, and when the seats was all gone —because nobody left—people kept coming until they was standing and sitting in the aisles, packed right to the doors, and even on the stage with him, nobody moving or making a sound, just getting sick in the stomach and hating it and loving it all at the same time.

So Uncle Wallace sang right until Saturday morning at four. And then we went home and I slept all day.

That was how we found out what Uncle Wallace was, or did. But for a while after he sang that Friday, he didn't sing no more. It was like before: Uncle Wallace going to work, him and my old man building their building, coming home and Uncle Wallace gassing himself on TV until one, then going to sleep.

But then the phone call came from Mister Friedlander and I answered it. He sounded real tired and said: "Hello? Is this the Bedlow residence? Do you have someone living with you or know of someone named Bedlow who sings folk songs?"

And when I answered the questions Yes, there was a silence and then I could hear sobbing on the other end of the line and through all the sobbing, him saying, "Thank God; Thank God," for about five minutes.

So at first I was about to hang up because I heard of guys calling up and cursing at women and all that mess, but then he said: "Who am I talking to?" I told him. "You were with that man who sang in my place four weeks ago? *The Lantern?* I'm Arthur Friedlander." So I said Hello, because I remembered him. He asked me what Uncle Wallace was to me and I told him.

"Carlyle," he said, "I've been trying to find your uncle for three weeks. I called Bedfords and Bradfords for the first two. It's like this, kid, every night a hundred people come into the place and ask for him and I have to say he isn't here and they get so mad they go away. He's ruining me! Where's your uncle now?"

I told him Uncle Wallace was at work.

"Listen, kid, there's a five in it for you if you can get him down here tonight by seven-thirty. And tell him I'll pay him thirty—no, make that fifty a week."

I said I could only *try* like I figured it might be hard to get Uncle Wallace to sing. Mister Friedlander give me his number and told me to call him back when I had an answer and hung up.

When Uncle Wallace come home, I said: "That man you sang for a month ago?—he wants you to come again . . . for money." I didn't have to add the money part because I could tell by his face, he was ready to go.

So I called back Mister Friedlander and told him we was coming. I said that to get Uncle Wallace to sing, which he hadn't wanted to do, I had to say Mister Friedlander was paying him seventy-five dollars a week.

Mister Friedlander didn't even seem surprised. He just said, "But you got him to come?"

"Yes, sir," I said.

"Good boy! I'm giving you ten dollars instead of five." Which is what I figured he'd do if I told him I had trouble.

When we turned the corner into *The Lantern*'s block there was a riot going on, with a hundred people, maybe even a thousand there, not all Village people neither. A whole bunch of them was in suits, and fur coats and jewels. Man, if I been a pickpocket I could-a retired on what I could-a got there that night. And there was cops in their green cars with flashing lights going off and on, and on horses. Folks was pushing each other into the gutter and throwing punches. I looked up at Uncle Wallace and said: "Hey, we better split. We ain't got nothing to do with this, and you know how cops pick on colored folks."

"But I promised the man I'd sing, Carlyle," he said. But I could tell it wasn't that: he just wanted to sing, promise or no promise.

So we tried to sneak around behind all the rioting to get into *The Lantern*. And we most made it, but someone said: "Is that him?"

And someone answered: "Got to be."

I poked Uncle Wallace and said: "Now we really better get out-a here. These white folks think you done something."

"What?" he asked.

"I don't know, but we better get out-a here, *now*." And I grabbed his arm and started to pull him away, out-a there. I could tell he didn't want to go; he wanted to sing, but I figured I had to keep him out-a jail if I could.

Then someone started to yell at us to stop and I turned around to see how big they was and if there was more than we could handle, because either Uncle Wallace could flatten them or we could outrun them. But it was Mister Friedlander, chugging up the stairs, yelling.

We stopped.

He got to us and said, "What's wrong?"

"They think Uncle Wallace did something. He didn't do nothing. We just got here. We don't know nothing about this riot."

"Come inside. I'll explain," Mister Friedlander said. So we went down the stairs, and inside and he locked the door.

The place was jammed! There was more people there than that first Friday night.

Mister Friedlander said: "After you called, I put a sign in the window saying: *Bedlow here tonight*. Those people, they're here to see him. That's what the riot is." Then he asked me if I read that New York Sunday paper which weighs so much and ain't got no funnies. I told him No.

"Well, that Friday night your Uncle Wallace was here, there was a guy here from that paper. And the next Sunday he wrote an article—wait, I'll show you." So he ran behind the counter and come out with this page of a newspaper that he got magnified around forty times and pasted on cardboard. At the top of the page was this title: *Big Voice Crying in the Wilderness*.

The article under it was about Uncle Wallace. It told all about that other Friday night and said that Uncle Wallace was a voice speaking for all the colored folks and that to hear him was to understand the pain of discrimination and segregation and all that kind of stuff, which seemed like a lot of B-S to me because I didn't understand Uncle Wallace hardly myself; I didn't understand why he sang folk songs when he could sing rock-and-roll or jazz. So how the hell could he be *my* voice or the voice of anybody like me? But that's what this writer said anyway.

When I looked up from the story I must-a been frowning, or maybe looked like I didn't get it because Mister Friedlander grabbed me by the shoulders and shook me. "Don't you see? Your uncle is the hottest thing to hit New York since the Chicago Fire. He's a fad!"

And all the time he was telling me this, Uncle Wallace was standing by the window looking out at the people, not realizing this was all about him. That was when I started to dig something about him I never had before, and when I started to really like him and decided I'd have to look after him, even though he was old enough and big enough and smart enough to look after hisself: Uncle Wallace was innocent. To him you didn't sing for money, or for people even, but because you wanted to. And I guess the most important thing was that he wasn't some guy singing about love who never loved, or hard work who never worked hard because he done all that, loved women and picked cotton and plowed and chopped trees. And even though he was in show business, he wasn't at all like anybody else in it. He was more real somehow.

Anyway, I could say he was better that night than he was before, but that wouldn't be really honest because I didn't dig his music so I don't know if he was better or not. I think the people liked him better, but I can't be sure of *that* either because when he finished, they was in so much pain, they never snapped their fingers for him, just sat staring, sad and hurting like before.

After he sung three sets and was sitting back in the kitchen drinking gin and fruit juice, this man come in with Mister Friedlander. "Bedlow, this is A. V. Berger. He wants to speak to you a minute."

This Mister Berger was five feet tall—tops—but weighed close to three hundred pounds with black hair, straight and greasy. He was wearing a black wool suit—this was in midsummer now—

with a vest and a scarf, which was black wool too. And the English this man spoke was fantabulous! I can only *try* to copy it. He hemmed and hawed a lot too so it sounded like:

"Mister Bedlow, (hem) I'm a concert producer. And (hem) I have been watching you perform. It seems quite likely that (hem) I can use you in a concert (hem) I'm staging at Carnegie Hall." He stopped there. I could see he was looking for Uncle Wallace to jump in the air and clap his hands. I knew what Carnegie Hall was, but I bet Uncle Wallace didn't. Mister Berger thought Uncle Wallace was playing it cagey.

"Mister Bedlow, (hem) I'm prepared to offer you a good price to appear in the show."

"What's it to be? A dance?" Uncle Wallace said. "Sure, I'll play for a dance. That's what I done down home."

"No, Mister Bedlow. You (hem) misunderstand. This will be a concert."

"Like what?" He turned to me. "Like what, Carlyle?"

"A concert, Uncle Wallace. That's when a whole lot of folks come and just sit and listen to you sing."

"You mean just like here?"

"No, Uncle Wallace. It's like a church." I was thinking about how the seats was arranged, but he didn't get me.

"But I don't sing church music, Carlyle. My songs is too dirty for church. They never let me sing in no church." He looked back at Mister Berger. "What kind-a church you running, mister, that they sing my kind-a songs in there?"

"(hem) I don't run a church, Mister Bedlow." Mister Berger looked sort-a bleak and confused.

"No, Uncle Wallace, it ain't in no church," I said. "It's in a big hall and they want you to sing for a couple thousand people."

"No stuff?"

"Yeah, sure," I said.

"That's (hem) right," said Mister Berger.

"Go on, Bedlow," chimed in Mister Friedlander.

So he did.

But that concert wasn't until October and Mister Berger asked him to appear in early July, so there was a lot of time in between, when Uncle Wallace was making all his records.

And there was that damn movie. It was about this plantation family and all their problems in the Civil War. It wasn't really such a bad movie, but Uncle Wallace made it worse. I mean, he was the best thing in it, but after he was on the screen you couldn't look at the movie no more.

The movie would be going on all right and then would come Uncle Wallace's scene. He be sitting on this log in raggedy clothes and they *even* had a bandana around his head. You know how they make movies about colored people in Hollywood; the slaves act like slavery was the best God-damn thing ever happened to them and all they did all day was sit around on logs and sing and love Old Master, instead of breaking their asses in his cotton field and waiting for the chance to run away or slit Old Master's throat wide open. But that wasn't the worst. Dig this! They made him sing *John Henry*. But it didn't matter. They didn't know Uncle Wallace. He started playing and singing and when he got through you had the feeling old John Henry wasn't no idiot after all. I mean, I heard some guy sing that song once and I said to myself: what an idiot this John Henry must-a been, killing his-self to beat a machine, when he could-a joined a union, like my old man's, and made twice the money and kept the machine out.

But when Uncle Wallace sang *John Henry* you didn't feel that way. You felt like old John Henry was trapped and he had to do what he did, like when a fellow says your Mama screws for syphilitic blind men, you got to hit him; you don't think about it; it don't even matter if he joking or not, you just got to hit him even if he beats all hell out-a you. Well, that's what Uncle Wallace did to you.

So when them white folks come back on the screen with their dumb problems, and started kissing it up, you could see they was cardboard; you could see they was acting and you got up and left out of there because you had to see real people again, and even when you got out in the street you sort-a felt like the people *out there* wasn't real neither, so what you did was go back in and stand in the lobby until the next showing when Uncle Wallace come on again for his two minutes and you'd go in and see him. Then you'd walk out again to the lobby. There was always a whole lot of folks out there waiting like you and not looking at you because you was as cardboardy to them as they was to you, and you'd wait for his two minutes again, and like that all day until you got too hungry to see.

After he made the movie he come back East and it was October and it was time for the concert at Carnegie Hall. And I guess you know what happened at the concert, but I'll tell it again and also some things I felt about it.

Mister Berger had-a told Uncle Wallace to play it cool and save his best until last, which meant that Uncle Wallace was to come out and sing a couple songs with only one guitar and then—bingo!—lay the two guitars on them. So they fixed me up in a tux and when the time come, I paraded out and give him the other guitar.

Uncle Wallace was tuning the second guitar when a voice come whispering up from the dark in the front row. "Hey, nigger, you the same one, ain't you."

Uncle Wallace squinted down, and there in the front row with all them rich white folks was this dark little Negro. There was a woman with him and a whole bunch of little kids, all shabby-looking, all their eyes shining like a row of white marbles.

"The same as what?" Uncle Wallace said.

And the voice come back. "The same fellow what played at a East Willson café in 1948."

"Yeah, I played there that year."

"There was one night in particular, when a cripple white man was taping you, and we all danced until the next day."

"Sure, it was!" Uncle Wallace snapped his fingers. "I remember you. You was with a *pretty* girl."

"You right, man. Here she is; my wife." He turned to the woman. "Honey, get up and meet Mister Bedlow." She did, and Uncle Wallace leaned over the edge of the stage and shook her hand. "Say, you know, I bought these big money seats because I wanted my kids to see you up close. Them is them." He pointed at the row of kids. "The oldest one, he's Bedlow. I named him after you because me and the wife wasn't getting on so good until that night." It was like they was all alone in that great big place, just those two down-home Negroes talking over old times. "And them others is Booker, Carver, Robeson, Robinson, and Bunche."

"Man, you do me proud. Pleased to meet you all. Say, you want to come up here and sit with me?"

"Now, you do *me* proud." So they all come up on stage like a row of ducks.

Then Uncle Wallace started to play and the littlest kid, that was Bunche—he was about three—he sat there for about one minute and then I saw him jump on his feet and start to do these wild little steps, just his feet moving like little pistons. Then the man got up and asked his wife to dance, and the next thing I knew, everybody was dancing—even me; I danced right out on stage—and all the rich white folks was on their feet in the aisles and their wives was hugging strangers, black and white, and taking off their jewelry and tossing it in the air and all the poor people was ignoring the jewelry, was dancing instead, and you could see everybody laughing like crazy and having the best old time ever. Colored folks was teaching white folks to dance, and white folks was dancing with colored folks and all the seats was empty and people was coming on stage to dance. Then the other singers backstage come out and started to back-up Uncle Wallace and we was all dancing, all of us, and over all the noise and laughing you could hear Uncle Wallace with his two guitars. You could hear him over the whole thing.

Then the air changed; you could feel it. It wasn't just air any more, it started to get sweet-tasting to breathe like perfume and the people started to run down the aisles toward the stage, and everybody on the stage started to dance in toward Uncle Wallace, and everybody, *everybody* in the whole place was sobbing and crying and tears was pouring down their cheeks and smearing their make-up and making their eyes red and big. I could hear Uncle Wallace singing louder than ever. The people was rushing toward him. They was all crying and smiling too like people busting into a trance in church and it seemed like everybody in the place was on stage trying to get near enough to touch him, grab his hand and shake it and hug him and kiss him even. And then the singing stopped.

I pushed my way through the crowd up to his chair. The first thing I seen was his two guitars all tore up and smashed and the strings busted. Uncle Wallace was sitting in his chair, slumped over, his face in his lap. And this was real strange; he looked like an old punctured black balloon, deflated and all. There wasn't a mark on him, but he was dead all right.

Mister Berger called in a whole bunch of doctors, but they just stood around shaking their heads. They couldn't figure out how he'd died. One of them said, "There isn't nothing wrong with him, except he's dead."

Now I know this'll sound lame to you, but I don't think anything killed him except maybe at that second, he'd done everything that he ever wanted to do; he'd taken all them people, and sung to them, and made them forget who they was, and what they come from, and remember only that they was people. So he'd seen all he wanted to see and there was no use going on with it. I mean, he'd made it. He got over.

It's kind of like that girl I was telling you about—the one who'd promised you some tail, and when you got it, you was sorry, because then you'd still have it to look forward to? Well, I think it's like that: getting tail and coming out of her house and there ain't nothing but pussycats and garbage cans in the street, and it's lonely and late and you wished you hadn't done it, but then you shrug and say to yourself: "Hell, man, you did, and that's it." And there ain't nothing to do but leave, because it's finished. But then there's something else. You're walking along and all at once you smile, and maybe even laugh, and you say: "Man, that was some *good* tail!" And it's a nice memory to walk home with.

KENNETH KING*

❧

SuperLecture

SOME WEIRD THINGS STARTED HAPPENING LAST SUMMER. ONE
FULL-MOON NIGHT I MET THE *m-o-o-n-l-a-d-y* ON MY ROOF AND
DANCED FOR HER. SHE WAS FORMERLY A COLLEGE FRIEND, I THINK,
THOUGH I COULD HARDLY RECOGNIZE HER. SHE LOOKED VERY DIFFER-
ENT NOW AFTER HAVING RETURNED FROM SOME AMBITIOUS JOURNEY.
ON THE COURSE OF HER TRIP SHE BLEW HER CIRCUITS ON A. SHE
KNEW IT. SHE ALSO KNEW SHE HAD TO FIND SOMETHING OR SOMEONE
BEFORE SHE DIED. WE TRIED TO FIGURE OUT WHAT IT WAS. SHE
WASN'T SURE IF SHE HAD BEEN BORN ON THE MOON OR EARTH OR JUST
WHERE.

LATER DURING THE SUMMER JANE SMITH PHONED AND SAID
SHE WAS LOCKED AWAY IN BELLEVUE HOSPITAL. SHE WAS THE FIRST
PERSON I EVER KNEW WHO READ E. E. CUMMINGS LETTER BY LETTER
INSTEAD OF CONNECTING-UP THE WORDS. SHE SAID THERE WAS ENOUGH
IN EACH LETTER. SHE WAS ALSO THE FIRST PFRSON WHO FELT VIBRA-
TIONS, WHO GAVE ME A PERSON FOR A GIFT, WHO HAD GONE ALL THE
WAY OUT, AND WHO KNEW THIS.

It was Immanuel Kant who unknowingly began Blowing Minds
and reprogramming circuits. History will record Kant in the near

* KENNETH KING, *born in 1945 in New York City, graduated in 1965
from Antioch College where he studied philosophy. He has contributed articles to* Film Culture *and two anthologies,* The New Art
(1966) *and* The New American Cinema (1967). *Primarily a dancer
and choreographer, he has performed with several companies and
created his mixed-means theater pieces. This published text was
originally a tape-recorded accompaniment for his first full-evening
theater work,* m-o-o-n-b-r-a-i-nwithSuperLecture (1966).

future as the Saviour of dance and theater. Another Jesus Christ. Kant began his Mission of wiring circuits through a phenomenological distinction between *phenomena* and *noumena*. What I Like about *noumena* is that nobody knows what they are, if they are, or anything about them. Like ether and the physicists a while back. Eventually though, the physicists had to Junk the ether premise because they couldn't find it.

Kant was a Head; the Head of Heads, just as Christ was the Head of the Church. But we had to wait until Sigmund Freud for Psychoanalysis and for Marcel Duchamp for the psychology of objects just as we had to Program Romanticism so we could get the Supremes. But it was without a doubt Jung who was quietly Taking Care of Business on the side. While Freud was Programming Jonathan Swift and Leonardo da Vinci, Jung was recircuiting *The Tibetan Book of the Dead*. Freud got Hung on tracing the roots of behavior to the pre-natal stages of embryonic development and on explaining behavior in terms of a Death Instinct; he postulated that even before the Birth Trauma the human embryo was Programmed for Action and Psychosis. But Jung, being the John Cage of psychology, wanted to Go all the Way Out—back before birth, before fertilization, to past Lives, whatever that Means. It was Jung who Connected-Up the Mainline to Death, and back beyond again into Life.

In the same way we had to wait for Rock 'n Roll and High-Gear electronic equipment to Establish Vivaldi as we had to wait for Isadora Duncan to recircuit ballet. Amplifications systems and other electronic Gear solve the problem of the harpsichord and other Baroque chamber instruments: sound is now a Super-Commodity—a Louder-than-Life Phenomenon. That's why Rock 'n Roll is so Great—if you play it Really loud enough you can't hear yourself and thinking anymore. That's why I Like Rock 'n Roll—it gives the transistors and cathodes a rest. When you play the Supremes Full-Blast you Short-Circuit Feedback. Human Feedback is like when thinking gets confused and garbled so that the Information Turns In On Itself and prevents a logical, or dialectical sequence of thought. Rock 'n Roll is a cool, sustained, and timeless High. And just you wait until the Beatles Program La Monte Young: not only will it be their Come Back—another historical Blow-Out, but another To-Be Landmark in Western Music. Now the problem, so to speak, is to make one *long* song, maybe one side of a 33 disk, perhaps a Rock 'n Roll equivalent to Mahler.

Sometimes a painting is about paint; paint on a canvas. Later the canvas was confused by the stage because paint became people and Action strokes. A dance was about dancing. Film and Television completely recircuited the Nineteenth Century concept of Modern Theater. It was René Clair in 1924 with his brilliantly telepathic movie *Entr'acte* who actually recircuited Modern Theater. If Martha Graham had Programmed *Entr'acte* she might never have Come Down to Nineteenth Century Idealism, that is to postulate her Carrying Out Isadora Duncan's Rape by dancing to the ready-made toilets of Marcel Duchamp instead of the neo-primitive sculpture of Isamu Noguchi.

Dancing was about Moving until moving got in the Way. The Abstract Expressionist expressed Everything. Now there is Nothing left to express: not even Alienation and Meaning-in-Life. Antonioni did that in *Red Desert*. What I Thought was so Great about *Red Desert* was that one Super-Colored shot of the giant ship cutting through the land because it looked just like the Staten Island Ferry. In fact, the Abstract Expressionists expressed Too Much. They got so much paint on the canvas that we forgot about the canvas. They made Art History by making painting be about a lot of (expressive) paint. And after all, painting used to be about canvas, just as choreography was about Space and Moving through it. What was so Radical about Cézanne was that he left some of his early canvases alone and only borrowed a little carner to Do his Business in. But if a child in today's Modern school system doesn't Use the Whole canvas, that is, if the child doesn't Do color, line, mass Business all over a clean, fresh, white piece of paper, his teacher recommends him for psychological counseling. That's what's so Great about school: they make sure you don't repeat the Past.

That's why THE MOST PERFECTLY IMAGINABLE DANCE would take place in some sealed-off, empty, white-walled room with Nothing in it. Not even a door for entrances and exits and no trap door either because that would be too Shakespearean. Only white *modern* walls. Very Modern. And you can be sure that Berkeley would have Blown his Cool—because I Think that the Best Things are those you can't never see. And you remember what Berkeley said happens to those Fucking trees in *that* forest when no one is around to see them. If no one is around to Observe, i.e., Perceive the trees, then they don't Exist, epistemologically speaking. That's what so Great about epistemology: no one knows What-the-Fuck anything's about. I think the Best Dance though, would have no movement because the movement would get in the Way of its being Original. I Mean movement was Invented a long Time ago already.

I Mean Moving is everywhere. Movement is Larger-than-Life. Television, you know. Movement Connects everything Up. Seeing, feeling, hearing, tasting, thinking etc. are Forms of Movement. A static image is *about* Moving, about the presence, the absence, the denial, the momentary alleviation of movement. Sex is about Moving and Electricity. Electricity makes pain and pleasure synonymous by instantly inducing kinesthesia in all muscles and nerves. There is no Way Out of all the Moving and Feeling except to deny it, of course. There is no need any more to make an issue of Moving. Our skin is one schizophrenic medium in which the Moving Under the skin is Connected-Up to the Other Moving Over the skin.

Besides, it Really doesn't matter—because it's next to an impossible situation anyway—Perfection, that is. And maybe THE MOST PERFECTLY IMAGINABLE DANCE wouldn't have any dancer either. Just like William Butler Yeats asking, "How does one tell the dancer from the dance?" Gosh, I didn't know you could separate them. Just like the task of philosophy: creating dualisms. With dualisms everyone gets Fucked-Up. With dualisms there is no Way Out, except to accept Contradictions. More about Contradictions later sometime.

It was the Souped-Up Eighteenth Century Ballet and the newly emerging Twentieth Century film medium which bombarded and resulted in the mutation: The Theater of the Absurd. It was Moira Shearer in *The Red Shoes* being asked *that* famous ontological question: DO YOU WANT TO DANCE, OR DO YOU WANT TO LIVE? That's what so Great about *Red Shoes:* all those philosophical issues. Even *Red Shoes* is about dualisms.

Without dualisms the theater would cease to be a public place of Rape. Without dualisms we have to give up the Notions of ourselves and the theater. Without dualisms we would not distinguish ourselves from the world. Without dualisms we wouldn't know who or what we are. With dualisms we are everything or nothing. With dualisms we cultivate a taste instead of sin. Without dualisms we cultivate sin as taste. With dualisms we stay inside of our skin. With dualisms everyone fights. And when everyone fights everyone loses. Just like war. Fuck dualisms. Fuck war. That's what I Like about the theater: everyone can leave any Time. I Mean, everyone is Free to leave the theater any Time they want to. Everybody's Free to Believe it.

With Television, though, it's different. Television is sort of like Lincoln Center for the Performing Arts: you just sit there in your comfortable soft chair and fall asleep. But the seats in most theaters are usually too Hard to sleep in and the Best theaters always have the shittiest seating equipment. That's what's so Great about theaters like this one: everyone Thinks they're paying attention.

BUT BACK TO THAT MOST PERFECTLY IMAGINABLE DANCE OR WHATEVER. ANOTHER ATERNATIVE IS TO HAVE AN IMPRESSIVE DANCER DO HIS IMPRESSIVE TRICKS. I LIKE IMPRESSIVE MOVEMENT BECAUSE IT'S IMPRESSIVE. MOST PEOPLE THINK IMPRESSIVE MOVEMENT IS GREAT. THAT'S PROBABLY BECAUSE IT LOOKS SO HARD. YOU CAN USUALLY BE SURE THAT IF SOMETHING'S HARD IT'S GOOD. BUT IT'S DIFFERENT WHEN YOU *DO* IT. WHEN YOU *DO* MOVEMENT YOU CAN'T SEE IT AND WHEN YOU CAN'T SEE IT YOU JUST *DO* IT. SO IT DOESN'T REALLY MATTER IF IT'S HARD OR NOT.

Once at Antioch College I did a dance in a telephone booth because dancers are supposed to get all Hot over Space. You know a Really Good dance is supposed to make a lot of Use of a lot of Space. I wonder if musicians get Hot and Bothered about Time. Because Time is just as Unreal. Kant knew that too. That is, Time is something we're automatically Programmed for. It's just like the problem of structure. THE MOST IMPORTANT THING ABOUT STRUCTURE IS MAKING SURE A DANCE TAKES A LOT OF TIME, LIKE WAGNER.

I LIKE IT WHEN THINGS TAKE A LOT OF TIME BECAUSE THEY'RE

MORE FUN THAT WAY IF A DANCE TAKES A REAL LOT OF TIME YOU
CAN BE SURE YOU WON'T NEED TO SEE IT TWICE AND YOU'RE REALLY
GLAD WHEN IT'S FINALLY OVER AND IF A DANCE TAKES A LOT OF TIME
YOU CAN BE SURE IT WON'T BE TOO MUCH ABOUT MOVEMENT BECAUSE
IF IT'S *ABOUT* MOVEMENT IT TAKES ONLY A LITTLE TIME UNLESS
YOU REPEAT THE STEPS AND POSITIONS A LOT OR UNLESS YOU DO IT VERY
SLOWLY IF A DANCE TAKES TOO LONG IT BEGINS TO WASTE TIME AND
IT BEGINS TO CONTRADICT ITSELF A DANCE THAT TAKES TOO LONG
DOESN'T GO ANYWHERE IT DEFEATS ITSELF BUT THIS IS BECAUSE WE
THINK OF TIME AS PASSING IN A CHRONOLOGICAL SENSE BUT IF THERE
IS NO TIME (LIKE THERE REALLY IS IN THE KANTIAN SENSE) THEN
THERE IS NO HISTORY AND IF THERE IS NO HISTORY THEN THERE IS NO
ACCUMULATION AND IF THERE IS NO ACCUMULATION THEN THERE IS
NO RETENTION AND IF THERE IS NO RETENTION THEN THERE IS NO
ANAL COMPLEX AND IF THERE IS NO ANAL COMPLEX THEN THERE ARE
NO SAVED-UP FECES AND IF THERE ARE NO SAVED-UP FECES THEN
THERE IS NO SHIT AND IF THERE IS NO SHIT THEN THERE IS NO HIS-
TORY. Just where we started. What do you know? A circular ar-
gument. That's what I Like about circular arguments: everything
Connects-Up.

Another alternative yet for the MOST PERFECTLY IMAGINABLE
DANCE is placing a sprayed white baby in the room and letting it
run around. You'd have to spray it white so it wouldn't detract
from the walls. Babies are free. I wish I could move just like a
baby because then I'd be an Original, Perfect Dancer (the Ideal)
and would never have to go to another class again. It's like dancing
to a strobe light. It doesn't Really matter what kind of movement
you Do or even if you're a Real dancer or not. Every movement
is Perfect with a strobe light.

Anyway, it doesn't matter much. When you realize that Nothing matters much and Nothing makes Too Much difference anyway, that is, about what you are Up to everyday, then whatever
you Do is Great. In that Way no one has to make too many De-
cisions.

This lecture was first presented at a conference of the United
Church at the Deering Conference Center in New Hampshire this
summer sometime. Someone asked me how I got the idea for this
SuperLecture. One day last summer I was Up on Tar Beach. That

Means the roof. When I have Nothing to Do, like everyday, I sit in the sun. From my roof there is a Great View: the whole panorama of New York City. I Like sitting in the sun because it's warm and makes you Feel Great and also because it makes you dark and then everybody Thinks you went to the Real beach and they wonder which one. I never go to Real beaches because all those people get in the Way. And what's so Great about Tar Beach is that when you get Really thirsty you can Come Down, and get some Free Cold orange juice Out of the refrig. Anyway, one day I was lying in the sun on Tar Beach and that's when I got the Idea for this SuperLecture.

In liberal theological circles I'm sure that Jesus Christ these days is synonymous with Electricity. That's because Liberals know that History has a lot of Tricks up its sleeves. Electricity is to the 1960's what God was to Spinoza's system. Only today there are fewer and fewer systems. Thank God. Electricity is instant and everywhere. Electricity is continuous and discontinuous, AC-DC, yes, I Know,—another Contradiction. More about Contradictions sometime later. Electricity is like Time, Space, Place, Motion, Structure, Emotion—ubiquitously Unreal, new expression.

ELECTRICITY SAVES DANCING. Because Electricity does away with steps and positions just as Christ does away with suffering and sins. Electricity does away with paint in painting and stories in novels and films. Alain Robbe-Grillet is a High-Gear novelist who certainly Understands the Power of the light bulb. Even More Better maybe than its Inventor, Thomas Alva Edison. That would be a Good Point for a dialectical argument if anyone is still Up on the Socratic Method.

Since we are living in an age of socialized electricity there no longer seems to be any Use in differentiating between theater and electrical engineering, nor between being a dancer or a programmer. Both spend their days wiring circuits, processing Information and Taking Care of Business. For the same reason there is no longer the need to differentiate between the representational and the abstract, between neutral and loaded situations, between the objective or positivistic and the subjective or the human response mechanism. That's because the process of Programming has a built-in, prefabricated Contradiction—that either Everything or Nothing matters or both. For a "good" Program is one in which the circuits are open, in the Sense of making a lot of Connections: like High voltage. Everybody's Head is like a bundle of electric circuits.

Advanced cybernetics and computing systems now make it possible for us to set up our own Programs, you might say our own *individual* Programs. With Programming we can Plug into any input or source of Information and Know anything we choose to Know. We can learn painting, dancing, history, writing and make Progress-Is-Our-Most-Important-Product at our own speeds. A Good Program Means Plugging into the Right Information. And the thing with Programming is that we can be or have whatever we want if we Know how to Get the Right Information. Programming fuses the mathematician's High-Gear rational sensibility with that of the poet's intuition because Programming makes everything possible: everything at once.

The electrical engineer Blew circuits with the Invention of the tape recorder. The tape recorder sounds the same Death-knoll for dancing as the film did for the novel. That is, the tape recorder was a spiritual rebirth for choreographers because it puts dancing in its place. The tape recorder redefines the phenomenon of "music" by breaking down the distinction between public and private experience as well as breaking down the distance between dancer and composer. They can now be one person. Private experience and the notion of expressing feeling is clearly a left-over, displaced, conceptual vestige which evolved and dissolves out of Romanticism. It was the tape recorder which contributed to Blowing-Out the concept of dance by short-circuiting a lyrical, private Point of View. The tape recorder gets rid of Point of View in dance as the camera gets rid of it in the novel. The tape recorder TRANsports the Real outside world into the interior of the Unreal theater. The tape recorder enables the theater to become truly bisexual because the theater is collectively sado-masochistic in the same Way that Electricity fuses the observer to the Thing observed. Electricity makes public and private experience synonymous just as it fuses male and female. The tape recorder thus provides an all-connecting, Electric Mainline with

Life. The tape recorder is the one machine which Expands the choreographic concept by contracting the Idea of movement.

ELECTRICITY CHANGED MY WHOLE CHILDHOOD. YOU KNOW WHEN I WAS IN SECOND GRADE WE GOT A TELEVISION. I THINK THAT IF YOU GREW UP ON TELEVISION PROGRAMS AND ADVERTISEMENTS YOU NEVER GOT BORED BECAUSE YOU COULD ALWAYS CHANGE CHANNELS. WHAT'S SO GREAT ABOUT TELEVISION IS THAT THERE IS ALWAYS SOMETHING GOING ON TO HOLD YOUR ATTENTION. IT DOESN'T EVEN MATTER WHAT THE PROGRAM IS ABOUT, YOU KNOW. YOU SAT THERE FOR HOURS WITHOUT MOVING. IF YOU GOT HUNGRY YOU'D HAVE TO WAIT UNTIL THE COMMERCIALS. BUT I ALWAYS THOUGHT THE COMMERCIALS WERE BETTER THAN THE PROGRAMS SO YOU HAD TO WAIT UNTIL THE NEWS TO RAID THE REFRIG. THE NEWS WAS A DRAG. IT BROUGHT YOU DOWN BECAUSE IT WAS THE ONLY REAL THING. I THOUGHT THE COMMERCIALS WERE BETTER BECAUSE I THINK THE MADISON AVENUE GUYS KNEW THAT EVERYBODY WAS COPPING-OUT OF THE COMMERCIALS SO THEY INVENTED A LOT OF NEW WAYS TO MAKE YOU LOOK AND LIKE COMMERCIALS EVEN THOUGH YOU KNEW THEY WERE JUST COMMERCIALS. WHAT WAS REALLY SO GREAT ABOUT TELEVISION WAS THAT YOU FORGOT ABOUT HAVING TO GO TO SCHOOL, ABOUT HAVING PARENTS AND ABOUT HAVING TO DO HOMEWORK. TELEVISION MAKES EVERYTHING UNREAL. TELEVISION MADE CHILDHOOD GREAT.

Electricity, in revamping values and remolding ideals, changes our notions of heroes and anti-heros. With television the radio sports idols like Mickey Mantle give Way to Batman and James Bond, America's arch-heroes, i.e., symbols of the Unreal. Batman and James Bond are more powerful than Real Life heroes because they can do phenomenal things. In the same breath, Allen Ginsberg and Timothy Leary become anti-heros, enshrined by LIFE and TIME magazines because they are the secret undercover agents for new values and ideals which Electricity and World War III are producing. But if we base our considerations of heroism on sex appeal and sexuality, then we get different numbers. The Real American Hero is Mr. Clean because he keeps the works Going by being the secret symbol of America's mass and amassed efforts at repressing the anal, and the anal-sadistic overt tendencies we all have. Mr. Clean is the secret Underground agent 007 and not James Bond. Mr. Clean is the rear-guard behind modern architecture, responsible for designing sterile Madison Avenue offices and Howard Johnson's motor lodges equipped with sterilized toilets. In short, Mr. Clean has become everybody's Super Secret, Rough Phantasy Fuck.

Maybe we are now living in an age or something when the Rock 'n Roll singer and the modern dancer can pull the rug from under the epistemologists or theologians. Electricity Spaces everything Out by Connecting everything Up. Except the theologians would be very unlikely to notice anyway because they are always floating a couple of feet off the floor. That's what so Great about theologians: they're so Light. That's what I Like Best about dancing. I spend most of the days at the typewriter. I Like Contradictions.

Contradictions are like William James and his Pragmatic friends: they make everything work. With Contradictions everything Connects Up. Ministers can say Shit and Screw, and if Kant had taken up ballet it would have been a Gas because in that Way we wouldn't have had to go through classicism. But we have gone through classicism and that's Cool because—uuuuuummmmmm-mmm—that's how we got to where we are: Bobby Dylan.

Cause if Kant had put on toe shoes we would have had to take off our watches. Then Robert Rauschenberg couldn't have immobilized his running clocks in the surface of a canvas, but that would have only been a minor loss. He painted a lot of Great stuff without clocks. Salvador Dali got closer to the pragmatic issue. Time isn't Really there. But take off your watch and then when would we Go Out to Lunch? Whenever we Felt the Urge.

It's just the same thing all over again with emotion and expression. Some modern artists thought they wanted to get rid of emotion because they thought it was expressive. But expression and emotion don't Mean hardly anything anymore because we've mixed them up. And besides they're always around somewhere anyway—like Time, Space, Place, Motion and stuff.

Anyway, without Time some people would finish up their Work or their lives before others. James Dean Did Life by the Time he was 24. Others, like Grandma Moses kept on Living and Liking everything because there is no Time: hence, Nothing to accomplish, nothing you have to learn or Do. If you spend your days getting ready to Die you get plenty of Living accomplished. That's why I dance. I Mean, what else is there to Do after Doing college and philosophy: drive trucks or sell shirts or Work for Olsten's Temporary Office Personnel or something? Dancing is as Good a distraction as any other kind of Working—once you manage to Junk the leftover childhood phantasy motivation.

That's what was so Great about playing with puppets as a kid: pulling the Wrong strings at the Right Time. Puppets can do anything: float, fly, walk without having their feet touch the ground —just like people. Puppets are luckier because they can Move anyway you want if you pull the Right strings.

JUST LIKE AT THANKSGIVING WHEN WE WATCHED THE MACY'S DAY PARADE. I ALWAYS REMEMBER LIKING THE GIANT INFLATED HELIUM PUPPETS LIKE MICKEY MOUSE BECAUSE I THOUGHT THOSE GIANT FLOATING PUPPETS WOULD MAKE THE GROWN-UPS FEEL LIKE LITTLE KIDS AND THEN THEY'D UNDERSTAND EVERYTHING. KIDS WANT TO BE LIKE PUPPETS BECAUSE PUPPETS CAN DO EVERYTHING. ANYWAY WHAT WAS SO GREAT ABOUT THE MACY'S THANKSGIVING DAY PARADE WAS THAT YOU DIDN'T HAVE TO GO SEE IT. YOU COULD STAY HOME IN YOUR COMFORTABLE CHAIR AND EAT YOUR CHOCOLATE TURKEY WITH THE FAMILY AND TURN ON YOUR TELEVISION AND SEE EVERYTHING MUCH BETTER. IT WAS ON EVERY CHANNEL.

JUST LIKE CHRISTMAS TIME TOO. AT CHRISTMAS TIME WE AL-WAYS GOT A LOT OF PLASTIC MODEL AIRPLANE KITS. I NEVER KNEW WHAT TO DO WITH ALL THE FINISHED PLASTIC AIRPLANES, I MEAN, SAVE THEM UP OR BREAK THEM. THE BEST THING, OF COURSE, ABOUT CHRISTMAS PRESENTS WAS BREAKING THEM. CAUSE THEN YOU GOT INTO A LOT OF TROUBLE BECAUSE BREAKING UP CHRISTMAS PRESENTS WAS DANGEROUS EXCITEMENT. THE BEST PART, TOO, ABOUT MAKING PLASTIC AIRPLANES WAS THE AIRPLANE GLUE. THE GLUE GOT ALL OVER EVERYTHING YOUR FINGERS AND ALL OVER YOUR CLOTHES AND MADE YOU STICKY AND MESSY. THAT'S WHEN I FIRST KNEW, I MEAN, THAT'S WHEN I FIRST *FELT* — uuuuuuuuummmmmmmmmmmm — THAT I WANTED TO BE AN ARTIST. I THINK MAKING-UP ART SHOULD BE LIKE GLUING PLASTIC AIRPLANES TOGETHER AND THEN DOING SOMETHING UNREAL LIKE MAKING THEM FLY.

And what do you think *Giselle* is Basically about? I Mean, what is *Giselle* about after you Junk the tutus, the chintz, the willies, the phantasy, the story, everything, even the ballet steps? One might say that the ethereal perfection is Basically a fixation with Death. I try to Think everything is Great even though everything is Basically dying. I Mean just because we Know that everything is Basically an explication of the Death Process doesn't prevent us from trying to Get Into Death. For after all, it is through phantasy participation with one's own Death that we Charge ourselves Up. Death is another Way to Connect everything Up.

Even Culture Vultures, and people who Dig Art because they Think it's Universal and because it Communicates. They Really Mean that they Like Art (people are never sure or never Really Mean so already Idealism defeats us) because Art is about Death.

A long Time ago Plato said in the *Phaedo* that Socrates said, "For is not philosophy the study of death?" Even Sartre writes in *Saint Genet:* "Life is impossible: death is the only possibility." Even philosophy is about Death. Death and dualisms.

And I guess we have to be careful to make some kind of distinction between dying and Death as we have to distinguish a funeral from a dramatic tragedy. For the funeral is a ritual, a celebration of the Dead in the same Way that a tragedy is a celebration of the Living. Only we'd have a lot of trouble these days finding evidence to support *that* notion. On the contrary, in order to Affirm theater and Life Samuel Beckett's play, *Happy Days*, has a femme fatale buried up to her Boobs in a fake stage set suggesting a barren desert location. But in terms of Death Everything is about Everything else. The Church is *about* burying the Dead—not about God, just as Kenneth Anger's *Scorpio Rising* is not about motorcycles or Carl Dreyer's *Joan of Arc* is not about Joan of Arc. Perhaps we had to wait until Freud with his positing a Death Instinct in human nature before scientists could Do synthetic drugs like LSD-25. But Freud is *about* Freud and the Aztec and other North American Indians already had magic peyote buttons and mescaline as well as the Magic Mushroom—all as a kind of Instant therapy in which the beholder could die without going through the ordeal of Death.

And after you Do dying you can wave goodbye to the shrink.
It was e.e. cummings' prophetic electrocution of poetry which
drove the Message home, like "Buffalo Bill": "Jesus/he was a
handsome man/and what i want to know is/how do you like your
blueeyed boy Mr. Death." The Beatles confirmed e.e.'s Point of
View a while back when John Lennon at a press conference wondered just which would die first: Rock 'n Roll or Christianity.
Christianity can't stand up erect to Electricity because it can't
Deal with Death—just as poetry couldn't Deal with the Invention
of the typewriter. Rock 'n Roll wins Out because it's the kind of
music one would have Fun dying to. And it's the most Accessible
—that's a fact because a lot of people are dying everyday with
transistor radios. If Christianity wants to keep the Institution and
the Churches open, it would be a Good Idea to find some Way of
celebrating Death, like chuck the confirmation and have a funeral
service as a SuperReal preparation for the young man embarking
on manhood. In that Way puberty would be a Mainline, a rite—
like Shooting-Up on Meister Eckhart and Norman O. Brown.

What's so Great about the theater is that it's so Unreal. It
doesn't matter what you Think or Believe anymore. I hope the
audience here doesn't expect anything from me because I have
nothing to give. I hope the audience here doesn't Believe in me or
in anything I Do. That's because everybody has spent so much
Time Being busy Becoming a Real, serious Carl Rogers Person
that he probably has enough to Believe In anyway.

Unreal things are Great because they aren't Really serious. Unreal things are the only things which make Sense. I will probably
have to get serious when I grow up. But I don't think I want to
grow up and make serious dances because that would be too Real.
But dancing is as Good a training for Life as anything else: all that
Moving around. I guess what's so Great about Being young is that
you're impressionable, i.e., everything is confused and confusing
so you can never Really Understand what's Going On, so don't
worry if you're confused, it just Means you're young. That's
what I Like about the Pepsi Generation: you Do middle-age at 22.
Shakespeare knew all about that: Ophelia knew more about Doing Love and Life at 14 than Blanche Du Bois ever did at 45. But

then Blanche Du Bois is truly a modern character like Pussy Ga-
lore. Tennessee Williams is the Grade B Shakespeare of the Real
Modern Theater—the Soap Opera.

And Unreal things are Metaphysical, too. That's because
Everything is Metaphysical. That's what you can count on about
Metaphysics: nobody loses—it's everywhere.

UNREAL THINGS AREN'T CREATIVE BECAUSE THEN YOU WOULD
BE ABLE TO ANALYZE THEM. BUT ANALYSIS IS FUN. YES, ANOTHER
CONTRADICTION. LIKE MY DANCES. MY DANCES SECRETLY HAVE CHAR-
ACTERS, AND STORIES BECAUSE I GREW UP ON STORY-PLOT-CHARACTER-
ARISTOTELIAN-BUSINESS AS A KID AND LEARNED TO PSYCH OUT NOVELS
IN SCHOOL. MY DANCES ALSO HAVE CLIMAXES. I THINK A CLIMAX
SHOULD COME AT THE BEGINNING OF A DANCE INSTEAD OF AT THE
END. I THINK A CLIMAX SHOULD COME AT THE BEGINNING OF A DANCE
SO EVERYBODY IN THE AUDIENCE CAN SIT BACK AND RELAX AND NOT
EXPECT ANYTHING FOR THE REST OF THE EVENING. TELEVISION, YOU
KNOW.

THAT'S WHAT'S SO GREAT ABOUT ANALYSIS: PSYCHING EVERY-
THING OUT. IT'S LIKE DOING A CROSS-WORD PUZZLE ONLY MORE IN-
TELLECTUAL. I MEAN, HOW ELSE CAN YOU UNDERSTAND WHAT'S GO-
ING ON? THAT'S WHAT HAPPENS WHEN YOU READ FREUD: YOU WANT
TO BE EVERYTHING AND EXPERIENCE EVERYTHING YOU'RE SUPPOSED
TO HAVE REPRESSED—LIKE BEING PRETENTIOUS EVEN, BECAUSE BEING
PRETENTIOUS SOMETIMES IS A LOT OF FUN. LIKE RIGHT NOW. AGGRES-
SION YOU KNOW. MORE ABOUT AGGRESSION IN ANOTHER LECTURE
SOMETIME MAYBE. I MEAN A DIFFERENT COMPLEX EVERY DAY. A LOT
OF EXPERIENCES. A LOT OF DOWNRIGHT HEALTHY FUN. AND INVOLVE-
MENT.

SOMETIMES I DON'T KNOW ANYMORE WHO OR WHAT I AM. I AM
NOT SURE IF I AM ONE PERSON OR A COUPLE OF PEOPLE OR A GROUP
OF PEOPLE OR THINGS OR WHAT. SOMETIMES I AM A LOT OF DIFFER-
ENT PEOPLE OR CHARACTERS. THAT'S WHY THERE'S NO NEED ANY
MORE TO INVENT ANYTHING OR TO TRY AND BE ORIGINAL, BECAUSE
OUR LIVES ARE *ABOUT* REPEATING EVERYTHING OVER AND OVER AGAIN.
EXCEPT WITH DIFFERENT DETAILS AND CIRCUMSTANCES BECAUSE THE
SAME EXACT THING OVER AND OVER IS IMPOSSIBLE AND EVENTUALLY
IT GETS DULL ANYWAY. THERE IS NO LONGER ANY USE IN TRYING TO

BE ORIGINAL BECAUSE WE CAN BECOME ANYTHING WE WANT: AN
ANIMAL, A SOUND, OR SOME OBJECT. I MEAN WE CAN IDENTIFY WITH
ANYTHING. I MEAN BEING ORIGINAL IS LIKE PLAYING A ROLE. YOU
CAN MAKE UP YOUR OWN ROLE. I DON'T THINK THERE IS ANY NEED
TO MAKE SOMETHING INVENTIVE BECAUSE EVERYTHING ALREADY
EXISTS.

(Poetry and theater Hung themselves Up because both Turned
In On themselves, that is, they started taking their talking seriously. What's so Great about talking though is the things we can't
talk about. Usually the things we say anyway we don't Really
Mean. The most Real things are said in the most Unreal moments:
when babbling, when half-awake, when insane or when play-
acting like right Now. It doesn't matter if my Ideas are right or
wrong, entertaining or boring, because there is always something
Better going on Out in the street—outside in the Real World.)

That's what's so American about the theater: it's always com-
peting with Life. If we saw Everything that was Going On we'd
never Think of going to the theater, because if we could see
Everything that was Really Going On we'd never Believe it. Not
in a Billion years even.

And that's what's so Great about Life: it's just like the Movies,
except the Movies are Really More Exciting. That's how we react
Basically when something Really Exciting Happens. When we
meet a friend unexpectedly for example. We remember how
Spontaneous it is because of some Television program or a Rock
'n Roll song. (Or a novel if you're middle-aged.) That's how we
react Typically because it makes us Feel Good to Know we are
like the Movies: full of Life.

Then what about opinions and things? It doesn't matter much
what we Do. You can Do anything if you Know how to Do it the
Right Way. We leave the Best Things undone and unsaid. We
could never do Real things in the theater like Make Love so we
Make-Up some Unreal things, like wearing masks and talking
trivia. Then we Realize how Life-like it is. There is nothing especially wrong with trivia if it's interesting. It has gotten us where
we are—in this room and this Far along.

I GUESS I'M SUPPOSED TO TELL YOU HOW I MAKE MY DANCES. IT'S

PRETTY OBVIOUS. NO USE HIDING ANYTHING, YOU KNOW. IF PEOPLE DON'T KNOW ME THEY ASK ME HOW I THOUGHT THEM UP. PEOPLE WHO KNOW ME DON'T BOTHER ASKING.

FIRST, I USUALLY THINK-UP A GOOD SOUNDING TITLE, BECAUSE THAT INSPIRES ME.

I ALWAYS HAVE IDEAS FOR SOUND BECAUSE SOUND IS REALLY GREAT. SOUND CAN t-r-a-n-sport YOU TO ANOTHER PLACE. SOUND CAN BE THE MOST IMPORTANT ELEMENT BECAUSE IT CAN MAKE YOU STOP THINKING. SOUND REALLY TURNS YOU AROUND.

THEN I GO TO THE GREATEST FIVE AND DIME STORE IN THIS CITY: LAMSTONS ON THE CORNER OF 23RD STREET AND 8TH AVENUE AND LOOK AT ALL THE GREAT GEAR. THERE'S SO MUCH GEAR THAT IT SPACES YOU OUT. ALL KINDS OF COLORED RUBBER GLOVES, PLASTIC FRUIT, PLASTIC FLOWERS (which are better than real flowers because they never die) PLASTIC BABIES, BALLOONS, BUBBLE PILLS, BUBBLE PIPES, ELASTIC STRING, CANDY CIGARETTES, SOLDIER'S OUTFITS, MARBLES, RUBBER SNAKES, FOAM RUBBER, CRAZY FOAM, ELECTRIC TOOTHBRUSHES, MASKS—EVERYTHING YOU NEED FOR A DANCE. THERE'S ENOUGH GEAR IN LAMSTONS FOR A LIFETIME OF DANCING. IT'S LIKE PAINTING BY NUMBERS ONLY MORE FUN. AND MORE ORIGINAL. AND MORE UNREAL.

THEN I HAVE TO HUSTLE-UP SOME MONEY TO BUY THE GEAR. MY DANCES HARDLY COST ANYTHING. I THINK A DANCE SHOULD BE DIRT CHEAP OR ELSE I'D HAVE TO GO TO WORK TO SUPPORT MY DANC-ING AND THAT WOULD BE TOO MUCH OF A COMEDOWN. I GUESS WHEN I GROW UP THOUGH, I'M SUPPOSED TO WANT TO MAKE BIG EXPENSIVE PROGRESSIVE DANCES WITH A LOT OF MODERN TECHNOLOGICAL GEAR BECAUSE TECHNOLOGY HAS CHANGED EVERYTHING, INCLUDING MAS-TURBATION. TECHNOLOGY EVEN RECIRCUITS MASTURBATION BECAUSE IT'S ONE OF THE FEW REMAINING ACTIVITIES WHICH REALLY IN-VOLVES YOUR WHOLE BEING. THAT MEANS MASTURBATION IS NORMAL BECAUSE IT'S EXISTENTIAL. JUST LIKE SARTRE.

THEN I THINK-UP A COSTUME BECAUSE A COSTUME IS VERY IMPORTANT. I MEAN YOU ALWAYS KNOW WHERE SOMEONE'S AT BY WHAT THEY WEAR. (KLEIDER MACHEN LEUTE) THEN I THINK ABOUT KANT OR SOMETHING METAPHYSICAL OR ABOUT CÉZANNE AND CUBISM AND TRY AND CONNECT IT ALL UP: LIKE WRITING A TERM PAPER. THAT'S WHAT'S SO GREAT ABOUT DANCING: THE PROPS BECAUSE THEY

GET IN THE WAY. AND THE SAME THING HAPPENS AS WHAT HAPPENS WHEN YOU DANCE WITH A STROBE LIGHT OR IN SUPERSLOW MOTION: IT DOESN'T REALLY MATTER WHAT YOU DO: ANY KIND OF MOVEMENT —PUSH-UPS OR PIROUETTES—IS GREAT IF YOU DO IT THE RIGHT WAY. ANYWAY, DURING THE LAST WEEK OR SO I SORT OF THINK-UP SOME MOVEMENT TO MAKE IT LOOK LIKE A DANCE.

What's so Great about going to the theater is that when it's finally over everybody can go home and Be just like he always is or go where he wants to go and Do what he Really wanted to Do. Theater is a Good Way to Waste Time. Also you can usually meet some friends or Pick Up someone. If the show's Good it entertains us for a while and makes us forget Something or Other. And I guess if it's Really Good there's some High-Gear intellectual Things to contemplate. I hope that when this lecture is Over, like it is Right Now, everybody will go home and Forget about it.

RICHARD KOSTELANETZ*

❦

*The New
American Arts*

> *The famous "modern break with tradition" has lasted long
> enough to have produced its own tradition.*
> —Harold Rosenberg, *The Tradition of the New* (1959).

Contemporary art demonstrates that the impetus to create
new forms and embody new themes, an ethos that has motivated
Western artists particularly since the time of Baudelaire, continues to be a prime force influencing artists, critics, and audience
alike. What prompts modern artists to create works which are
distinctly new is, first, a dissatisfaction with what other artists are
doing and, second, their truly felt need to engage the evolving
spirit of their times. Thus, in the past hundred years, all the important painters, film-makers, dancers, composers, and writers, in
Europe and America, have created works that were decisively and
propitiously original; and their new styles and/or themes, in turn,
influenced their artistic successors and, of course, also provided
the young with an "old" against which to rebel.

Moreover, history itself seems to be an accomplice of the im-

* RICHARD KOSTELANETZ, *born in New York City in 1940, studied at
Brown, Columbia, and London universities. He has written essays on
various subjects for over three score magazines, edited two antholo-
gies*—On Contemporary Literature (*1964*) *and* Twelve from the
Sixties (*1967*)—*and a collection of criticism, on* The New American
Arts (*1965*), *and authored a forthcoming book on* The Theatre of
Mixed Means (*1968*).

238

pulse to create new styles; for with each great historical change in the twentieth century, in America as well as Europe—World War I, the Depression, World War II—an era of art came to an end only to be followed in all arts by styles appreciably different. In this respect, the twentieth century epitomizes art's entire history in which, as the cultural historian Meyer Schapiro has observed, "Important economic and political shifts . . . are often accompanied or followed by shifts in the centers of art and their styles."

In recent years, the two-fold processes of social and aesthetic change have, I believe, accelerated considerably—instead of passing through an overhauling alteration every fifty or twenty years, the world seems to be transformed every ten; and contemporary art, with each year, departs more rapidly and radically from the past. This acceleration is a key reason why newness as such has, in recent years, become a more important value in our understanding of art and in art's understanding of itself. Given the influx into art of new ideas and new compositional materials, given a contemporary historical predicament rapidly distinguishing itself from those of the far- and near-past, given the widespread aesthetic cross fertilization that the tradition of the new produces, one must say that no artist today or tomorrow will be considered significant unless his work either offers an expansion of formal range, an original reordering of materials within the spectrum of possibility, or a new preception of the changing aesthetic and/or human situation of our time. When hypothetically confronted with two recent artworks of equal substance, most modern artists and critics will usually consider an achieved newness to be the crucial criterion that distinguishes the competent from the imaginative, the enjoyable from the invaluable, the acceptable from the brilliant.

For several reasons, then, to understand the overall direction of today's art and to appreciate the best recent works in Europe and America, an onlooker cannot depend upon modes of perception and criteria of judgment based on the past—he will surely wallow in misapprehension and confusion. Rather, he must slough off aesthetic commitments to prior work to gain the open-minded attitude that initiates a rapport with new art.

What I would describe as realism—the humble subordination of the artist before the natural phenomenon—is very rare in America.
Sir Herbert Read, "Some Observations on Art in Ameria."

After many years of cultural isolation, American artists are no longer exempt from the dynamics of European art; for although Americans until 1920 seemed unaffected by European modernist developments (and vice versa), since that date American culture, in becoming a major contributor to world art, has assumed many of the characteristics and values of the international scene, among them a commitment to the tradition of the new. Despite the recent proclamations of conservative and theory-haunted native critics that the age of revolt has exhausted itself or is stalled in aesthetic dead ends, American artists continue to produce works of dance and literature, cinema and music that have no precedent in our culture or, sometimes, that of the world. In sum, they enliven and extend America's participation in the modernist tradition. Moreover, the continuing aspiration to true originality is evidenced, on one hand, in statements by the artists themselves— John Barth's and Saul Bellow's on the recent novel, Edward Albee's on the development of American theater, and Merce Cunningham's on the dance—and, on the other, by the impact that the work of these and other original artists have upon knowledgeable segments of the American art public.

Though the idea of the tradition of the new spread from its European origins to America, *avant-garde* arts in America assume a cast quite different from those abroad, largely because the isolated environment of the experimental American artist both defines his condition and influences the character of his work. Just as the individual pitted against an indomitable Nature was a frequent protagonist in nineteenth-century American painting and literature, so, in fact, this same aloof, eccentric, impatient, perhaps Faustian spirit, wrestling with art's limits, inhabits the major American artists. If nearly all European *avant-garde* artists gravitate toward the cultural centers—usually Paris, but sometimes Rome or one of several German cities—and develop their originality in an atmosphere of camaraderie and criticism, American artists start their careers as rather isolated figures scattered around the country, out of touch with the centers of established modern art, unapprenticed to recognized masters. Often in their later success they reaffirm the isolation of their youth, as William Faulkner clung to Mississippi, Charles Ives to Northwest Connecticut, Robinson Jeffers to his California cliff, and William Carlos Williams to his New Jersey medical practice.

Today, although nearly all the leading figures in the non-literary arts and theater live in New York, the gravitational center of the cultural mainstream that runs from Boston to Philadelphia, only a few were born or educated there (while, in contrast, most of the important critics are A-to-Z New Yorkers); the prime activity in creative literature is widely scattered—John Barth writes about his native Eastern shore, Maryland, from a Western Pennsylvania university town; James Wright and Robert Bly live in Minnesota; William Stafford, in Washington; Thomas Pynchon, as a recluse in Mexico; John Ashbery, in Paris; Vladimir Nabokov and William Burroughs, in Europe and North Africa; and Sylvia Plath, until her death, had been living in England. Also, largely because culture in New York is so diffuse, young artists achieve a kind of isolation there, apart from universities, cliques, alliances of sympathy and promotional establishments. For its first ten years in Manhattan, The Living Theater was hardly noticed, and Merce Cunningham, who has lived there for twenty years, still suffers the indignity of infrequent New York recitals. In short, the alienation that European artists of the twentieth century "discovered" had, from the start, defined the American cultural condition.

This isolation, in turn, influences the character of our advanced arts; for our archetypal creative artist is the "pathfinder" who leaves, often with naïve motives, the confines of "civilization," a metaphor for conventional, largely European notions of artistic possibility, to explore the uncharted frontier, sometimes achieving a "breakthrough" into aesthetic country that Europe had never seen before. America becomes Europe's artistic virgin land, for so many of the compositional ideas that have strongly influenced the organized European *avant-gardes,* from Edgar Allan Poe's symbolist poetic theory, through Henry James' and Faulkner's fictional techniques to John Cage's notions of aleatory music, have been American in origin; and this tradition accounts for why America's greatest representational arts, fiction as well as painting, tend to be more visionary and mythic—penetrating to the hidden essences of life—rather than concrete and realistic—encompassing a wealth of verifiable experience.

In an age when the quest and response to the "new" moves artists everywhere, what particularly characterizes the American's explorations is his willingness to pursue aesthetic ideas literally, wholeheartedly and unselfconsciously to ultimate and unprecedented ends. In a culture where politics at its best is very much the art of the possible, the best art exemplifies the politics of the impossible. Thus, not until The Living Theater's production of Kenneth H. Brown's *The Brig* (1963) were the influential, semi-mad ideas of the Frenchman Antonin Artaud's *The Theatre and Its Double* fully realized—ideas which Europeans had pondered over, discussed, re-interpreted, and faintly reproduced in the nearly quarter-century since the book's publication. It is similarly appropriate that thoroughly radical experiments at both extremes of the compositional spectrum in music, intentionally arbitrary and totally planned, should be attempted by American composers—respectively, Morton Feldman and Milton Babbitt; that the notion of using the products of mass production for artistic purposes which had remained dormant since constructivism and the prime of Marcel Duchamp should blossom again in the American Pop artists; that the literary tradition of irony should be so inclusively utilized in cinema by Stanley Kubrick in *Dr. Strangelove;* that John Cage should provide a rationale for "composing" a piece of four minutes and thirty-three seconds of sheer silence (though no one has yet claimed its visual analogue, an unadorned sheet of cellophane, is "art"); and that the French idea of absurd literature, which has permeated European theater, should father a school of fiction unlike any other, anywhere—the absurd novels of Joseph Heller, Thomas Pynchon, and John Barth.

Of course, this passion to follow a suggestive idea to its extreme conclusion reflects, in general, a certain innocence about fixed ideas—the naïve belief that they can be true and ultimate—but out of this obsession has sprung that peculiarly American tradition of works of art whose originality and imaginative strength exceed and eventually transform the going notions of artistic appropriateness and possibility. Walt Whitman, Herman Melville, Albert P. Ryder, Charles Ives, William Faulkner, Jackson Pollock, John Cage, D. W. Griffith, E. E. Cummings, Frank Lloyd Wright, Isadora Duncan all invented or adapted ideas that pushed their arts into new realms, single-handedly initiating changes that influenced scores of younger artists in America and (but for Ives) Europe.

What the Europeans find so appealing in American art, I think, is its seemingly untutored, law-defying, concentrated (rather than broad), somewhat violent imaginative energy. As the American critic Kenneth Rexroth once tellingly characterized the enthusiastic French response to American action painting, "[They] got hold of the wrong catalogue and were under the impression the pictures were painted by Wyatt Earp and Al Capone and Bix Beiderbecke." But Wyatt Earp is an apt metaphor of the American artist, for the optimistic spirit of the frontier lawman—performing old tasks in new ways by taking the laws of form into one's own hands, with little awareness of the tragedy of *hubris*—still dominates *avant-garde* American art. Once Europeans can understand and reproduce the American's rule-defying, original techniques, they often show up, in more premeditated forms, in their own works. Out of Faulkner, for instance, come the cerebral novels of Claude Simon; out of Cage, the systematized change and indeterminacy of Karlheinz Stockhausen. For another example, the tone-cluster (the sounding of whole blocks of notes simultaneously) was invented by Charles Ives and independently re-invented by Henry Cowell, only to be more shrewdly used by Bela Bartók. (Perhaps this trick, along with John Cage's prepared piano, belongs in the great American tradition of inspired gimmickry.) Indeed, some American artists, such as John Cage and Barnett Newman and, perhaps, Henry Cowell and Ezra Pound, are more important for the aesthetic innovations they propagate than for any single realized work.

The origins of this risk-taking individualism probably lie in the singularities of the American experience—in the exploitation of the frontier, in our pervasive belief that man is superior to natural materials and can, therefore, freely and successfully impose his will upon them, in our basic assumption that in America everything is possible, in an educational system that encourages from an early age the child's individual initiative, in our related commitment to the irrelevance of paternal authority, and, more deeply in our religious and economic traditions: in the self-help capitalist ethos that atomizes rather than syndicates a society, coupled with the Protestant inclination for individual revelation which produces so many religious sects and which contrasts with the European Catholic tradition of communal revelation. In America, most of the very successful artists, moguls, salvationists, and secular reformers are, particularly early in their careers, inspired independent operators, each stamping his achievement with a highly individualized mark.

Just as capitalism and Protestantism are responsible for both the achievements and disasters of American life, the pioneering stance is paradoxically the source of the key achievements and most disappointing deficiencies in the American artistic experience. On one hand, the American art scene as a whole or the scene in each of the arts is generally not as broadly sophisticated or significant as that in European countries—surely, for instance, neither American theater nor cinema is one-half as rich as French; on the other hand, in each American art are works which in crucial respects completely transcend anything in the European arts today—the paintings of Jasper Johns, Robert Rauschenberg, and Frank Stella, Jack Smith's *Flaming Creatures*, the fiction of John Barth, the productions of The Living Theater, the poetry of John Berryman, the dance of Merce Cunningham and the Judson Church movement, the great static spatial compositions of Stepan Wolpe and of Ralph Shapey (particularly his *Evocations*).

Similarly, the careers of nearly all the greatest American artists are equally uneven, characterized by sporadic achievements amidst masses of debris, loss of severe diminution of creative talent, sometimes a lack or slowness of recognition, and early decline or death. So many of our most significant novels, from *Moby-Dick* to *The Sound and the Fury*, from *The Great Gatsby* to *The Sun Also Rises*, are written by men about 30 who never do as well again. Charles Ives did little composing after he turned 45; after publishing at 30 his great novel *Call It Sleep* Henry Roth finished little else. Jackson Pollock, Isadora Duncan, Stephen Crane, and Nathanael West all died much too young. H. L. Mencken, much-quoted and perceptive at 45, was unread and irrelevant at 55. In what other culture did so many major artists voluntarily expatriate themselves, their work usually suffering a falling off; and where else do so many great imaginations, from Griffith to Melville, spend their last years in undeserved obscurity. In an essay on the jazz guitarist Charlie Christian, who died at 23, Ralph Ellison, himself the author of one and only one great novel, so perceptively noted, "Jazz, like the country which gave it birth, is fecund in its inventiveness, swift and traumatic in its development, and terribly wasteful to its resources."

Similarly, just as American art reflects the virtues of unsophistication—an originality stemming from a certain kind of innocence—it also embodies the perils of naïveté—a general inability to fashion neat wholes and an obsession in even the best artists with pursuing ideas to ridiculously unsuccessful ends. Charles Ives spent nearly forty-five years thinking about, and many of his last years working on, an unfinished *Universe Symphony* in which, write his biographers Henry and Sidney Cowell, "Several orchestras, with huge conclaves of singing men and women, were to be placed about in valleys, along hillsides, and on mountain tops." Who else but The Living Theater, for example, would attempt with utter failure a theatrical work constructed on principles of chance. Who else but an American, Kenneth Koch, would produce an interminable poem of such arbitrary meaninglessness as *When the Sun Tries To Go On*. Where else could a composer like La Monte Young claim that his burning of a violin was a piece of music (because it made a noise) and, like the most eccentric backwoods preacher, attract a small but vociferous following.

For all the inventive arts maintain, as it were, a sympathetic connection between each other, being no more than various expressions of one internal power, modified by different circumstances.

—Percy Bysshe Shelley

Along with their commitment to the tradition of the new, most of the new American artists continue the modernist tradition of non-causal and spatial, rather than syllogistic and narrative-linear, relations—the artwork's basic connections coalesce across space, rather than in immediate, chronological succession—and, thus, of the unhindered exploration of abstract relational possibilities. As the structure of plays and films has become flat, as opposed to the pyramid of classical five-act drama, so painting in recent years, from the color fields of Morris Louis to the geometric designs of Frank Stella, discounts visual depth in favor of flatter, "planar" tensions and interests. Likewise, the best recent literature, from Edward Albee's *Who's Afraid of Virginia Woolf?* to John Berryman's *Dream Songs*, achieves its coherence and makes its points less through sequences of time, as a story in which one thing follows after another, than through space—by repeating images, attitudes, incidents, comments, rituals, fragmented feelings, aspects of character—so that we comprehend the whole by grasping the resonant details spatially, at once. That is, in Kenneth Burke's terms, our developed systems of formal comprehension—of expectations and fulfillments—honed on architectonic structures, must be superseded by response systems that are attuned to formal coherence achieved by repetition—spatial systems of expectation and fulfillment. This change is exemplified in the history of dance—contrast a typical ballet with Merce Cunningham's pieces —as well as music, where most advanced contemporary composers de-emphasize the developmental movement of harmony, polyphony, melody and accompaniment and instead create complex multi-layered spatial forms built on juxtaposition of events and gestures, often abetted by some form of structural repetition.

This shift toward spatial form generally accompanies, but does not determine, other aesthetic trends, such as the tendency toward visionary, non-naturalistic styles which focus upon hidden phenomena and metaphysical themes where the function of the artist becomes rendering the invisible visible rather than the documenting of social and factual experience. (Thus, much of the greatest nineteenth-century American art is "modern" before its time.) Precisely because these artists reject any commitment to the realities of external subjects to concentrate on purifying the techniques of their art and using "facts" primarily for artistic purposes, aesthetic form in some works, particularly in music, becomes by itself the major "content" while the aesthetic line distinguishing form from subject is blurred. Just as Merce Cunningham's dances are primarily about the techniques and possibilities of non-referential dance and *The Brig's* subject is as much Artaud's theories of the theater as it is the violence of contemporary life, so *Dr. Strangelove* is more about the resources of irony in film than the absurdity of contemporary nuclear politics.

To explain this widespread transition from narrative to spatial structures, the American critic Joseph Frank makes historical comparisons by relating it to man's changing attitude toward life around him. When mankind confidently understands his universe, he feels able to present it in depth—seeing experience in various planes—and in time. In contrast, two-dimensional form arises, Frank believes, "when the relationship between man and the cosmos is one of disharmony and disequilibrium," and, as in our time, man loses "control over the meaning and purpose of life [especially] amidst the continuing triumphs of science and technics."

In his *Understanding Media*, Marshall McLuhan attributes the rise of discontinuous spatial forms to technological development: As the printing press shaped an era of narrative form, so the new electronic instruments of communications create an age of spatial form. "Electricity," he writes, "ended sequence by making things instant," adding that, "The movie medium [itself represents] a transition from lineal connections to configurations." The physical sciences, too, in the Quantum theory, insist that traditional concepts of linear causality are undemonstrable and irrelevant. In sum, Joseph Frank's and McLuhan's analyses complement each other; for both suggest that, although much recent art may not explicitly describe the contemporary world, it cannot help but reflect it.

At the same time that they embody extensions of the modernist tradition, each of the new American arts has rebelled against entrenched hierarchies dominant, in most cases, in the early and middle fifties; for as the era of Universal Threat replaced that of the Cold War, new artists keyed to a new sensibility, sought to overthrow their artistic step-fathers, often pursuing to unprecedented lengths the impulse to rebel. In cinema, the enemy was that complex of clichés we call Hollywood; in painting, out of the lull that fell over art about 1955 with the decline of what Clement Greenberg christened Painterly Abstraction, arose the new styles of Jasper Johns, Pop Art, and others. In theater, Albee, The Living Theater's playwrights, and others have reacted against the psychology of Tennessee Williams and the sociology of Arthur Miller, while the new novelists conspicuously avoid creating a hero for our time or conducting a search for one. The best contemporary composers, such as Elliott Carter, Stepan Wolpe, Salvatore Martirano, and Charles Wuorinen, reject at one extreme the dogmatic chance and formlessness of Cage and his followers and, on the other, European total serialism, as well as American neo-classical developmental styles (of Samuel Barber and the like) for a music that intelligently exploits the entire range of musical possibility, while the new dance discards the conventions of movement and the dependence upon an extrinsic subject for a dance of pure form and total possibility of movement. When Merce Cunningham says he wants "to make a space in which anything can happen," the dancer James Waring echoes him with, "I try to get rid of ideas and the Self. I don't like metaphor, or symbolism."

In the same spirit, some artists have endeavored to dismiss the categories of art as irrelevant by fusing two or more arts into a single whole—Rauschenberg's "combines" link painting and sculpture, "happenings" combine theater, music, dance, and sometimes painting, The Connection and The Brig produce an original synthesis of drama and music, and there are several just reasons for defining many music compositions, such as David Tudor's performance of 4'33" of John Cage's silence, as closer to theater and even dance than music. Sometimes, the artist's motives in creating combinations are ironic—Max Kozloff likens some happenings to "the Wagnerian dream of synthesis of the art upon which has been superimposed junk culture." Reflecting, more modestly, the same impulse toward crossfertilization, some artists have taken the aesthetic ideas from other arts and applied them to their own, producing abstract poetry, chance dance, a serially organized theater piece, and the like.

As the revolutions got underway, in most of the arts there was a moment of conflict as the old challenged the new—when the new was condemned as "anti-art" and, in turn, the old as decadent and irrelevant; but as soon as the issues were drawn, the younger audience championed the new. Indicatively, all the major young American drama critics were enthusiastic about *The Brig* and, in unison, severely criticized Arthur Miller's *After The Fall;* and the new works in other arts received parallel critical responses. Thus, there is good reason to believe that the audience which enthusiastically supports new works today comprises a membership considerably different from that which admired the new works of, say, fifteen years ago. All too often, one encounters a devotee of Arthur Miller who detests Albee and The Living Theater, a fan of Martha Graham who walks out on Merce Cunningham, an *aficionado* of Hemingway who "can't read" *The Moviegoer* or *Catch-22*, or, even more tellingly, an admirer of the thirties' and forties' Aaron Copland who is put off by his recent, more complex serial works, *Piano Fantasy* (1957) and *Connotations for Orchestra* (1962); for the new works initiate not only a shift in style but also a change in the audience.

Not only do the young seem to comprehend the formal revolutions embodied in Pynchon's V and in *The Connection* with an ease that often baffles their elders, they also appear to have a strong sympathy for the content of new art. For instance, the totally negative sensibility—so thoroughly dissentient it finds nothing but the act of truth-telling worthy of loyalty or admiration—which some older critics and, more typically, parents, find objectionable, is precisely the quality that the younger generation finds so attractive in *Who's Afraid of Virginia Woolf?* and *Dr. Strangelove*, in Nathanael West (revived in the late fifties to gain popularity in the sixties), the novels of John Barth and Joseph Heller, and even the fad-nihilism of Terry Southern and Mason Hoffenberg's *Candy* and knee-jerk-No literary critics such as Dwight Macdonald. To the younger audience, so many of whom since early youth guffawed at the sentimentalities of Hollywood and whose sensibilities were honed on *Mad*, an acute, truly felt nay-saying offers the most immediately satisfactory explanation of their experience.

Intrinsic in this critical, negative attitude toward life today, is an irreverence toward tradition. Whereas the writers and artists of, say, forty years ago would use the technique of quotation, as T. S. Eliot did in *The Waste Land* and Charles Ives in his Second Symphony, largely to weave resonant motifs into their work, almost all quotations in the best recent art function, often comically, as irony. From John Barth whose references to history in *The Sot-Weed Factor* are inverted or ridiculously distorted, to Stanley Kubrick who juxtaposes the quoted Hollywood cliché of the cripple who learns to walk against a thermonuclear explosion, to Jack Smith who in *Flaming Creatures* has transvestites enact stock cinematic situations, to John Cage who indiscriminately mixes quoted noise (sometimes identifiable music!) with nondescript sounds, to Kenneth Koch, Arthur L. Kopit, and the Pop artists, all of whom show an affinity with French pataphysics ("The science of imaginary [i.e., parody] solutions."), the art of the past, just like the external scene, is so ludicrously irrelevant that it is used, in the Eliotic sense, largely as fuel for irony.

As they are unable to speak through the past to the present, so the major recent artists (except for some of the film-makers and poets and William Burroughs in his early works) do not employ art as a vehicle for pure self-expression. They believe that art is a craftsman's product, to be put together consciously and critically, often to employ pre-determined aesthetic and thematic ideas, that it reflects more upon itself than upon its author or external reality, evoking symbols rather than images of meaning; therefore, because it resists immediate assimilation, it must be interpreted, often in a multiplicity of ways, before it is truly understood. As the English critic David Sylvester perceptively noted in an essay on Pop art, "Modern artists . . . use art as a form of meditation about art and its relation to reality." In muffling their own voice to speak wholly through the mask of artistic form, often with techniques of irony, these artists do not believe their work can program extra-aesthetic effects upon their audience, repudiating again and perhaps once and for all the heresy that swept over and nearly choked American arts in the 1930s. Quite consistently, then, those recent artists who find artistic examples in the American past, draw from pre-1930s culture—playwrights and poets from Cummings and Eliot, composers from Ives and early Varese, and painters from Marcel Duchamp (who has lived here nearly fifty years)—thus making themselves heirs to the artistically most fruitful decade in American history, the 1920s.

Most of the revolutions in the American arts started around 1958, and many artists presented their crucial opening or transitional works in the year 1959 and 1960: Carter's Second String Quartet, Babbitt's Composition for Tenor and Six Instruments, Rauschenberg's *Monogram*, Reinhardt's Black Paintings, Barth's *The Sot-Weed Factor*, Albee's *The Zoo Story*, Gelber's *The Connection*, Koch's *Ko*, Lowell's *Life Studies* and the first dances of the Judson Church choreographers. The explanation of this blossoming would seem to lie in two historical changes—one domestic, the other international—in the years just preceding 1959 which probably affected every sensitive American. By the late fifties, the constrictive forces we call McCarthyism had weakened considerably, reducing the general anxiety over eccentrically individualized expression and nonconformity that plagued creative Americans in the early fifties. The second event was the rise of Sputnik in October, 1957, which with a variety of other incidents influenced the change in our attitudes to world politics from *we-they* (i.e., us and Russia), probably the dominant mode of political understanding since the rise of Hitler and the revelations of Nazi atrocities, to *it-us*, "it" being thermonuclear holocaust and "us" as *all* the world's peoples. At this time, most of us became aware that the predicament of contemporary man was universal—since all of us could in a few swipes be erased from the earth, we-they distinctions, even in lesser social affairs, became less relevant. One recognized that in a world cemented to peace by a genuine balance of power—an equal capacity to threaten and retaliate—the two major powers are now ultimately more dependent upon tacit trust in each other than upon faith in their allies. Just as Khrushchev became in 1959 the first Russian supreme leader to set foot in the United States, so in 1960 appeared Herman Kahn's *On Thermonuclear War* which, more than any other book, clarified the new world situation. In this same vein, much narrative literature of the 1960s, from *Virginia Woolf* though Peter Kass and Ed Emshwiller's movie *Time of the*

Heathen to *Catch-22*, refuses to suggest that one person's predicament is less critical than another's. (The exception is that strain of cinema which, in dealing with domestic issues of outsiders and civil rights, finds good reasons for seeing the world as we-they.) These historical forces which produced a shift in moral emphasis, coupled with lack of sympathy for the directions of art in the recent past, led artists, particularly younger ones, to work out new ways of dealing with the formal problems of art and of looking at the reality around them.

Just as world politics seem to be in fast flux in the mid-sixties, with the patterns of authority and loyalty being constantly realigned and an endless series of minor crises continually threatening precarious balances, so the world of American arts is permeated with varied and sprawling activity—energies extending in all directions, numerous schools (some with a few members) forming and dissolving, practitioners gaining enthusiastic, but limited and often temporary, followings; so that the scene as a whole resembles, in contrast to the programmed production line around us, a primitive workshop where everyone is off in his own cubbyhole doing his own work. In art, times of flux are times of ferment; and although any final evaluations should be held in abeyance, I would say that the past six years of American art have witnessed an expansion of artistic possibility and of relations within that increased range, as well as numerous works of originality and substance. These years were considerably more fruitful than the preceeding half-dozen, and tentatively I would say we are passing through a period of a minor renaissance in our culture.

[1965]

PETER MICHELSON[*]

❦

I Dream Profuse

Panther Pam, extravagant in public,
strips—fifteen pair of eyes, intense
with nonchalance, anticipate each new
exhibit of her charms and strain uneasy,
waiting for her black and velvet groin
in two/four time to rape their fantasies.
Pam facilitates imagination. . . .
the lights turn green and blue and grimly white,
the darkening drummer drums the driving time,
Pam's rhythmic fingers smooth her mocha skin—
her glowing chocolate torso draws me in . . .

I feel with her, I dance I dance I must,
she flaunts with me, her haunch she swivels lust
and strokes her nipple rising to her touch—
those practised hands obscenely promise much.

Perspiring now I know that she is more
than such a lust as mine prepares me for—
but heat and lights infuse my sweating glands
and I too dance obscene as she demands.

* PETER MICHELSON, *born in Chicago in 1937, took his B.A. from Whitman College and his M.A. from the University of Chicago, where he edited the* Chicago Review *from 1962 to 1965. He has published poems and critical essays in* Tri-Quarterly, The New Republic *and other magazines, as well as taught at Jamestown College in North Dakota, Northwestern and, currently, Notre Dame.*

Flannel my mouth my tongue too thick to cry
I ache, sweat, Sweet, I ache—deny
her sweet, my ache to suck her body dry

Contempt she laughs my fumbling heart
in blatant loving private shows her arts
and laughing smacks her lips her lewdly parts

In heave my hips by her directing hands
and dance I too as she obscene demands . . .

In dance I joy my Pam to make I scheme
and follow beat at cymbal clang I dream
profuse and caper canal caper thrust
I steamy pour my magnifying lust
in sweat I joy says rattlesnare and drum
she visions me and fear I sometime come
to face her facing out and sheeny skin
she laughs me sweating breathing hard is sin—
I frighting: does she seek my secret smell
wherewith my fetished brain in damn to dwell
me will she give me loving pleasure such
her hands her lips as promise seek me much
I want I fear in rage her massive beauty
jangle sings me husband father duty
halts her hungry breath alluring hands
I dance dance dance as drum and she demand
the snare and clang go *stop*.
                    I gape as caught
my panther dancing there is dancing not
she cheshire mocks my dreaming wet and hot.

HEATHER ROSS MILLER*

🌢

Chel

Chel leaned against the wall. The mid-sun, shining between the slatted white blinds, striped her cheek. She closed her eyes.

"Are you comfortable?" asked the doctor.

"Yes," her answer, like the slow lisp of a child, came once, and then again, "yes."

The counting began. One, two, five, seven. At the count of seven, she fell asleep. And opening her eyes that were sealed against waking, looked upon the doctor. He had removed his white jacket and sat in his shirt sleeves, holding in his palm a round flat watch, like those grandfathers used to carry. Chel could not blink. She frowned, a little shyly, and followed the dance of the dust motes weaving through slanted beams of light.

"How do you feel?"

"Just fine."

"Are you still comfortable?"

"Yes, very comfortable." She melted into the blank wall and was soon evaporated into sunbeams. Her cells dipped and bloomed in translucent corollas, her blood lisped its dark way through channels and was ejaculated in bright streams over a precipice.

"Hold out your arm. Your right arm."

Obediently and without question, the arm, the right arm, lifted and stiffened. The doctor sat and followed the needle of his

* HEATHER ROSS MILLER, *born in 1939 in Albemarle, North Carolina, received her B.A. from the University of North Carolina (Greensboro). She has published three novels,* The Edge of the Woods (*1964*), Tenants of the House (*1966*), and Gone a Hundred Miles (*1967*), and one collection of poetry,* The Wind Southerly (*1967*).

watch. Piteously it tore away shreds of time, of Chel's time, and then devoured them politely, obediently. He turned to the girl before him, on the other side of his desk. She sat so quietly, placidly holding out her arm, like a statue of warm rose flesh left in a ruined garden. He tapped the wrist. He pressed upon firm bone and resilient muscle around which was clasped a thin gold chain of charms. It held. He grasped her arm and tugged, gently at first, then harder. She resisted.

"Why are you holding your arm out like that?"

"Because."

"Because I told you?"

"No, because it feels good."

The doctor snapped shut the watch and began pulling on his jacket. "One, two, three."

Chel opened her eyes again. They felt weak. They felt they might possibly look red and old if she were to examine them in a mirror.

The doctor was standing at the open door, smiling officially.

"See you next Wednesday. And try to remember all we've said."

She went out, heavily, smoothing the wrinkles in her blue smock, and the sun met her in a dazzling flood along the corridor.

II

At home, on the gallery, the rocker squeaked comfortably and before her the mountains rose in emerald billows, bristling with unruly pine. Bees droned monotonously in the big hydrangeas. She was marooned in a sea of honey. The sun on her face was thick and sweet and smelled of August in the country. It stretched like a lazy beast, a beast furred in gold, claws sheathed, its tawny throat vulnerable. She would be alone this way until six.

"Are you comfortable?" she asked herself. And answering, "Yes, I am comfortable," sank into the heavy sea of honey. All afternoon, she rose and sank, a blue sail blown full by the scent of hydrangea, soaking in the pull of the bees and illuminated under the pleasant indifferent torpor. Inside her, the child trembled.

Slowly, toward the wane of the afternoon, Chel opened her

eyes, one at a time, cautiously, peep-eyeing. Over the dark green mountains, the sun spread a thin yellow veil, winking in dust. She was filled with languor and her eyes felt red again. The tissues of her brain echoed with the curlicues of the dense hydrangea and her blood lay flat as the long shadows across the sagging porch.

"Where have you been?"

"Hold out your arm."

"Are you comfortable?"

At six, Roy came, big, exhausted, his shoulders wet.

"How's my girl?"

Laboriously, she prepared the supper and set it steaming in bowls on the table. The chianti was bitter.

"I don't like it."

"It's just to sip," he said, pouring out a lipful for her glass. "Just to sip."

"But I want to *drink* it!" Chel shook back her hair, long and fine as cornsilks, the stale gold color of vermouth.

"Wine is to sip," Roy insisted. "Beer is to drink. And," he took a bite and chewed thoughtfully and swallowed and continued cheerfully, "we have no beer."

In the night, as Roy slept good-naturedly, one sunbrowned arm struck carelessly across her pillow, Chel arose and went out to the gallery where stars blossomed profusely in the black. The rocker squeaked under her and she looked down at her arms folded limply across her thick belly. They were pale. They seemed weak upon the mighty weight of her belly. It was drawing full due. Roy's son would burst forth and blossom like one of the infinitesimal stars in the dark firmament.

"Are you comfortable?"

The honey fell in slow drops, coiling and recoiling, swirling, spinning on an oaken wheel, bubbling in tiny star-specks. Over a hundred miles away, a thundercloud hammered the sky and Chel's white arms felt the vibration.

III

On Wednesday, she sat before the doctor's desk. He counted. She slept.

"Look at the rosebud in my lapel."

Chel obediently looked.

"It's pink now, but watch it turn into red."

She watched. The small tight bud unfurled and a scarlet glow ignited the points of her eyes and ballooned and usurped the place where the doctor had been.

"Can you hear?"

"Yes."

"What time is it in London?"

She heard the bells ringing sharp and dissonant, sprinkling the hours like flecks of steel grain through the cloudy air. The time was three, then nine, then twelve, not noon and not midnight twelve, but an indiscernible twelve. Chel gave way to the visitation: houses of Parliament, spires of Buckingham where soldiers march in red, a curling strand of Thames.

"Are you comfortable?"

"Yes." Lisping, lisping, these are the first words you ever learned. You saw a red rose and its thorn pricked your fingers and you bled red drops all over your white organdy. Yes.

When Chel waked, he said to her, flushing with pride, "You are a perfect somnambule. You have absolutely nothing to fear. The baby will be born alert and the memory of labor will fade rapidly."

August did not fade rapidly. It burned away unyieldingly, and September came, still burning. The mountains before the long gallery withered. The earth parched hard and pine needles broke with a crisp snap underfoot. All around her, the heavy honey surged incessantly in hues of amber and rose gold, streaked through with sienna, umber, ochre, coagulating to burnt blood, dried drops on a loom of organdy.

"Are you asleep?"

"Yes."

"Where are you?"

"I'm not anywhere yet."

More honey, more heat, accented with the crisp rattle of brown hydrangea and the drone of wearied bees.

"Where are you now?"

"I'm in the cellar. Hiding. They call me 'Rochelle. Rochelle.' Louder. 'Row-chelle!' How I hate the sound of their voices calling me 'Row-chelle.' "

"Do they find you?"

"No. I slip out and surprise them at their play. I am dirty from the black cellar. My fingernails are ringed in dirt."

"Are you comfortable?"

"Yes."

"Why are you holding your arm out like that?"

A trellis of roses unfurl to the clashing of iron bells. There is a flounce of spotted organdy. *I took a ride on a Ferris wheel and I was sick and I tried to jump out and they jeered at me. The pocket on my dress was torn and a fistful of hot cinnamons spilled out.*

"You have a fine healthy boy."

"No. It's impossible."

"Why do you say that?"

"It's not time. I'm still comfortable."

"You have a fine healthy boy."

"I have no child."

IV

Roy entered her room. It was all brightness without sunshine and no dust motes teeming in the air. He held a bouquet of fresh flowers.

"How's my girl?"

Grinning, his white teeth sharp and firm, his big certain hands plumping the pillow, cigars bulging his lapel, he was no more, no less, than Roy.

"I've told everybody." Roy scraped up a chair. He put the flowers on her tray, right between the water vessel and the thermometer. "But, honey, what's his name?"

Chel searched the air for dust. The sun was sterile here. The pillow smelled of carbolic and soap. Roy squeezed her hand. "Honey, what's the baby's name?"

Chel looked at him. Her cornsilk-fine hair felt dry, and her mouth, bitter and disappointing as chianti, cracked with the reply, "I don't know." And she closed her eyes, feigning sleep.

In her white soapy bed, Chel slept. Above and beneath her, thrusting endlessly, were rooms with beds where people slept, grew well again or sickened and died. At 2:00 A.M., the nurse, masked and whisper-soft, appeared with a child in her arm. She wakened Chel.

"Are you comfortable?"

"No."

"Why not?"

"I have this child at my breast. Can't you see! I can no longer hold out my right arm."

When the child had gone away, filled, Chel tried to sleep again. But no honey swam beside her bed, no warm sun melted the sterile dustless air. The easy chain would not unclasp. She held out her arm, her right arm. It faltered in the dim light and fell to her flattened empty belly, a broken wing.

ROBIN MORGAN*

The Improvisors

Crouched by your boots, I look along your body
            to that mouth, smiling
wreathed in the circle of the whip you coil,
but lunge free from your grasp in time to run
    unerringly to that other door
            the huge woman, the nursemaid,
flings back expectantly, grinning my welcome,
                my false safety.
She drags her charge to another room
            where the father rises,
black coat, stiff collar, accent, switch, to chide
    the daughter pleading she is naughty.
        As your hand falls, I scream,
scuttle away to the hall museumed with chains,
    belts, sticks, knouts, leather,
                past open doors
that expose the sultan's stern command,
the thin schoolmaster's frown, the pirate's anger,
    the eluded priest's ecstatic curse.
        To the corridor's farthest end
I crawl, to the chamber's center, to the bed
        with crimson hangings

* ROBIN MORGAN, *born in Lake Worth, Florida, in 1941, has written a* play, Their Own Country (1961), *and has had poems published in* Sewanee Review, Antioch Review, Poetry Northwest, Hudson Review, *and other magazines. Her first book of poems, just completed, will be entitled* War Games. *Married to the poet and novelist Kenneth Pitchford, she lives in New York City and works as a free-lance editor.*

261

I know will muffle all my cries.
Naked you wait,
whip coiled at your thigh, for my demand.

Hours, nights, and years
behind my lidded curtain
—a long, successful run—
I watched my characters

who, scorning their producer,
refused to improvise.
At last, I gave them notice
and locked the theater,

the stage dark ever since.
Only now new actors
hold me by their postures,
a captive audience.

I do not know them. I did not call them up.
But they are rude with indifference,
stroll a stage-
street real to the sound of late-night traffic,
calmly light slow cigarettes in doorways,
and watch for some approaching shape.
Then you appear, by chance,
windbreaker tight against the cold, and stop,
ask for a light?
(I cannot seem to hear the words)
Casually you talk,
then you recede together, you and he
(or they) past any imagined following.
Sometimes there is a bar,
and a blond broad man, tall, always laughing
(I cannot seem to hear the joke)
your arm around him,
then your departure, easy, together.

Or clouds of steam, from some dry-ice department
    of my brain, blend and blur
        the movements of you both—
only a line of muscle, a limb
        delineated.
    But always it ends, and this I fear,
        more than my rack-suite
or the bed looming behind a crimson shroud:
    always it ends with me among them,
        too swift to tell
which arms embrace women, which men,
caressing beards, full breasts, until we fall
        to that carpet
of living bodies, some dismembered,
        calves haired and soft,
torsos planed unlike a woman's.
Her nails on my breast describe his triangle hips
    beside us, narrowed from shoulders that curve
        as your fingers mold them. Her hair
brushes my lips as whose hands
        widen my thighs,
    and mouths open all like flowers
soundless, stroboscopic, slow, to darkness,
    opening to the room where you and he
        and all of them squirm, then stiffen
        oh beyond
my help or hurt or memory.

        You curl beside me, sleeping,
        unreachable, alien, known.
        How can I finish the scene
        that betrays me to such waking?

        Each night the actors play
        this ritual of vengeance:
        I murder every stance
        by which I watch them die.

They jerk, badly strung puppets
dancing on broken film
to no music. The lights dim.
The paint cracks on the sets.

Soon I will have nothing
but our own reality. Listen
before I can be heard,
before my voice can reach you through these hangings:
However strange I seem, learn me
at least to the limit
my foreign body will allow
or split the flesh, risk sight of the familiar.
You love perceptive mourning.
I prefer
even this daily confrontation
with what we never meet
to all you could see, know, love, too late.
Though a reluctant Prospero,
I've buried all my books,
paid and discharged my actors, struck my sets.
Break your sleep and look at me
before their gesturing
reclaims the dark proscenium.
See that I acknowledge you a stranger
but hold whatever I can learn
like your flesh, inside me.

Asleep in our marriage bed,
so I call out, while you
lean through the steaming day
to rouse me from my dead.

CHARLES NEWMAN*

✼

A Dolphin in the Forest, a Wild Boar on the Waves

THREE SCENES

"We must act as if we were lost, desperate . . ."
—Van Gogh to his brother

1

We sat there for awhile looking at the snow and the sky. We had come all the way through the Preserve, catching our breath among the great oaks of the Golf Club. We cleared away some snow and squatted down on the frozen sod, a finely quilted grass for future divots. Sand for the traps was heaped among the trees, and above us stretched the powder-blue watertower of Precious Blood Retreat.

They had bought the land when it was still wild onion. Their tower was the highest thing outside the city. When we first moved in, I lay in bed at night and listened to the water running out of the tower and into all the houses. They grew horse-radish for years until the ground turned blue. Then they sold the west

* CHARLES NEWMAN, *born in St. Louis, Missouri, in 1938, took his B.A. at Yale University and did graduate work at Oxford. Currently teaching English at Northwestern University, he is editor of* Tri-Quarterly *and author of* New Axis *(1966) and a second novel tentatively entitled* The Promisekeeper.

forty to the state for an airport, they sold the east forty to developers for a golf club, they sold the south forty to the city for a garbage dump, they sold the north forty to Irma Nadler's husband, Dr. Nadler, and he sold it to us and thirty-nine others.

Before they sold the south forty they took out all the rock and sold it to the airport for concrete. Before they sold the west forty they took off all the sod and sold it to the Gold Club for grass. When they put garbage where the rock and sod had been, the gulls from the lake moved inland with us. The gull is a clean and quiet bird. But they heckled the clippedwing swans down at the swan pond, and one gull flew into the mouth of an executive jet and blew it up.

The tower was a real landmark. At Christmastime they put messages on it in lights. This year it said: CHRIST WANTS MORE!

There was a good deal of comment about that. It attracted attention because it stretched around the entire tank, and to get the whole message, it was necessary to drive an everwidening circle through the countryside. Otherwise, from a single perspective, you could get only a few letters. From our house, for instance, all you could see was ANTS. Airliners used it for a pylon, and when a pervert annually took its child in the Preserve, official observers were seen at the tower railing, flashing signals through the night to search parties in the forest. They go up there when a little girl is late for dinner. Rewards are offered, the State Police are summoned, the hounds go out, the creek is dragged, the air is full of helicopters, but it's never any use. The dogs always find them the same way, half buried, decomposed, their underclothes in their mouths. The newspapers run a picture of the cop giving a little shoe to a big dog to smell. Sometimes, the body is dismembered and the police are around for weeks. Tell me, why do they have to find *all of it*, once they know?

The Cloister itself was yellow stucco with a red tile roof and a bell-less campanile. We went there several times a year to vote. Our precinct polls were in the foyer of the chapel, the only public place around. My parents always took me when they voted, a nice touch, although we never discussed who was to be chosen. While they were doing their duty, I stayed in the foyer, and it always surprised me, next to the pamphlet rack towered a big stuffed polar bear rearing up on his hind legs. You put a penny on his grooved tongue, shoved it back through scissor teeth and for a good minute his head swiveled, his eyes rolled, and from deep inside came a siren roar. Err-*err*-Err-Err! It was for orphans.

I mention this because something happened while we were sitting there, all tired out, with nothing to do, that nearly made the day. Moulton and I were in pretty bad shape; we didn't have too much more to say to each other. Our supply lines were overextended. We had, as he said, "defined the problem." So, we were just sitting there, resting, "free from constraint," as he would say, heads between our tails, and I had even begun to hear the water dripping out of the tower again after so many years, at my age, when three men came out of the forest. They were running crazily, zig-zagging, and they all carried huge sticks with which they beat the ground. It looked like some fool medieval Mad Dance.

It is a fact of modern living that we don't question what a man is doing as long as we understand what he's wearing. So when I saw they were wearing B-29 parkas, not hooded robes; sweatpants not pantaloons; football cleats not *clochepied*, and their weapons merely fiberglass polevault poles, I was prepared to give them a chance.

What they were doing was hunting. Their plan, apparently, was to run the length of the field in tandem, flushing rabbits and then busting them with their poles. And sure enough, on their third sally, one rabbit zigged when he should have zagged, and got clouted by the center hunter. They gathered round to finish the job, and by that time we were up to them. Moult was fascinated.

"By God, you got him!" he exclaimed. "That was terrific!"

The three of them grinned and leaned on their poles. They were stocky flushed types and the fur of their hoods was drawn in perfect circles about their faces.

"First one today," the center hunter spoke for the others, "tough going."

"I'll bet," said Moult. "What a fine idea!"

They didn't say anything but just kept grinning. They were

probably wondering what we were doing there. I was getting worried.

"You fellahs with Precious Blood?" I broke in.

"For a time," the center one spoke again. "Until the spring when we take orders."

"Oh, Monks?" Moult said.

"Brothers," they grinned.

"Where will you go from here?" I said.

They shrugged collectively, shifting their weight on the poles. I wanted to ask them "orders for what," but I was afraid Moult might start an argument if it was one of those with vows of silence or celibacy or something.

There was a light in Moulton's eye as he looked down at that rabbit pounded fresh on the snow; a light not for the killing or even the hunting, but for the lengths they had gone to before they did kill.

"Lemmie see one of those poles, will you Pal?"

When Moulton got it he held it in his hands like a presentation. Then he choked up on it, backed away, and took a few swings. Then he took several vicious swings, grunting and letting the momentum throw him off balance. Then he arched it back over his shoulder and flung it like a javelin. It sailed and bore quivering into a thicket. He plunged in after it, emerged in a minute with snow clinging to his hair, the pole over his shoulders like a yoke.

When he returned he looked down at their cleats.

"You guys must have a pretty good athletic set-up."

"You ever play anybody in anything?"

They shook their heads.

"Well, for not playing anybody they sure give you a lot of equipment."

Moult bent the pole in the snow, letting it snap back. I was afraid he was going to insult them and I wanted to get out of there.

"Just rabbits?" he pondered, "why not owls and quail too? And there's muskrat down by the creek."

"The rabbits get into the garbage," the center one said, "and the vegetables in the spring."

"We can't shoot them," another spoke for the first time, "It's against the law."

"We can't even eat them," said the third morosely.

I knew Moult was going to ask *why* they couldn't eat them and it might have been embarrassing so I interrupted.

"You fellahs got a nice chapel here," I said. "We go there a lot to vote." They smiled.

I was trying to figure out how to ask them the story behind the polar bear without getting involved when I saw Moult screwing the pole into the snow and getting a very troubled expression on his face. And we were in no position to protest.

"Well, better be going," I said. "Nice to meet you guys."

We shook hands all around but as I thought we were free, Moult did it.

"Could I have the rabbit?"

They looked at each other. They shuffled their feet, folded and unfolded their arms. The center one made sure we were not being watched, then smiled benignly. Why not? And we shook hands again before they ran off, brandishing their poles silently, running in cadence.

"Well, it's not exactly the Great White Whale," Moult said, fastening his prize to his belt by the ears, "but it's perked me up."

We weren't talking as we turned back across the divot field. My balance had made his leverage possible, I thought.

II

We cleared the forest, startled. The Christmas lights had been turned on! The houses, normally disparate, had reconnoitered in an electrical pageant, and now marched upon us full of jolly fury. The sky was smoked at the rooftops, extinguishing the stars; a wintry rose dusk. It was as if the sun had fallen into the ocean.

Strands of light lay everywhere. Hung in winking festoons from the trees, strung through the gristle of hedges; entwined about telephone poles, gascapsules, septictanks; they framed windows, crowned doorways, shrouded chimneys, garlanded mailboxes, stumps, balconies. Some lay in the winter brush like foxfire, others straddled gutters or dangled from frozen conifers, and some simply lay scattered on the snow where they had been thrown, like broken atoms.

Windowpanes had been carefully flocked, in special predrifted patterns, but, sad to say, real frost had filled these in. And through this ice, cellophane wreaths revolved, while on ribboned trees, electric candles bubbled colored waters. Enormous aluminum lollipops and stalks of peppermint were anchored in the snowbanks, and plastic life-size Santas, squatting in their own glow, waved convincingly as parking-lot attendants. Here and there a horseless driverless sleigh laden with massive hollow packages embarked across a yard. Golden doves with pipe cleaners in their claws strained on their wires in the wind. The Millers had a Kodachrome enlargement of the family in their window, framed with those birds of peace. The children were as happy as the birds and the birds as cute as the children. The Simmons had chosen Raphael's *Alba Madonna* for their front porch. The Wrights had a snowman with a nose which blinked in the night like an airliner. The Nelson's four papier-mâché lambs huddled for warmth in a spotlight. Elves worked feverishly at an assembly line in the Johnson's patio, grinning to themselves, while the Cooper's bevy of imported tinsel partridge hooted prerecorded hoots from collapsible pear trees. Baseboard silhouettes of wise men and camels strode across the playground towards the Memorial: Mother holding child untrembling, the swirling snow filling in their eyesockets.

We were almost home. The Christmas lights gilded the road, chained tires bit through the ice, stung sparks from the pavement. At an intersection, two plainclothesmen in a pastel ranchwagon were setting up a radar speed-trap.

We climbed the cyclone fence and cut through Mrs. Parker's bird sanctuary, to save time. The Parker place was the largest and the most magnificent around. Mr. Parker had been Dr. Nadler's first customer, as Dr. Nadler had first entreated upon the Church. They have eschewed each other since. A successful engineering career had been cut short by a hunting accident in Parker's case. Part of his frontal cortex had been shot away, making it subsequently impossible for him to think in terms of the possible. He had retired with his wife, early in life, and both devoted themselves to the photography of the wild life within their acreage.

Parker himself had died recently, but the crescent paths which were his testament were kept up by his wife. His woods were still webbed with the rusty wires he used to trip his secret cameras. And the Parker foyer was fully decorated with testimony to his skill; hundreds of startled animals gazed down from the walls, like beautiful movie stars trapped in some profane indulgence—raccoons with fish, deer stripping bark, birds atop rodents, snakes sucking eggs, rabbits with each other.

Suddenly, Mrs. Parker appeared ahead of us, turning one of her husband's serpentine bends, leading her black Labrador, Beodyboy.

"Get that rabbit out of sight," I hissed to Moult, "she'll think we've been poaching."

Moult disposed of the corpse in his coat. And we met a minute later, Mrs. Parker brimming with that gentleness which has no object, pleased that we were taking advantage of her privacy. I said the good things and remembered to introduce Moult who shook hands stiffly like a foreigner as he had the rabbit in his armpit. We would have gotten out of it cleanly, in fact, if it weren't for Beodyboy. He sauntered up, nosed Moult, and dropped into a solemn point. I don't think Mrs. Parker had ever seen Beodyboy on point before; nothing had been dead and bleeding that close to her. It embarrassed all of us of course. Particularly when Beodyboy jammed his nose into Moulton's groin. Mrs. Parker apologized and tugged on Beodyboy's collar but Beodyboy just stood his ground and growled. Moult grinned terribly and I patted Beodyboy's head as fast as I could. What we should have done, I suppose, was to let Mrs. Parker see what was up, explain things, throw the body for Beodyboy and get home for dinner. But there were so many things involved I don't think Mrs. Parker could have stood it. This was no time to start that. It would be easier, in a way, just to stand there, being pointed at, until Mrs. Parker either left or collapsed from the cold, and we could beat the pee out of Beodyboy and make it for home. For when we move, we leave nothing behind. No scraps, no ribbons in the trees, no graves, no dung. We leave things clean—if not precisely as we found them, still clean—bequeathing a footprint so wide, so equally pressured, that our predecessors will have no idea what passed their way.

But as it turned out, we didn't have to. Because Mrs. Parker just picked up a branch and started to whale Beodyboy about the shoulders. Exactly as we would have done, except for different reasons. Beodyboy didn't differentiate and took off for home. It was nice of Mrs. Parker to do that because she loved Beodyboy; he had been Mr. Parker's favorite after all. At least she knew something was wrong and that this was no time for a tug-of-war. It was hard to believe she was part of the conspiracy.

We commended her as best we knew how, and then she excused herself, returning around the bend to the enormous house which lit up the apple sky like an ocean liner. Her plotting was now confused, I suspect, and we were free again.

III

There are no hills near the Lake so they built one. They dug a hole for the necessary dirt, called what was left a reservoir, and that was all right. But inadvertently, they inverted the mountain. That is, they piled first what they dug first, so that the mountain is built on clods of topsoil small as walnuts; the peak is enormous rectangles of clay and striped granite. So our mountain tends to collapse into itself each year, and is only maintained by the constant ministrations of a corps of steam shovels and dumptrucks. In any case, the hill arose tentatively out of the fields before us, settling like a fallen meteor in its rim of shale. It was on the way and we climbed it for the view and to rest.

In the dark, at the top, things were indistinct. Across the fields, I could make out our house, set in the prairie turf like an axblade. The forest was darker than the sky; the sky had seeped through the horizon and ran like lymph throughout the electric patches of our Christmas. The water tower was spotlit, its fine message warped as always by parallax. From the hill tonight, it read WAN. The monastery's turrets glowed red; the Lake, still white and ribbed with frozen currents, angled away like a gull's wing. We squatted down and rested.

It was quite still. The airbase had shut down for the holidays;

the bluntnosed orange planes, aerodynamics bulged with radar, were down. The submarines were in their pens. The commuters were home.

I blinked down into the Sunset Estates, down into the converging lights, into those homes designed with so little thought that years of grooming could not give them warmth or character, but only a slight diffidence to one another. I was very cold and very tired. All day, it seemed, we had been addressing a vague audience that was not ourselves, an audience which refused to be taken seriously. We have destroyed the Proscenium forever.

In the dark, of the stillness, at the top, I heard the water backing up in the tower, the silence too of more solid fuel cached in our Preserve, frost splitting brickpaths, drone of precision thermostats, lubric drip of idle engines; waiting only for the coordinates to intersect, ignite . . . in order to retaliate. . . .

"My God," yelled Moult. "There's someone down there!"

I peered down into the great white field. There was someone there all right. But if it was someone, they looked dead. He was lying right in the center of the field with arms and legs outstretched, an illiterate signature on the snow.

We ran down the hill as fast as we could and into the field. At first I thought the perverts were rushing the season, but they would never have left things that way. Perhaps heart disease or cancer. We crashed down through the ice and into nettles as we ran. Moult was getting short of wind and tears were freezing to his face. Once he tripped and cut his ankle on the edge of his own deep track. He clutched at his wound but I got him by the back of the neck and hauled him to his feet. Then we were going again, and he soon outdistanced me. We galloped on, knee deep now, the nettles cutting our socks to pieces. A great volume of blood pressed against my eyes—the adrenalin hadn't started yet, I wasn't excited, I was going on pure intent. I had been feeling mean; now maybe we could make a rescue.

It was a kid all right. About ten, in a purple snowsuit, an abandoned princeling. Moult arrived first but didn't know what to do. I drew up, dropped to my knees to see if the kid were breathing. Moult fell on the other side of him and began to retch. The kid was fine. His eyes were wide open and he was breathing clouds of frost. There was nothing wrong with him at all except his nose was running.

"What ya want, bub?" he said, and not too pleasantly.

"What happened? You fall down?"

"Are you kidding?"

"Does your family know you're out here?" He rolled his eyes indifferently.

"Lost?"

"No," he pouted.

I started to grab him under the arms to pick him up—perhaps he had a fight and was sulking—but as soon as I touched him he winced and bellowed.

"No. Don't!"

"What? You break something?"

"No. Stupe. Can't you see? You'll ruin it! The angel!" I didn't know what he meant and took a deep breath.

"Just get away, will ya? And I'll show ya."

I rolled away a few feet to watch. Moult seemed better, and was eyeing the kid from a safe distance. Very solemnly and deliberately the kid sat up, holding his arms out to the side. Then in one motion he sprang to his feet and turned on us proudly. "There," he said, pointing. He was right. In the snow was the impression of an angel in full flight.

"A little didactic," Moult mumbled, "But still, an angel." He rolled over closer, intrigued. "Hey," he said, "how'd you do that?"

"Easy," the kid said, wiping his nose. "Just lie on your back without moving and sweep your arms up and down like you were flying."

Moult put the rabbit beside him and lay down. But the kid yelled and stamped his feet.

"No. Naah! You gotta do it easy!"

He took Moult's head in his hands and eased him back. He still lay too eagerly, however, and again broke the outline.

"I told ya buddy, you gotta do it *easy*."

"Try it over here," I said. "There's a good smooth spot."

Moult came over, careful not to damage the fresh snow, and began again, gingerly.

"You can do it on your stomach if you want," the kid continued, "but you'll get snow up your nose."

Moult was down and I tried it next to him. The kid looked down at us.

"OK," he said. "Now fly."

I wound my arms slowly in a half circle. Moult did the same. At one point in the arc, our knuckles brushed.

"Slow," warned the kid. "Easy does it."

We continued. I took short breaths, careful not to arch my back and ruin the mold.

"OK," the kid said again. "That's good. OK! OK!!" Moult and I looked to him.

"OK. Now's the hard part. Gotta get up. But no hands, see? Or you'll break it."

Then he held my feet. I sat up slowly. My groin burned from the running. But after some effort I was up. And Moult was too. With the kid's help. We rolled forward on our haunches, up and away from the impressions.

"Not bad," the kid said, "pretty good."

They were too. Two big gruff angels on either side of the kid's little perfect one. Ours seemed to career more, like helicopters. But they were good, considering.

"Say," Moult said, "Say. That's all right."

The kids wiped his nose. "OK."

"Moult," I interrupted, "Moult. We got to go." He nodded.

"And you," I said to the kid, "You getter get home. Your mother's probably going crazy wondering where you are." The idea seemed to strike him as a fact; but he lay down again.

"Sometimes," he said, "I make 'em with just one wing. Then they look sadder, or they look like somebody carrying a fan or a horn or a big ax."

"Yes, that is what they would look like," said Moult, caching our carcass within his parka again.

"We got to get going," I said. "So long kid."

"Yeah bub," he said. "I'd wave but I'd break it."

We crossed the field at a trot. We didn't look back or talk.

JOYCE CAROL OATES*

❦

Upon the Sweeping Flood

One day in Eden County, in the remote marsh and swamp-lands to the south, a man named Walter Stuart was stopped in the rain by a sheriff's deputy along a country road. Stuart was in a hurry to get home to his family—his wife and two daughters—after having endured a week at his father's old farm, arranging for his father's funeral, surrounded by aging relatives who had sucked at him for the strength of his youth. He was a stern, quiet man of thirty-nine, beginning now to lose some of the muscular hardness that had always baffled others, masking as it did Stuart's remoteness, his refinement, his faith in discipline and order that seem to have belonged, even in his youth, to a person already grown safely old. He was a district vice-president for one of the gypsum mining plants, a man to whom financial success and success in love had come naturally, without fuss. When only a child he had shifted his faith with little difficulty from the unreliable God of his family's tradition to the things and emotions of this world, which he admired in his thoughtful, rather conservative way, and this faith had given him access, as if by magic, to a communion with persons vastly different from himself—with someone like the sheriff's deputy, for example, who approached him that

* JOYCE CAROL OATES, *born in Lockport, New York, in 1937, holds degrees from Syracuse and Wisconsin universities. A 1967 Guggenheim Fellow and an associate professor of English at the University of Windsor (Ontario), she has published two novels—*With Shuddering Fall *(1964)* and A Garden of Earthly Delights *(1967)—and many short stories, collected in* By the North Gate *(1963)* and Upon the Sweeping Flood *(1966),* as well as several critical and scholarly articles.*

day in the hard, cold rain. "Is something wrong?" Stuart said. He rolled down the window and had nearly opened the door when the deputy, an old man with gray eyebrows and a slack, sunburned face, began shouting against the wind. "Just the weather, mister. You plan on going far? How far are you going?"

"Two hundred miles," Stuart said. "What about the weather? Is it a hurricane?"

"A hurricane—yes—a hurricane," the man said, bending to shout at Stuart's face. "You better go back to town and stay put. They're evacuating up there. We're not letting anyone through."

A long line of cars and pickup trucks, tarnished and gloomy in the rain, passed them on the other side of the road. "How bad is it?" said Stuart. "Do you need help?"

"Back at town, maybe, they need help," the man said. "They're putting up folks at the schoolhouse and the churches, and different families— The eye was spost to come by here, but last word we got it's veered further south. Just the same, though—"

"Yes, it's good to evacuate them," Stuart said. At the back window of an automobile passing them two children's faces peered out at the rain, white and blurred. "The last hurricane here—"

"Ah, God, leave off of that!" the old man said, so harshly that Stuart felt, inexplicably, hurt. "You better turn around now and get on back to town. You got money they can put you up somewheres good—not with these folks coming along here."

This was said without contempt, but Stuart flinched at its assumptions and, years afterward, he was to remember the old man's remark as the beginning of his adventure. The man's twisted face and unsteady, jumping eyes, his wind-snatched voice, would reappear to Stuart when he puzzled for reasons—but along with the deputy's face there would be the sad line of cars, the children's faces turned toward him, and, beyond them in his memory, the face of his dead father with skin wrinkled and precise as a withered apple.

"I'm going in to see if anybody needs help," Stuart said. He had the car going again before the deputy could even protest. "I know what I'm doing! I know what I'm doing!" Stuart said.

The car lunged forward into the rain, drowning out the deputy's outraged shouts. The slashing of rain against Stuart's face excited him. Faces staring out of oncoming cars were pale and startled, and Stuart felt rising in him a strange compulsion to grin, to laugh madly at their alarm. . . . He passed cars for some time. Houses looked deserted, yards bare. Things had the look of haste about them, even trees—in haste to rid themselves of their leaves, to be stripped bare. Grass was twisted and wild. A ditch by the road was overflowing and at spots the churning, muddy water stretched across the red clay road. Stuart drove, splashing, through it. After a while his enthusiasm slowed, his foot eased up on the gas pedal. He had not passed any cars or trucks for some time.

The sky had darkened and the storm had increased. Stuart thought of turning back when he saw, a short distance ahead, someone standing in the road. A car approached from the opposite direction. Stuart slowed, bearing to the right. He came upon a farm—a small, run-down one with just a few barns and a small pasture in which a horse stood drooping in the rain. Behind the roofs of the buildings a shifting edge of foliage from the trees beyond curled in the wind, now dark, now silver. In a neat harsh line against the bottom of the buildings the wind had driven up dust and red clay. Rain streamed off roofs, plunged into fat, tilted rain barrels, and exploded back out of them. As Stuart watched, another figure appeared, running out of the house. Both persons— they looked like children—jumped about in the road, waving their arms. A spray of leaves was driven against them and against the muddy windshield of the car that approached and passed them. They turned: a girl and a boy, waving their fists in rage, their faces white and distorted. As the car sped past Stuart, water and mud splashed up in a vicious wave.

When Stuart stopped and opened the door the girl was already there, shouting, "Going the wrong way! Wrong way!" Her face was coarse, pimply about her forehead and chin. The boy pounded up behind her, straining for air. "Where the hell are you going, mister?" the girl cried. "The storm's coming from this way. Did you see that bastard, going right by us? Did you see him? If I see him when I get to town—" A wall of rain struck. The girl lunged forward and tried to push her way into the car; Stuart had to hold her back. "Where are your folks?" he shouted.

"Let me in," cried the girl savagely. "We're getting out of here!" "Your folks," said Stuart. He had to cup his mouth to make her hear. "Your folks in there!" "There ain't anybody there— *God-damn* you," she said, twisting about to slap her brother, who had been pushing at her from behind. She whirled upon Stuart again. "You letting us in, mister? You letting us in?" she screamed, raising her hands as if to claw him. But Stuart's size must have calmed her, for she shouted hoarsely and mechanically: "There ain't nobody in there. Our pa's been gone the last two days. *Last two days.* Gone into town *by himself.* Gone drunk somewhere. He ain't here. He left us here. LEFT US HERE!" Again she rushed at Stuart, and he leaned forward against the steering wheel to let her get in back. The boy was about to follow when something caught his eye back at the farm. "Get in," said Stuart. "Get in. Please. Get in." "My horse there," the boy muttered. "You little bastard! You get in here!" his sister screamed.

But once the boy got in, once the door was closed, Stuart knew that it was too late. Rain struck the car in solid walls and the road, when he could see it, had turned to mud. "Let's go! Let's go!" cried the girl, pounding on the back of the seat. "Turn it around! Go up on our drive and turn it around!" The engine and the wind roared together. "Turn it! Get it going!" cried the girl. There was a scuffle and someone fell against Stuart. "It ain't no good," the boy said. "Let me out." He lunged for the door and Stuart grabbed him. "I'm going back to the house," the boy cried, appealing to Stuart with his frightened eyes, and his sister, giving up suddenly, pushed him violently forward. "It's no use," Stuart said. "Goddamn fool," the girl screamed, "goddamn fool!"

The water was ankle deep as they ran to the house. The girl splashed ahead of Stuart, running with her head up and her eyes wide open in spite of the flying scud. When Stuart shouted to the boy, his voice was slammed back to him as if he were being mocked. "Where are you going? Go to the house! Go to the house!" The boy had turned and was running toward the pasture. His sister took no notice but ran to the house. "Come back, kid!" Stuart cried. Wind tore at him, pushing him back. "What are you—"

The horse was undersized, skinny and brown. It ran to the boy as if it wanted to run him down but the boy, stooping through the fence, avoided the frightened hoofs and grabbed the rope that dangled from the horse's halter. "That's it! That's it!" Stuart shouted as if the boy could hear. At the gate the boy stopped and looked around wildly, up to the sky—he might have been looking for someone who had just called him; then he shook the gate madly. Stuart reached the gate and opened it, pushing it back against the boy, who now turned to gape at him. "What? What are you doing here?" he said.

The thought crossed Stuart's mind that the child was insane. "Bring the horse through!" he said. "We don't have much time."

"What are you doing here?" the boy shouted. The horse's eyes rolled, its mane lifted and haloed about its head. Suddenly it lunged through the gate and jerked the boy off the ground. The boy ran in the air, his legs kicking. "Hang on and bring him around!" Stuart shouted. "Let me take hold!" He grabbed the boy instead of the rope. They stumbled together against the horse. It had stopped now and was looking intently at something just to the right of Stuart's head. The boy pulled himself along the rope, hand over hand, and Stuart held onto him by the strap of his overalls. "He's scairt of you!" the boy said. "He's scairt of you!" Stuart reached over and took hold of the rope above the boy's fingers and tugged gently at it. His face was about a foot away from the horse's. "Watch out for him," said the boy. The horse reared and broke free, throwing Stuart back against the boy. "Hey, hey," screamed the boy, as if mad. The horse turned in mid-air as if whirled about by the wind, and Stuart looked up through his fingers to see its hoofs and a vicious flicking of its tail, and the face of the boy being yanked past him and away with incredible speed. The boy fell heavily on his side in the mud, arms outstretched above him, hands still gripping the rope with wooden fists. But he scrambled to his feet at once and ran alongside the horse. He flung one arm up around its neck as Stuart shouted, "Let him go! Forget about him!" Horse and boy pivoted together back toward the fence, slashing wildly at the earth, feet and hoofs together. The ground erupted beneath them. But the boy landed upright, still holding the rope, still with his arm about the horse's neck. "Let me help," Stuart said. "No," said the boy, "he's my horse, he knows me—" "Have you got him good?" Stuart shouted. "We got—we got each other here," the boy cried, his eyes shut tight.

Stuart went to the barn to open the door. While he struggled with it, the boy led the horse forward. When the door was open far enough, Stuart threw himself against it and slammed it around to the side of the barn. A cloud of hay and scud filled the air. Stuart stretched out his arms, as if pleading with the boy to hurry, and he murmured, "Come on. Please. Come on." The boy did not hear him or even glance at him: his own lips were moving as he caressed the horse's neck and head. The horse's muddy hoof had just begun to grope about the step before the door when something like an explosion came against the back of Stuart's head, slammed his back, and sent him sprawling out at the horse.

"Damn you! Damn you!" the boy screamed. Stuart saw nothing except rain. Then something struck him, his shoulder and hand, and his fingers were driven down into the mud. Something slammed beside him in the mud and he seized it—the horse's foreleg—and tried to pull himself up, insanely, lurching to his knees. The horse threw him backwards. It seemed to emerge out of the air before and above him, coming into sight as though out of a cloud. The boy he did not see at all—only the hoofs—and then the boy appeared, inexplicably, under the horse, peering intently at Stuart, his face struck completely blank. "Damn you!" Stuart heard, "he's my horse! My horse! I hope he kills you!" Stuart crawled back in the water, crab fashion, watching the horse form and dissolve, hearing its vicious tattoo against the barn. The door, swinging madly back and forth, parodied the horse's rage, seemed to challenge its frenzy; then the door was all Stuart heard, and he got to his feet, gasping, to see that the horse was out of sight.

The boy ran bent against the wind, out toward nowhere, and Stuart ran after him. "Come in the house, kid! Come on! Forget about it, kid!" He grabbed the boy's arm. The boy struck at him with his elbow. "He was my horse!" he cried.

In the kitchen of the house they pushed furniture against the door. Stuart had to stand between the boy and the girl to keep them from fighting. "Goddamn sniffling fool," said the girl. "So your goddamn horse run off for the night!" The boy crouched down on the floor, crying steadily. He was about thirteen: small for his age, with bony wrists and face. "We're all going to be blownt to hell, let alone your horse," the girl said. She sat with one big thigh and leg outstretched on the table, watching Stuart. He thought her perhaps eighteen. "Glad you come down to get us?" she said. "Where are you from, mister?" Stuart's revulsion surprised him; he had not supposed there was room in his stunned mind for emotion of this sort. If the girl noticed it she gave no sign, but only grinned at him. "I was—I was on my way home," he said. "My wife and daughters—" It occurred to him that he had forgotten about them entirely. He had not thought of them until now and, even now, no image came to his mind: no woman's face, no little girls' faces. Could he have imagined their lives, their love for him? For an instant he doubted everything. "Wife and daughters," said the girl, as if wondering whether to believe him. "Are they in this storm too?" "No—no," Stuart said. To get away from her he went to the window. He could no longer see the road. Something struck the house and he flinched away. "Them trees!" chortled the girl. "I knew it! Pa always said how he ought to cut them down, so close to the house like they are! I knew it! I knew it! And the old bastard off safe now where they can't get him!"

"Trees?" said Stuart slowly.

"Them trees! Old oak trees!" said the girl.

The boy, struck with fear, stopped crying suddenly. He crawled on the floor to a woodbox beside the big old iron stove and got in, patting the disorderly pile of wood as if he were blind. The girl ran to him and pushed him. "What are you doing?" Stuart cried in anguish. The girl took no notice of him. "What am I doing?" he said aloud. "What the hell am I doing here?" It seemed to him that the end would come in a minute or two, that the howling outside could get no louder, that the howling inside his mind could get no more intense, no more accusing. A goddamn fool! A goddamn fool! he thought. The deputy's face came to mind, and Stuart pictured himself groveling before the man, clutching at his knees, asking forgiveness and for time to be turned back. . . . Then he saw himself back at the old farm, the farm of his childhood, listening to tales of his father's agonizing sickness, the old peoples' heads craning around, seeing how he took it, their eyes charged with horror and delight. . . . "My wife and daughters," Stuart muttered.

The wind made a hollow, drumlike sound. It seemed to be tolling. The boy, crouching back in the woodbox, shouted: "I ain't scairt! I ain't scairt!" The girl gave a shriek. "Our chicken coop, I'll be gahdammed!" she cried. Try as he could, Stuart could see nothing out the window. "Come away from the window," Stuart said, pulling the girl's arm. She whirled upon him. "Watch yourself, mister," she said, "you want to go out to your gahdamn bastardly worthless car?" Her body was strong and big in her men's clothing; her shoulders looked muscular beneath the filthy shirt. Cords in her young neck stood out. Her hair had been cut short and was now wet, plastered about her blemished face. She grinned at Stuart as if she were about to poke him in the stomach, for fun. "I ain't scairt of what God can do!" the boy cried behind them.

When the water began to bubble up through the floor boards they decided to climb to the attic. "There's an ax!" Stuart exclaimed, but the boy got on his hands and knees and crawled to the corner where the ax was propped before Stuart could reach it. The boy cradled it in his arms. "What do you want with that?" Stuart said, and for an instant his heart was pierced with fear. "Let me take it. I'll take it." He grabbed it out of the boy's dazed fingers.

The attic was about half as large as the kitchen and the roof jutted down sharply on either side. Tree limbs rubbed and slammed against the roof on all sides. The three of them crouched on the middle beam, Stuart with the ax tight in his embrace, the boy pushing against him as if for warmth, and the girl kneeling, with her thighs straining her overalls. She watched the little paneless window at one end of the attic without much emotion or interest, like a large, wet turkey. The house trembled beneath them. "I'm going to the window." Stuart said, and was oddly relieved when the girl did not sneer at him. He crawled forward along the dirty beam, dragging the ax with him, and lay full length on the floor about a yard from the window. There was not much to see. At times the rain relaxed, and objects beneath in the water took shape: tree stumps, parts of buildings, junk whirling about in the water. The thumping on the roof was so loud at that end that he had to crawl backwards to the middle again. "I ain't scairt, nothing God can do!" the boy cried. "Listen to the sniveling baby," said the girl. "He thinks God pays him any mind! Hah!" Stuart crouched beside them, waiting for the boy to press against him again. "As if God gives a good damn about him," the girl said. Stuart looked at her. In the near dark her face did not seem so coarse; the set of her eyes was almost attractive. "You don't think God cares about you?" Stuart said slowly. "No, not specially," the girl said, shrugging her shoulders. "The hell with it. You seen the last one of these?" She tugged at Stuart's arm. "Mister? It was something to see. Me an' Jackie was little then— him just a baby. We drove a far ways north to get out of it. When we come back the roads was so thick with sightseers from the cities! They took all the dead ones floating in the water and put them in one place, part of a swamp they cleared out. The families and things—they were mostly fruit pickers—had to come by on rafts and rowboats to look and see could they find the ones they knew. That was there for a day. The bodies would turn round and round in the wash from the boats. Then the faces all got alike and they wouldn't let anyone come any more and put oil on them and set them afire. We stood on top of the car and watched all that day. I wasn't but nine then."

When the house began to shake, some time later, Stuart cried aloud: "This is it!" He stumbled to his feet, waving the ax. He turned around and around as if he were in a daze. "You goin' to chop somethin' with that?" the boy said, pulling at him. "Hey, no, that ain't yours to—it ain't yours to chop—" They struggled for the ax. The boy sobbed, "It ain't yours! It ain't yours!" and Stuart's rage at his own helplessness, at the folly of his being here, for an instant almost made him strike the boy with the ax. But the girl slapped him furiously. "Get away from him! I swear I'll kill you!" she screamed.

Something exploded beneath them. "That's the windows," the girl muttered, clinging to Stuart, "and how am I to clean it again! The old bastard will want it clean, and mud over everything!"

Stuart pushed her away so that he could swing the ax. Pieces of soft, rotted wood exploded back onto his face. The boy screamed insanely as the boards gave way to a deluge of wind and water, and even Stuart wondered if he had made a mistake. The three of them fell beneath the onslaught and Stuart lost the ax, felt the handle slam against his leg. "You! You!" Stuart cried, pulling at the girl—for an instant, blinded by pain, he could not think who he was, what he was doing, whether he had any life beyond this moment. The big-faced, husky girl made no effort to hide her fear and cried, "wait, wait!" But he dragged her to the hole and tried to force her out. "My brother—" she gasped. She seized his wrists and tried to get away. "Get out there! There isn't any time!" Stuart muttered. The house seemed about to collapse at any moment. He was pushing her through the hole, against the shattered wood, when she suddenly flinched back against him and he saw that her cheek was cut and she was choking. He snatched her hands away from her mouth as if he wanted to see something secret: blood welled out between her lips. She coughed and spat blood onto him. "You're all right," he said, oddly pleased. "Now get out there and I'll get the kid. I'll take care of him." This time she managed to crawl through the hole, with Stuart pushing her from behind; when he turned to seize the boy, the boy clung to his neck, sobbing something about God. "God loves you!" Stuart yelled. "Loves the least of you! The least of you!" The girl pulled her brother up in her great arms and Stuart was free to climb through himself.

It was actually quite a while—perhaps an hour—before the battering of the trees and the wind pushed the house in. The roof fell slowly, and the section to which they clung was washed free. "We're going somewheres!" shouted the girl. "Look at the house! That gahdamn old shanty seen the last storm!"

The boy lay with his legs pushed in under Stuart's and had not spoken for some time. When the girl cried, "Look at that!" he tried to burrow in farther. Stuart wiped his eyes to see the wall of darkness dissolve. The rain took on another look—a smooth, piercing, metallic glint, like nails driving against their faces and bodies. There was no horizon. They could see nothing except the rushing water and a thickening mist that must have been rain, miles and miles of rain, slammed by the wind into one great wall that moved remorselessly upon them. "Hang on," Stuart said, gripping the girl. "Hang on to me."

Waves washed over the roof, pushing objects at them with soft, muted thuds—pieces of fence, boards, branches heavy with foliage. Stuart tried to ward them off with his feet. Water swirled around them, sucking at them, sucking the roof, until they were pushed against one of the farm buildings. Something crashed against the roof—another section of the house—and splintered, flying up against the girl. She was thrown backwards, away from Stuart, who lunged after her. They fell into the water while the boy screamed. The girl's arms threshed wildly against Stuart. The water was cold, and its aliveness, its sinister energy, surprised him more than the thought that he would drown—that he would never endure the night. Struggling with the girl, he forced her back to the roof, pushed her up. Bare, twisted nails raked his hands. "Gahdamn you, Jackie, you give a hand!" the girl said as Stuart crawled back up. He lay, exhausted, flat on his stomach and let the water and debris slosh over him.

His mind was calm beneath the surface buzzing. He liked to think that his mind was a clear, sane circle of quiet carefully preserved inside the chaos of the storm—that the three of them were safe within the sanctity of this circle; this was how man always conquered nature, how he subdued things greater than himself. But whenever he did speak to her it was in short grunts, in her own idiom: "This ain't so bad!" or "It'll let up pretty soon!" Now the girl held him in her arms as if he were a child, and he did not have the strength to pull away. Of his own free will he had given himself to this storm, or to the strange desire to save someone in it—but now he felt grateful for the girl, even for her brother, for they had saved him as much as he had saved them. Stuart thought of his wife at home, walking through the rooms, waiting for him; he thought of his daughters in their twin beds, two glasses of water on their bureau. . . . But these people knew nothing of him: in his experience now he did not belong to them. Perhaps he had misunderstood his role, his life? Perhaps he had blundered out of his way, drawn into the wrong life, surrendered to the wrong role. What had blinded him to the possibility of many lives, many masks, many arms that might so embrace him? A word not heard one day, a gesture misinterpreted, a leveling of someone's eyes in a certain unmistakable manner, which he had mistaken just the same! The consequences of such errors might trail insanely into the future, across miles of land, across worlds. He only now sensed the incompleteness of his former life. . . .

"Look! Look!" the girl cried, jostling him out of his stupor. "Take a look at that, mister!"

He raised himself on one elbow. A streak of light broke out of the dark. Lanterns, he thought, a rescue party already. . . . But the rain dissolved the light; then it reappeared with a beauty that startled him. "What is it?" the boy screamed. "How come it's here?" They watched it filter through the rain, rays knifing through and showing, now, how buildings and trees crouched close about them. "It's the sun, the sun going down," the girl said. "The sun!" said Stuart, who had thought it was night. "The sun!" They stared at it until it disappeared.

The waves calmed sometime before dawn. By then the roof had lost its peak and water ran unchecked over it, in generous waves and then in thin waves, alternately, as the roof bobbed up and down. The three huddled together with their backs to the wind. Water came now in slow drifts. "It's just got to spread itself out far enough so's it will be even," said the girl, "then it'll go down." She spoke without sounding tired, only a little disgusted—as if things weren't working fast enough to suit her. "Soon as it goes down we'll start toward town and see if there ain't somebody coming out to get us in a boat," she said, chattily and comfortably, into Stuart's ear. Her manner astonished Stuart, who had been thinking all night of the humiliation and pain he had suffered. "Bet the old bastard will be glad to see us," she said, "even if he did go off like that. Well, he never knew a storm was coming. Me and him get along pretty well—he ain't so bad." She wiped her face; it was filthy with dirt and blood. "He'll buy you a drink, mister, for saving us how you did. That was something to have happen—a man just driving up to get us!" And she poked Stuart in the ribs.

The wind warmed as the sun rose. Rain turned to mist and back to rain again, still falling heavily, and now objects were clear about them. The roof had been shoved against the corner of the barn and a mound of dirt, and eddied there without much trouble. Right about them, in a kind of halo, a thick blanket of vegetation and filth bobbed. The fence had disappeared and the house had collapsed and been driven against a ridge of land. The barn itself had fallen in, but the stone support looked untouched, and it was against this they had been shoved. Stuart thought he could see his car—or something over there where the road used to be.

"I bet it ain't deep. Hell," said the girl, sticking her foot into the water. The boy leaned over the edge and scooped up some of the filth in his hands. "Lookit all the spiders," he said. He wiped his face slowly. "Leave them gahdamn spiders alone," said the girl. "You want me to shove them down your throat?" She slid to the edge and lowered her legs. "Yah, I touched bottom. It ain't bad." But then she began coughing and drew herself back. Her coughing made Stuart cough: his chest and throat were ravaged, shaken, he lay exhausted when the fit left him and realized, suddenly, that they were all sick—that something had happened to them. They had to get off the roof. Now, with the sun up, things did not look so bad: there was a ridge of trees a short distance away on a long, red clay hill. "We'll go over there," Stuart said. "Do you think you can make it?"

The boy played in the filth, without looking up, but the girl gnawed at her lip to show she was thinking. "I spose so," she said. "But him—I don't know about him."

"Your brother? What's wrong?"

"Turn around. Hey, stupid. Turn around." She prodded the boy, who jerked around, terrified, to stare at Stuart. His thin bony face gave way to a drooping mouth. "Gone loony, it looks like," the girl said with a touch of regret. "Oh, he had times like this before. It might go away."

Stuart was transfixed by the boy's stare. The realization of what had happened struck him like a blow, sickening his stomach. "We'll get him over there," he said, making his words sound good. "We can wait there for someone to come. Someone in a boat. He'll be better there."

"I spose so," said the girl vaguely.

Stuart carried the boy while the girl splashed eagerly ahead. The water was sometimes up to his thighs. "Hold on another minute," he pleaded. The boy stared out at the water as if he thought he were taken somewhere to be drowned. "Put your arms around my neck. Hold on," Stuart said. He shut his eyes and every time he looked up the girl was still a few yards ahead and the hill looked no closer. The boy breathed hollowly, coughing into Stuart's face. His own face and neck were covered with small red bites. Ahead, the girl walked with her shoulders lunged forward as if to hurry her there, her great thighs straining against the water, more than a match for it. As Stuart watched her, something was on the side of his face—in his ear—and with a scream he slapped at it, nearly dropping the boy. The girl whirled around. Stuart slapped at his face and must have knocked it off—probably a spider. The boy, upset by Stuart's outcry, began sucking in air faster and faster as if he were dying. "I'm all right, I'm all right," Stuart whispered, "just hold on another minute. . . ."

When he finally got to the hill the girl helped pull him up. He set the boy down with a grunt, trying to put the boy's legs under him so he could stand. But the boy sank to the ground and turned over and vomited into the water; his body shook as if he were having convulsions. Again the thought that the night had poisoned them, their own breaths had sucked germs into their bodies, struck Stuart with an irresistible force. "Let him lay down and rest," the girl said, pulling tentatively at the back of her brother's belt, as if she were thinking of dragging him farther up the slope. "We sure do thank you, mister," she said,

Stuart climbed to the crest of the hill. His heart pounded madly, blood pounded in his ears. What was going to happen? Was anything going to happen? How disappointing it looked— ridges of land showing through the water and the healthy sunlight pushing back the mist. Who would believe him when he told of the night, of the times when death seemed certain . . . ? Anger welled up in him already as he imagined the tolerant faces of his friends, his children's faces ready to turn to other amusements, other oddities. His wife would believe him; she would shudder, holding him, burying her small face in his neck. But what could

she understand of his experience, having had no part in it? . . .
Stuart cried out; he had nearly stepped on a tangle of snakes.
Were they alive? He backed away in terror. The snakes gleamed
wetly in the morning light, heads together as if conspiring. Four
. . . five of them—they too had swum for this land, they too
had survived the night, they had as much reason to be proud of
themselves as Stuart.

He gagged and turned away. Down by the water line the boy
lay flat on his stomach and the girl squatted nearby, wringing out
her denim jacket. The water behind them caught the sunlight and
gleamed mightily, putting them into silhouette. The girl's arms
moved slowly, hard with muscle. The boy lay coughing gently.
Watching them, Stuart was beset by a strange desire: he wanted
to run at them, demand their gratitude, their love. Why should
they not love him, when he had saved their lives? When he had
lost what he was just the day before, turned now into a different
person, a stranger even to himself? Stuart stooped and picked up a
rock. A broad hot hand seemed to press against his chest. He
threw the rock out into the water and said, "Hey!"

The girl glanced around but the boy did not move. Stuart sat
down on the soggy ground and waited. After a while the girl
looked away; she spread the jacket out to dry. Great banked
clouds rose into the sky, reflected in the water—jagged and bent
in the waves. Stuart waited as the sun took over the sky. Mist at
the horizon glowed, thinned, gave way to solid shapes. Light did
not strike cleanly across the land, but was marred by ridges of
trees and parts of buildings, and around a corner at any time
Stuart expected to see a rescuing party—in a rowboat or something.

"Hey, mister." He woke; he must have been dozing. The girl
had called him. "Hey. Whyn't you come down here? There's all
them snakes up there."

Stuart scrambled to his feet. When he stumbled downhill, embarrassed and frightened, the girl said chattily, "The sons of
bitches are crawling all over here. He chast some away." The boy
was on his feet and looking around with an important air. His
coming alive startled Stuart—indeed, the coming alive of the day,
of the world, evoked alarm in him. All things came back to what

they were. The girl's alert eyes, the firm set of her mouth, had not changed—the sunlight had not changed, or the land, really; only Stuart had been changed. He wondered at it . . . and the girl must have seen something in his face that he himself did not yet know about, for her eyes narrowed, her throat gulped a big swallow, her arms moved slowly up to show her raw elbows. "We'll get rid of them," Stuart said, breaking the silence. "Him and me. We'll do it."

The boy was delighted. "I got a stick," he said, waving a thin whiplike branch. "There's some over here."

"We'll get them," Stuart said. But when he started to walk, a rock slipped loose and he fell back into the mud. He laughed aloud. The girl, squatting a few feet away, watched him silently. Stuart got to his feet, still laughing. "You know much about it, kid?" he said, cupping his hand on the boy's head.

"About what?" said the boy.

"Killing snakes," said Stuart.

"I spose—I spose you just kill them."

The boy hurried alongside Stuart. "I need a stick," Stuart said; they got him one from the water, about the size of an ax. "Go by that bush," Stuart said, "there might be some there."

The boy attacked the bush in a frenzy. He nearly fell into it. His enthusiasm somehow pleased Stuart, but there were no snakes in the bush. "Go down that way," Stuart ordered. He glanced back at the girl: she watched them. Stuart and the boy went on with their sticks held in mid-air. "God put them here to keep us awake," the boy said brightly. "See we don't forget about Him." Mud sucked at their feet. "Last year we couldn't fire the woods on account of it so dry. This year can't either on account of the water. We got to get the snakes like this."

Stuart hurried as if he had somewhere to go. The boy, matching his steps, went faster and faster, waving his stick angrily in the air. The boy complained about snakes and, listening to him, fascinated by him, in that instant Stuart saw everything. He saw the conventional dawn that had mocked the night, had mocked his desire to help people in trouble; he saw beyond that his father's home emptied now even of ghosts. He realized that the God of these people had indeed arranged things, had breathed the order of chaos into forms, had animated them, had animated even Stuart himself forty years ago. The knowledge of this fact struck him about the same way as the nest of snakes had struck him—an image leaping right to the eye, pouncing upon the mind, joining itself with the perceiver. "Hey hey!" cried the boy, who had found a snake: the snake crawled noisily and not very quickly up the slope, a brown-speckled snake. The boy ran clumsily after it. Stuart was astonished at the boy's stupidity, at his inability to see, now, that the snake had vanished. Still he ran along the slope, waving his stick, shouting, "I'll get you! I'll get you!" This must have been the sign Stuart was waiting for. When the boy turned, Stuart was right behind him. "It got away up there," the boy said. "We got to get it." When Stuart lifted his stick the boy fell back a step but went on in mechanical excitement. "It's up there, gotten hid in the weeds. It ain't me," he said, "it ain't me that—" Stuart's blow struck the boy on the side of the head, and the rotted limb shattered into soft wet pieces. The boy stumbled down toward the water. He was coughing when Stuart took hold of him and began shaking him madly, and he did nothing but cough, violently and with all his concentration, even when Stuart bent to grab a rock and brought it down on his head. Stuart let him fall into the water. He could hear him breathing and he could see, about the boy's lips, tiny flecks or bubbles of blood appearing and disappearing with his breath.

When the boy's eyes opened, Stuart fell upon him. They struggled savagely in the water. Again the boy went limp; Stuart stood, panting, and waited. Nothing happened for a minute or so. But then he saw something—the boy's fingers moving up through the water, soaring to the surface! "Will you quit it!" Stuart screamed. He was about to throw himself upon the boy again when the thought of the boy's life, bubbling out between his lips, moving his fingers, filled him with such outraged disgust that he backed away. He threw the rock out into the water and ran back, stumbling to where the girl stood.

She had nothing to say: her jaw was hard, her mouth a narrow, line, her thick nose oddly white against her dirty face. Only her eyes moved, and these were black, lustrous, at once demanding and terrified. She held a board in one hand. Stuart did not have time to think, but, as he lunged toward her, he could already see himself grappling with her in the mud, forcing her down, tearing her ugly clothing from her body—"Lookit!" she cried, the way a person might speak to a horse, cautious and coaxing, and pointed behind him. Stuart turned to see a white boat moving toward them, a half mile or so away. Immediately his hands dropped, his mouth opened in awe. The girl still pointed, breathing carefully, and Stuart, his mind shattered by the broken sunshine upon the water, turned to the boat, raised his hands, cried out, "Save me! Save me!" He had waded out a short distance by the time the men arrived.

JOHN PERREAULT*

❦

Boomerang

Why is everything I do in my life like a boomerang?
I throw the paper airplane out the window
and the wind sends it back.
I spit against the wind.

You bought me a fur boomerang for my birthday.
I hate you now. You are so rich.
You are such a consumer.
And I hate your boomerang.
But I can't throw it away.
It keeps coming back and hitting me
in the back of the head.

In a rooming house I lived in once
I knew a boy who had a handmade boomerang.
It was fifteen inches long.
What a beautiful gigantic handmade boomerang!
Every Sunday he practiced throwing it away,
in Central Park, by that sailboat lake.

People always talked to him and followed him.
Everybody wanted to see his boomerang.

* JOHN PERREAULT, *born in New York City in 1938, is currently the art critic for* Village Voice *and associate editor of* Art News. *He has edited a mimeographed magazine entitled* Elephant *and exhibited his paintings in one-man shows. His articles on art and his poems appear in many magazines, and the latter he collected in* Camouflage (1966).

. . . But boomerangs are dangerous.
When you fool around with boomerangs
you have to know what you're doing.

Congratulations, incidently, on the birth
of your brand new baby boy boomerang.
How amazing
that no matter where you leave him
in the morning he is always
in that basket, on your doorstep.

I had a dream about a boomerang race.
I lost.

I kiss your amorous aluminum boomerang
and the edges are so sharp
my tongue gets sliced,
my words get sliced
and my lips are able to smile in two directions.

And I think it would be nice to own a boomerang store.
Glass boomerangs.
Australian aborigine boomerangs.
Rubber safety boomerangs.
Regulation boomerangs for boomerang contests.
And even
automatic talking doll boomerangs.

But why is everything I do in my life like a boomerang?
I throw away my life
and my life comes back.

❦

Heart

I saw a picture of my heart
but it wasn't at all heart-shaped
It wasn't my real heart.
My real heart is red and heart-shaped
like a valentine.

Heart, I don't need you anymore.
You have cheated on me
and when I wasn't looking
you started chasing after everyone
and you chased them all away.

(My heart keeps getting caught in my throat.
What is it doing there?)

In the Benjamin Franklin Museum, Philadelphia,
I walk around inside a gigantic heart
that is a cave, a wound, a womb.

. . . Today I got a valentine in the mail
with a cupid on it and a heart
with an arrow through it.
Whose heart? Whose arrow?

I show my new movie called St. Valentine's Day
on a heart-shaped screen
and my heart is full of gangsters.

(I walk around with my heart in my pocket.
I walk around with my heart between my legs.)

Heart, I haven't the heart to disown you.
But you keep trying to jump up into my head
and you keep making my mouth say funny things.

You make my mind do somersaults
until it as limp as the slub of my tongue
is as loose as the wind.

I wear my heart on the sleeve of my new disguise.
I am a heart-specialist in a big hospital.
I wear my heart on my wrist like a box of candy.

Heart, I wear you on the arm-band of my mourning
for that afternoon in the heartlands
that opened up my heart
to this incredible landscape concealed by my head.

ED SANDERS*

❧

Poem from Jail

VI.

Goof City,
Infinite cock
& granite snatch,
& whiteness
as almond
out of the husk,
& strange sounds
    There,

temple of
Aphrodite
Kallipugos,

O City
"whose Terraces
are the color
of stars,"

* ED SANDERS, *born in Kansas City, Missouri, in 1939, took his B.A. from New York University where he majored in Greek. Among his pamphlet collections of poems are* Peace Eye (*1965*), Toe Queen Poems (*1965*) *and* Poems from Jail (*1963*). *He has founded the Peace Eye Bookstore in New York's East Village, edited a magazine entitled* Fuck You, a Magazine of the Arts, *and become "Orgiastic Microphonist" for a rock group called The Fugs.*

your monuments
the reflection
of crystal,

O City,
thou art beautiful
as the rubies
in thy women's
navels,

thou art as
carefully painted
as thy dancers,

The blueness of
your water
is as a
tinted eyelid,

you are a
nipple
on a mountain,

your streets
are as cross-cords
over belly-flesh,

your gates
are as parted lips;

Goof City,
where every choice
is allowed,
   Goof City,
the city of the
Trembling Flank,

Smile & Crotch

without fester,

City without
the Great Cancer

& Cancer not
worshipped
on its Altars,

nor bloated motion,

Goof City,
laughter
laughter
and flaming Teeth.

DAVID SHAPIRO*

❧

For Son

1

I kept spinning in all kinds of grass. An unmarried woman
came and pointed out the stems to me. In my light fast
motor-cycle, she read each letter in order. My hands are
resting on an arched roof, horse allowed to roam at night.

2

She gave me a damp cheek, to explain why her copy didn't
fly through the night. The telephone operator heard a
coin, "This is very good." A bread accused me of the
hatefully long absence. In this, was I fit to be imitated?

3

A soft unbleached ape in the carburetor due to weak
mixtures, while being launched. You blunt-nosed dolphins—
Decorating hat, shoe, etc. Who supported the vessel
while being launched? The Bishop of Rome of gas and air.

4

The peony is a plant with showy flowers, no it is a race, a com-
munity

* DAVID SHAPIRO, *born in Newark, New Jersey, in 1947, is currently
an undergraduate at Columbia College. He has published poems in*
Art and Literature, Location, Minnesota Review, *and other magazines.
His first collection,* January (1965), *received the Gotham Book Mart
Avant Garde Poetry Award. Also an accomplished violinist, he has
performed as soloist in many concerts.*

stocked with irritable qualities of red, pink, and white.
So back to the rules of penance, that shed standing with its roof
against the higher wall "Enter a place, somewhat young."

5

She gives body to the words. She will come into the camp of
retired governors, she will insert herself between the mould and
the emotion. Bright green is her hair, and the shadows follow.
A husband carries on, I love you, the tide of the river said.

6

The course of life on earth tends to repay an injury in kind.
Silent man takes a repeated test, a second photograph.
"She made him quiet, she will again, stars finding amends in stag-
    nation."
Gravel is the ship's bottom, and the fireplace its frame of bars.

Six Poems

FOR J.V.H.

1

I went ahead up the rapist road
Wondering whether she would follow me.
The trees were thin and foreign
Like a crowd of undressed French boys.

She came into my hand
Or she talked of coming
Like dim rain falling through the trees.

2

Then came the eel with the two-nosed suit,
Grandma of the jazz joints with a dollar bill.
"That is transient currency" I reminded her
But she came, she leapt, she dove into our cafe.

Enchantment is not vulgarity:
Somewhere, at the moment, a man is grasping gloom
While giraffes smooch April branches in my mind.

3

Fold a dead hand over your brother.
Life goes on even before the dawn compositions.
At 7:30 the Chapel holds communions,
The wife snores, the sleepers trick, there's laughter.

Later you and I will be sincere like Banker's Trust—
Talking about the ghostly girls we faced—
We have given our hearts back to the dust.

4

At day's end I was resting in Wichita:
Ethos and eros have gone to bed in Wichita:
Stuart hugs a map of his own Wichita.

Wichita, town of heat and copper and anguish.
Where boys ride pintos to school or get born
When their mothers undress themselves in the barn
For teams of restless rangers.

5

You will not let Benjamin kiss Sarah
You will not let him drink his milk from a skull.
Finally humiliation and more emotional people—
When will the watchman come?

When will the blood come to clean us?
Benjamin's blood is not the right type, we're strangers
Living on the wheat farm's wiry threshold.

6

Oh blue night of Esther
That you are wrapped in last hotel vacations—
A little further away is cancer—
Oh my mother's mother, crawl away.

She disappears to the tombs.
We are closest to dead people.
There is not the slightest jealousy.

❦

Canticle

What has been lost waves
     Could too have been convolutions

In the brain myself possessing
     Where the cold emotions get theirs

Dropping the pearl on stage
     Nakedness hiding all that doubt

Starting with the jangle clock
     Finish with the tiny bee

In Louisiana they hold prayer meetings
     Still, in the darkest lavatory

The guilty party is the cave
>And the lessons have their "right"

Dry tongues
>Are an excrescence

The Alcatraz prison
>Swirls in the wind

Al Capone himself
>Tipped his cape

This is not solitary enough
>And they will sink

What initially had so much tension
>Indifferently picking her hair

What began in the axis energy readership
>Ends athlete, smiler, dauber

She will be married
>Amid gowns and lions

After all, voices rumble
>Even science, errata

There is no more penis
>The fetch-me give-me age

Born in Wichita
>Went on thinking unquestionably deep

And the Tulsa post cards
>This little woman hits me deep

I whirl and drink
>Hit this hammer

Take up the square block
        Assemble a man's head

Underneath the whitest plaster
        It looks silly, man's head

While it should be in love
        Like *Herodias,* a "clear" novel

Otherwise I dance to strip
        This is a funeral song

Camerado
        I will not escape his hate

We work in dream logic
        The French come closer "mystique"

Emphasis downward among the pups
        We have our crack-up historian

In the symphony orchestra
        He plays his silver flute

All that tremolo for the Duke
        Degradation in my voice

The brick-after-brick energy
        Hankering for some news

That's what he emphasized
        In the cliff-cave getting up

Toward the rainbow in the wall
        To signals, whims, maxims

My hair's being pulled off by God!
        Oh rough arms

MITCHELL SISKIND[*]

❦

On a Sculpture of Dr. Albert Einstein

A few questions are asked.

My reply: I'll begin work, of course. But you see we need first to know each other.

An introduction is arranged. Dressed in sweaters of different colors one Sunday we meet in a park.

I open the conversation.

Doctor, I say. How do you do?

So for a while we walk, following a path. Right, then left, up a small hill.

Well, at least there are no clouds in the sky . . .

No, he says. Shall vee valk across ze river?

The path goes along the summit of the hill and then drops down.

Later, I plan a statue forty feet in height. Of bronze.

(Though I'd been asked to work in stone. Bronze, I argue, is necessary. Don't think it will be easier for me. It means a trip to Italy.)

Each Sunday we meet in the park. And I begin sketching in a month.

One day we watch the sunset developing between two trees like a huge sore.

* MITCHELL SISKIND, *born in Chicago in 1945, attended high school in Winnetka, Illinois, and college at Columbia. He has written poems as well as fiction, some of which has appeared in* Art and Literature. *He lives in New York.*

Zehr is somting I vant to tell you. Two years ago, ze university vuz loaned a large statue. But it vuz demeged by shtudents leaving a basketball game.

I reply: Our statue will be invulnerable—owing to its position *above* the entrance to the Hall, you see.

A shtatue of zat enormous size?

Certainly. I envision a statue forty feet tall.

But when I see the plaster miniature, I am disgusted.

My face sweats!

Since we are in my house, I tell him, you cannot see this statue. What a discourtesy that would be.

(I had forced him to stand—motionless in the din of passing buses in a room intensly lighted.)

But though balanced in the unnatural position I have required, he does not seem ridiculous. Only the statue seems ridiculous.

And he is far from ridiculous when slowly he tells me: Read ze letters of Kepler. Zehr, vun is confronted vit a sensitive personality devoted to a qvest. Dis man reached ze exalted goal he set for himself in shpite of all internal and external difficulty.

(It is later—when I realize that the disquieting motion of his face as he speaks, or at least the sense to me conveyed by that motion, I find somehow akin to that rarely perceptible yet of course ever delibrate motion accomplished on the faces of certain old clocks—that I know after all I must work in stone.)

Suddenly temperatures drop.

But Sunday we are in the park, and I tell him: The sculpture will be of stone.

(Dressed in overcoats—his reaching to the ankles—walking is difficult. But we keep moving. Temperatures require it.)

But is it not true zet shtone vill present certain shtructural problems? Vutt of ze *positioning* of ze shtatue in ze location planned?

I should have told you, I reply, that in fact all original plans called for a work in stone. Only at the last moment did I opt for bronze.

At the rounded crest of a hill we agree upon the day I will begin a second miniature.

But when a "statue" is formed—little more really than a toy, being but twenty-eight inches in height—I raise my eyes slowly from my work.

He is alert.

Stone, I begin. What a medium! To work it. To touch it. Have you seen "The Bound Slaves"?

His voice is calm.

Now I vill reveal ze source of your travail. Vunce, somvhere, a shepard boy said to a horse: You, ze noblest beast zett treads ze ert, deserve to live in untroubled bliss. Indeed, your happiness would be complete vere it not for ze treacherous shtag. But from his yuss ze shtag practiced to excel you in schviftness of foot. His pace allows him to reach ze vawter before you do. You unt your foal are left to tirst. Shtay vit me! My visdom unt guideance vill deliver you from zis shtate! Blinded by envy unt hatred for ze shtag, ze horse agreed. He yielded to ze shepard boyce bridle. He lost his freedom and vuz ze shepard boyce shlave.

He has not moved.

My hammer . . .

I begin a final miniature, eight feet in height.

(But at night in my room I lie on the bed and as outside a bus passes that bed goes floating off. I sit up and touch the wall to stop it.)

Sunday, dressed in shorts, we climb steadily up the path. Large round rocks stick up through the ground; there's grass beside the road. Looking back we can see buildings. Towers and spires mark the horizon; they seem strangely shaped. Somehow, the decision to work in wood seems a redemption. Wood, I think, you are sanctified, I think.

We are in a grove of birches, and the sun comes through in patches. And birds are moving in the trees. We have made arrangements. A wooden miniature will be made. He is beside me walking gracefully.

RONALD TAVEL*

❦

Shower

*First performance, July 29, 1965, at the Coda Galleries,
New York City, with the following cast:*

TERENE	*Beverly Grant*
X-35	*John Vaccaro*
MISS TERMITE	*Elsene Sorrentino*
PETER	*Larry Drago*
DICK	*Patrick Michaels*
DUMMY	*Mark Duffy*

*Directed by John Vaccaro; music by Tony Conrad and
Granchan Moncur III*

*Scene: Two adjoining showers with their shower curtains drawn
and the water running in both. After several moments the shower
curtain at stage right slowly draws away, revealing X-35 standing
under the running water, fully clothed, but wearing a shower
cap. He rubs himself up and down, as if with soap. Then the
shower curtain at stage left draws aside, revealing* TERENE *under
the running water, fully clothed but wearing a shower cap. She
rubs herself luxuriously up and down.*

X-35 *shuts off his faucet.* TERENE *listens: she has heard his water
go off. She presses her ear to the stall side nearest his.* X-35 *presses*

* RONALD TAVEL, *born in Brooklyn in 1940, studied literature and
philosophy at Brooklyn College and the University of Wyoming, and
later traveled widely. He has written several plays, including* Gorilla
Queen *(1967), which ran off-Broadway, scenarios for over a dozen
Andy Warhol movies, an unpublished novel,* Street of Stairs, *and
many poems.*

310

his ear close to the same side, listening to hear what she is doing.

TERENE *turns off the water in her shower. Both stand wringing the water from their soaking clothes.*

Then x-35 *pokes his head out of his shower and stretches it around until he can see into* TERENE's *stall. She is startled by his head and says, as if apologizing:*

TERENE Oh—er—cleanliness is next to godliness.

x-35 (*standing upright in his stall, trembling from his glimpse at her beauty*) The shape of things to come!

TERENE Can you come with this shape?

x-35 If you will come into my shower (*lowering his voice*) . . . heh-heh . . . said the spider to the butterfly.

TERENE (*innocently*) Why do you ask me to come into your shower?

x-35 Because I am lonely.

TERENE If I came in your shower, wouldn't you still be lonely?

x-35 Yes, after you came, I would still be lonely. . . . It is certainly worse to be lonely with someone than it is to be lonely alone. So don't come in my shower.

TERENE I won't.

(*Long pause*)

x-35 I mean, can you think of any loneliness that is greater than the loneliness you feel when you are with someone?

TERENE Yes.

x-35 So can I!

(*Long pause*)

x-35 What are you doing in that shower?

TERENE Getting cold.

x-35 I mean, why are you in that shower?

TERENE (*cautiously*) I'm waiting for someone.

x-35 Who?

TERENE (*very sexy*) I don't know—but when he comes along I will!

(*Long pause*)

x-35 How will you know him when he comes along?

TERENE (*thinking hard*) Hey, you, this country once belonged to the Indians. Right?

x-35 (*cautiously*) Right. . . .

TERENE This whole country was full of Indians. They owned the country. Right? So where are all the Indians now? Why aren't they here?

x-35 (*cautiously*) Well, dey was old. . . .

TERENE Hmmmmmmm . . . very interesting. Listen: In the book *The Last of the Mohicans* there are two Mohicans: Chingatumadre and his son, Uncas. Uncas gets killed in the end but Chingatumadre lives. So who is the last of the Mohicans then?

x-35 (*thinking hard*) . . . The Last of the Mohicans. . . . *Les derniers des Mohicans:* both of them are!

TERENE Hmmmmmmmmmm . . . very interesting. Listen: Do Scotchmen wear underwear under their kilts?

x-35 That's easy: Of course, Scotchmen *don't* wear underwear under their kilts. If they did, no one would ever have dreamt up the question, "Do Scotchmen wear underwear under their kilts?"

TERENE Do you wear underwear under your kilts?

x-35 Only one way to find out.

TERENE What's that?

x-35 By putting your hand up.

TERENE (*angry*) Who do you think I am—your Roto-Rooter woman or something?! You foul-mouthed pig!

x-35 (*angry*) Say that again and I'll close my fly and starve your mother.

(*Long pause; both are furious at each other*)

TERENE Listen—you have only one more question to answer.

x-35 (*very interested*) And what is that?

TERENE Which came first, the chicken or the egg?

x-35 Come into my shower, Chicken, and we'll find out soon enough.

TERENE (*overjoyed*) Marvelous—you answered all the questions correctly! You must be the man! You must be Mark. . . .

x-35 Stark!

TERENE Mark Stark Naked! The man I was to meet!!!

(TERENE *and* x-35 *rush out of their showers and fall into each other's arms. They embrace and kiss madly.* PETER *enters from the left and* DICK *from the right.* PETER *and* DICK *snoop around, spy on the kissers and rush into their showers, examining everything there*)

TERENE Oh, darling, darling, do you have sex with your eyes open or closed?

x-35 It depends on how ugly my partner is.

TERENE Enough, enough of this madness! We may be watched!
(x-35 *breaks out of her arms and rushes downstage to deliver an aside with a foreign accent*)

x-35 Terene and Mark Stark Naked embrace madly, unaware that they are both being watched—by eyes filled with DESIRE!!!!!
(*When* PETER *and* DICK *hear this aside, they look up frightened and rush out.* x-35 *runs back to* TERENE *and resumes kissing her*)

TERENE Oh, Seymour! Seymour! Seymour!!!
(PETER *pokes his head out from behind the right shower stall*)

PETER No, thanks, lady, I seen enough!

x-35 Darling, my name isn't Seymour.

TERENE (*pulling away from* x-35, *becoming very continental*)
I know, Mark Stark. I was just testing you.

x-35 Are you still suspicious of me?

TERENE (*quickly, testing him*) —What's my name?

x-35 Terene. . . . Terene, the Terrible Tart of Terra Cotta!

TERENE (*cautiously*) . . . That is correct. . . . . . .

x-35 Terra Cotta—he's a no gotta—I'm a gotta!

TERENE (*overjoyed*) Correct! Correct! You're my man!
(TERENE *and* x-35 *fall into each other's arms once again and kiss madly.* PETER *and* DICK *rush in, play the Peeping-Toms, rubbing their hands, drooling from their mouths. As the lovers pull apart, the spies scramble off again*)

TERENE Enough of this insanity, Mark! We have important business to attend to.

x-35 I'd like to let you see my business.

TERENE People like us can't afford to fall in love. If we do, we're all washed up.

x-35 Let's wash up together, Terene—in my shower!

TERENE Well, we certainly have enough dialogue. Now all we need is a washcloth—and we'd have a movie.

(TERENE *and* x-35 *hold hands and walk into the left shower stall*)

PETER (*pokes his head out again, rubs his hands libidinously, and says juicily*) Out of the solitude of a tranquil monastery comes the secret of a truly satisfying kosher bread.

(PETER *disappears;* TERENE *and* x-35 *begin to undress in the left stall. In the meantime,* DUMMY, *a deaf mute, and* MISS TERMITE *enter and walk into the right shower stall.* MISS TERMITE *laughs lecherously, and they draw the curtain closed, but the curtain stays open in the left shower. From time to time,* MISS TERMITE's *delicious laughter can be heard.* x-35 *pinches* TERENE's *cheek*)

TERENE Why did you pinch my cheek so hard, Mark Stark?

x-35 So you'll still remember me three days from now.

TERENE You mean like an icky, don't you?

x-35 Rosey cheeks and lips within time's bending suckle's compass come.

TERENE Mark Stark, do you like Art Nouveau?

x-35 Art Nouveau? It's the call letters of the stars.

TERENE But, I mean, do you like it?

x-35 I'm open to all suggestions.

TERENE (*sexy*) How suggestive. . . .

(x-35 *removes his shirt and* TERENE *fingers his nipples and chest muscles*)

TERENE (*very, very sexy*) Mmmmmmmmmm, what wonderful definition you have—you ought to write a dictionary!

x-35 I'm open to all suggestions.

TERENE To a dildo, too?

x-35 All this talk is making me horney!

TERENE Don't get so upset, Mark Stark. It isn't like this is going to last forever. Because someday we'll all be dead.

(TERENE *and* x-35 *strip down to their underpants*)

PETER (*pokes his head practically into the shower, then turns around, looks up and down, and says in a looming, seaman's voice*) Have ye seen the White Whale?

(MISS TERMITE *is heard laughing;* PETER's *head disappears*)

TERENE If you were only a little older.

x-35 If you were only a little younger.

TERENE Wait a minute—just how old do you think I am?!

x-35 Oh, don't be sensitive. It isn't that we get older—it's that we pass into another phase—which is the same amount of radius length from the center as Youth was.

TERENE (*very sexy*) Hmmmmm . . . radius? What did you say the length was? Mmmmmmmm. . . .

(TERENE *turns, removes her high-heel shoe, and begins spilling the water out of it*)

x-35 (*regarding* TERENE's *backside with popping eyes*) Oh, God! Whats givels!

(*singing, as if shower-singing*)

Give me some givel

Oh, please be civil

Enough of this drivel

Before they shrivel

Give me some givel!

TERENE (*regarding his backside*) You've got quite a bass. Voice, I mean.

x-35 (*kneeling; singing*)

Ass of ages!

Cleft for me!

Let me hide myself in thee!

Oh today I'm yet uncome

As I climb into thy throne—

Then, ass of ages,

Cleft for me!

Let me hide myself in thee!

Amen!

(TERENE *and* x-35 *giggle happily and* x-35 *draws the shower curtain closed. The water runs in both showers. Much lecherous and suggestive laughter is heard coming from both showers.* PETER *enters and snoops around; he listens to the giggling with anger. Suddenly the water is turned off.* PETER *does an eeny-meany-miny-mo in front of the showers, makes a decision, and rushes over to the right shower, tears open the cur-*

tain reveals MISS TERMITE *and* DUMMY *in an embrace, fully clothed, dripping wet*)

PETER (*yanking* MISS TERMITE *from the stall*) Ah-ha! I caught you! What were you doing in that Japanese shower, you unwholesome harlot!

TERMITE My whole and then some yourself! Who do you think you're talking to?

PETER Listen to me Termite. . . .

TERMITE Miss Termite to you, Peter Pecker!

PETER Miss Termite, what were you doing in that shower?

TERMITE I thought I'd clean up a bit before going on the set.

PETER Didn't we agree upon a tryst?

TERMITE Sure, Peter Pecker.

PETER Well, never double-twist a tryst. You might find it very unhealthy!

TERMITE Keep your pecker dry, Peter. I take my orders from headquarters.

PETER (*pointing to his crotch*) This is your headquarters from now on!! Did you get the information?

TERMITE Sure, I did. I got it from hindquarters.

PETER Then tell me quick. Wait a minute—who's the stud?

TERMITE Oh, that's Dummy. Don't worry about him. It don't matter what he hears—he won't tell—he's deaf and dumb, see?

(MISS TERMITE *and* PETER *both laugh sadistically.* DUMMY *laughs too, without sound*)

PETER Excellent, Miss Termite, excellent. I always said you were one of our cleverest agents! (*putting his hand around her hip*) I could get you a lot ahead, with my backing your front.

TERMITE It's what's in back of what's up front, I always say.

PETER Do you, my little bug, do you? Okay, what's the information? Wait a minute: did you fill out the female forms?

TERMITE (*taking a short sexy stroll*) Just take a look!

PETER Mmmm . . . I see, I see. Okay. What's the info?

TERMITE (*to the audience*) Well, the part of Terene is played by
——————. And the part of Mark Stark Naked is played

by ——————. They were last seen together in *Kitchenette*, and are co-starring once again by popular demand!

PETER In whose kitchenette were they last seen together?

TERMITE In —————'s kitchenette.

PETER (*rubbing his hands*) Ah-ha! I thought so! Just as I thought. Excellent sleuthing, Miss Termite! (*hearing laughter from the right shower; annoyed*) What are the two of them doing in there so long?

TERMITE (*slowly, deliciously*) They're mixing sex and seriousness. (*Laughter and movements in the shower curtain*)

PETER (*becoming thoughtful; his chin is in his hand*) Tell me, Miss Termite, is this a sixteen-millimeter movie?

TERMITE Yeah, what of it?

PETER Then X-35 will be quite upset about that. He should be informed immediately!

TERMITE Why, Peter?

PETER Because X-35 is a spy for thirty-five-millimeter movies.

TERMITE But who is X-35?

PETER I don't know. Nobody knows. That's what we've got to find out. But one thing I'm sure of!

TERMITE Yeah? What?

PETER (*confidentially*) X-35 is somewhere very close. He may be spying on us this very moment!!

X-35 (*poking his head out of the shower*) Peter Pecker and Miss Termite conspire together, unaware that they are being spied upon by—X-35!!!

TERMITE Peter, what do thirty-five-millimeter movies need a spy for? What is X-35 spying for?

PETER For ideas, of course. Thirty-five-millimeter movies haven't had a new idea since *Bride of the Gorilla*.
(*The sound of a recorder playing an eery tune is heard*)

TERMITE (*shivering*) You hear that, Peter? It's that strange music again.

PETER (*frightened*) Yes . . . I hear It! I always hear it. Every time someone mentions the word "gorilla," that music starts. It's gorilla music! It's music for gorilla movies; they use that same hack recorder player—that sexy kid with the phallic

symbol recorder! As if gorillas weren't sex symbols enough
—they have to enhance it with a recorder. If mine's not made
to order, use my recorder. Well, I've had enough of it,
enough of it, I tell you! I quit gorilla flicks because of that
recorder music. *Tim Tyler's Luck* was the last gorilla flick
I made. Did you see it? I was the second gorilla from the left
in the cliff scene.

TERMITE No, I don't think I seen that pic. I'm too young. It was
before my time.

PETER Just how old are you, chicken?

TERMITE I'm only twenty-two.

PETER Oh, say it again—I'll cream in my pants!

TERMITE I'm only twenty-two.

PETER (*waxing romantic*) There's cream in me plenty, for sweet
two and twenty!

(*The recorder music grows louder*)

PETER It's coming closer—the recorder's coming closer! The eery
competition is advancing. Flee! Flee! The Romans are coming!

(DICK *enters from the right, playing the recorder, as* PETER
and MISS TERMITE *take to their heels and disappear.* DICK *plays
his strange tune, pokes about, peeks into the shower, and
winds his way offstage. The shower curtain is drawn away,
revealing* TERENE *and* X-35, *both exhausted*)

TERENE Mark Stark, darling, do you think your ass is really
photogenic?

X-35 How should I know? I never saw it.

TERENE Oh, yes, of course. How silly of me!

X-35 (*stepping out of the stall, drying himself*) Come out, Terene.

TERENE No, I'm scared!

X-35 What is there to be scared about? What are you hiding in
the shower for? It's only a movie!

TERENE But it's a pretty realistic movie—you've got to admit that
much.

X-35 Come on out. Nobody's going to hurt you. I'm here. (*flexing his muscles*) I'll protect you.

TERENE Is anybody looking?

x-35 No. Just the audience. And they're not really here. I mean, the audience isn't here now.

TERENE (*innocently*) When are they coming?

x-35 Well, that depends on the promotion. But don't you bother your little female head about technical problems. Come on out, I say.

TERENE (*stepping from the stall; abstractly*) Excuse me, Mark, I have to make a phone call. (*She walks in her high-heels to a telephone; she lifts the receiver, dials, and waits a moment; x-35 eavesdrops on her conversation*) Hello—Dick's Delicatessen? (*pause*) Do you deliver?—I mean food (*pause*) Yes, I'd like a tongue sandwich. No, no, don't slice it. I want a nice, long wet tongue. Yes, that's it. Thank you, Dick. (*She hangs up*)

x-35 Any luck?

TERENE Yes, Dick's bringing up a tongue.

x-35 That *is* luck.

TERENE Yes, it's Tim Tyler's Luck.

x-35 (*standing as if transfixed by her words, studying her face with great suspicion*) Would you repeat what you just said, Terene?

TERENE (*cautiously*) I said, "Yes, it's Tim Tyler's Luck."

x-35 That's what I thought you said. All right, Terene, you haven't been leveling with me!

TERENE You leveled me, didn't you? What else do you want?

x-35 You are—

TERENE Terene, the Terrible Tart of Terra Cotta.

x-35 So you have said. But can I believe you?

TERENE Why can't you believe me?

x-35 Because of certain things you've said. Because of certain slips you've made!

TERENE What slips? I haven't made any slips. How can I, Terene the Terrible Tart from Terra Cotta, make a slip? How can a master spy slip up slip shod before a mere amateur like Mark Stark Naked?

x-35 I may not be quite the amateur you so confidently esteem me!

TERENE I'm cold. I feel cold.

X-35 Stop avoiding the issue.

TERENE But, Mark, I feel cold!

X-35 If you come clean, I'll warm you up.

TERENE Come clean? You mean, you want me to go back into the shower?

X-35 Talk, Tart!

TERENE (*suddenly capitulating*) All right, all right, I'll make a clean breast of everything! (*about to pull a breast out from the towel covering her*)

X-35 No, stop—wait a minute. (*clamping his hand over her mouth*) I hear someone coming.

(DICK *enters with the sandwich. During the entire exchange between him and* X-35, X-35 *stands behind* TERENE *with his hand held over her mouth. Dick is not fazed by anything he sees or hears; he acts as if all were completely normal*)

DICK I have an unsliced long wet tongue sandwich for Miss Terene the Terror of Tarta Cotta.

X-35 (*high-pitched, feminine voice*) Oh, yes, thank you.

DICK Are you Miss Terene?

X-35 Yes, I am. Are you Dick's Delicatessen?

DICK No, I am just Dick. The unsliced long wet tongue is the delicatessen.

X-35 I see. Please put the sandwich down.

DICK Where shall I put the sandwich, Miss Terene?

X-35 Oh—er—put it in the shower, please.

DICK Won't it get wet there, Miss Terene?

X-35 No, it is already a long wet tongue.

DICK I see. Thank you.

(*He goes to the right shower and drops the sandwich inside next to* DUMMY, *who proceeds to nibble on it.* DICK *returns to where* TERENE *is still struggling to free herself from* X-35)

X-35 Er—thank you, Dick.

DICK Thank you, Miss Terene.

(*Long pause*)

X-35 I said, "Thank you, Dick."

DICK Thank you, Miss Terene.

x-35 Well, what are you standing around for?

DICK My tip, Miss Terene.

x-35 (*releasing* TERENE *and reverting to his normal voice in a fury*) Your Tip! Idiot! Can't you see I'm in my underwear? How can I give you a tip? Do you think I keep money in my underwear?

DICK I'm sure I don't know what you keep in your underwear, Miss Terene. Presumably, a very bulky Modess.

x-35 Will you get out of here before I bend you over and drive you back to that delicatessen!!

DICK Thank you, Miss Terene. (*starting to leave, transforming himself into an altogether different disguise as he speaks*) I find it most interesting and not a bit curious and not a very bit revealing that Mark Stark should be masquerading as Miss Terene. But I am not hoodwinked for a single instant.

(*He exits.* TERENE, *freed, is not ruffled in the least; she speaks as if she had been standing there calmly all the time*)

TERENE What a strange fellow. So ugly.

x-35 Yes, he was ugly.

TERENE I can't stand ugly people. Can you, Mark?

x-35 Not any more than you can, Terene. You want your sandwich now?

TERENE No, thank you. Your hand sufficed my hunger.

x-35 You couldn't have been very hungry.

TERENE I wasn't. The salt in your skin sufficed me. It was only a momentary hunger pang.

x-35 That's fortunate . . . (*scheming*) . . . You have *luck.* . . .

TERENE Yes, Tim Tyler's Luck.

x-35 (*grabbing her and shaking her violently*) Okay!!! You slipped again. I caught you in a second slip. I want the truth now, Terene. I want the terrible truth! I'm warning you: my patience is at its end!

TERENE All right, all right! I'll tell you the terrible truth! Just let me go, will you?

x-35 (*releasing her*) Let's hear it, Miss Tart.

TERENE (*recomposing herself*) Er—just what is it that you want to know?

x-35 You know!

TERENE Of course, I know. But you don't know. So what is it that you want to know?

x-35 I want to know what your mission is! I want to know why you are here. I want to know what you're doing in the shower!

TERENE Some men just have to know everything—don't they?

x-35 Quit stalling. You ain't so sexy.

TERENE You thought differently just a short while ago. (*sobbing*) Yes, you thought differently just a short while ago. All men thought differently but a short while ago. That was before— before this mission was necessary. All right, I'll tell you why I'm here. I'll tell you why Terene the Terrible Tart of Terra Cotta is here. She is looking for . . . she is in search of . . . she is trying to recover . . . a stolen good.

x-35 A stolen good?

TERENE Yes. . . .

x-35 *A* stolen good?

TERENE Yes, *a* stolen good. What is so strange? Aren't all goods, isn't everything that is good, stolen? Stolen away from their owner?

x-35 So far so good.

TERENE (*dreaming, distracted*) No . . . no . . . not good.

x-35 (*impatient*) Well, Terene, what good?

TERENE Yes, what good? What good is anything any more?

x-35 I mean what stolen good are you seeking to recover?

TERENE My cherry.

x-35 Your—

TERENE (*loud voice*) I said, "My cherry." . . . And, now, Mark Stark, if you will excuse me, I have to take a shower. I feel dirty . . . somehow. . . .

(*She drifts into the right shower. x-35 is dumfounded; he turs and walks into the left shower; they both soap up*)

x-35 (*shower-singing*)

Once broken, never mended!

How the ladies are offended!

At the first they are befriended

At the second rarely tended
At the third they are commended
After that most condescended!
Then suddenly they are distended,
And once broken, never mended!

So spread, spread, spread!

When their bottoms are extended
And our parts are interblended
To our friends they're recommended
And we from them are transcended
And they're left unattended,
Once broken never mended!
So spread, spread, spread!

O how splendid, splendid, splendid!
Once broken, never mended!
So spread, spread, spread!
And the ladies wish that they were dead!

(*Both draw their shower curtains and turn on their faucets.*
DUMMY *wanders about briefly, carrying towels as if he were
a bath attendant*)

TERENE (*turns off her water and opens her curtain. She is shivering. She reaches for the towel* DUMMY *is holding*)
I'm cold. I'm freezing. Nothing seems to keep me warm.
(*she steps from the stall and paces back and forth*) Is there
no way to be clean and warm at the same time?

X-35 (*turns off his water, opens his curtain, and steps out. He takes
a towel from* DUMMY *and begins drying himself*)
How do you feel now, Terene?

TERENE Cold.

X-35 Frigid?

(*Long pause*)

TERENE I think I'm catching a cold.

X-35 It's from the showers you're taking.

TERENE No, it's not from the showers. (*staring at him*) God needs men . . . massing toward the maneuver of His composition . . . How am I less by need?

(*slowly*) How am I more as part than your wholeness, Mark? Give me your grasp.

x-35 Are you saying something?

TERENE Aren't I saying something?

x-35 I don't know. I'm not a woman.

TERENE You and I are friends, Mark.

x-35 We're not as delicious as other couples.

TERENE But we're both good-looking.

x-35 We're both good-looking, but we're not so delicious.

TERENE Give me your grasp! (*taking desperate hold of the arm he extends to her*) Those boys. Those gentle boys. . . . There was something so gentle about those boys. . . .

x-35 (*as if eavesdropping*) Which boys?

TERENE The boys in our spy ring. The boys with the rings on their fingers. The gentle boys with gentle rings in our gentle spy ring. They were gently men. They were what I call real gentlemen. (*suddenly, directly*) That's what a gentle man is.

x-35 What?

TERENE (*not hearing him*) An image of hatred! Hatred is the momentum behind my mission. Images of hatred I shall be seeking always, every midnight to know to express them. . . . And come up pale in a morning of Mondays emptied into— a yawn. . . .

x-35 What are you walking around naked for if you're so cold?

TERENE You know what I feel like, Mark Stark?

x-35 Like a Sabine woman?

TERENE Exactly. You read my thought.

x-35 Sure. That's why you got raped. The Sabine women ran around nude—remember? You've seen the Rubens' painting. And all that sculpture. Remember? Who told them to run around naked?

TERENE I don't know who told them.

x-35 Who told you to run around naked?

TERENE Nobody. I told myself.

x-35 Well—why?

TERENE Because before I felt that I was bound, that I was postured in as many ways as my lifted nightslip was . . . (*musing, wandering away from* x-35) And then . . . and then. . . .

x-35 And then, what?

TERENE And then I felt that things might really be facilitated so. I felt that when I'm nude and armored only in my hair—I might with more precision know the one who knew me first . . . and rise in the morning out of bed quite free, to walk the foyer—or descend the stair.

x-35 And the guy who got your cherry?

TERENE (*suddenly furious*) For him hatred! Hatred! Images of hatred! Ultimatums! What do I really want to say about loneliness? That I won't have it! That I won't have it!!

(PETER *and* MISS TERMITE *suddenly appear*. PETER *is holding an espionage gun*, MISS TERMITE *a small purse*)

PETER So you don't have it!

x-35 She won't have it. She wouldn't have it.

PETER Stop pretending! Just how stupid do you both think I am? She has it, and I know it!

TERENE The impeccable Peter Pecker!

PETER At your service, Terene! Hands up, both of you!

TERENE So—you speak English!

PETER Of course—and Coptic, Syrian, Sanskrit, and Greek and Latin, too. You see, my dear Miss Terene, I was born abroad, but I was educated in your country—at Northwestern University!

TERENE (*innocently*) You were born a broad?

PETER Yes, but I visited Denmark and thereafter took the then more appropriate name of Peter. Peter Pecker, if you please.

TERENE With two "Ps"?

PETER It pees. And with two "Ps" for alliteration, with two "Ls"? And now, hands up, both of you!

TERMITE (*opening her purse, removing a miniature gun and cocking it*) I just cocked this. He said hands up!

x-35 Who's your ladyfriend?

PETER I am never friendly with ladies. Ladies are a waste of time. This spy's name is Miss Termite.

x-35 Miss Termite?

PETER Yes. She is called Miss Termite because she works from the bottom up.

x-35 I'd like to let her try my bass.

TERENE Voice, he means.

PETER And what is your name, O bass one?

x-35 My name is Tony. Tony—you like that, huh?—it excites you!

PETER Say it again—I'm coming in my pants.

x-35 Tony! Tony!

PETER Shut up! Enough of this! Your name is not Tony. We will settle this matter of the names. Miss Termite, do you have the information?

TERMITE Yeah. The part of Peter is played by —————— and the part of Miss Termite is played by —————— and I played damn well, I might add.

PETER How embarrassing!

TERMITE (*sexy*) Just chalking up credits in heaven, honey.

PETER But the technical information?

TERMITE You wanna get technical?

TERENE Hurry up, will you!

TERMITE The technical assistants are Mr. —————— and Mr. ——————.

PETER All right, where do you two hide out?

x-35 We have orders not to disclose that.

PETER (*regarding the two of them practically naked*) Why not? You've disclosed nearly everything else.

x-35 Our lips are sealed.

PETER But that's about all of you that must be. Look, you two are in no position to hold out.

TERMITE (*sexy*) They're in a better position to put out.

TERENE (*suddenly hysterical*) All right, all right, we'll talk! We hide out on the West Side. In the twenties.

PETER How unfashionable! You two ain't even worth the bullets we are about to waste on you! Where in the twenties?

TERENE The early twenties.

TERMITE (*sexy*) Hmmmm. The early twenties. Just like me.

TERENE There is nothing just like you.

PETER All right, you two, for the last time—hands up!

DICK (*enters from the left with a gun in his hand*) All wrong, you two, for the first time—all four hands up. I mean, all eight hands up!

(*The four immediately obey; they turn and face* DICK)

PETER Who are you?

DICK I'm Dick, the private dick.

TERMITE Why private? Nobody else around here is particular.

TERENE I thought you were Dick's Delicatessen!

DICK (*pointing to his crotch*) Dick's delicatessen is here, lady. You're all under arrest.

TERMITE What for?

DICK We're picking up all undesirables.

TERMITE (*sexy*) On the contrary—I think I'm quite desirable. But you can pick me up for that!

TERENE What do you want, you fugitive from a frankfurter factory!

DICK You know what I want.

TERENE You know what you want.

DICK I want to know, Who is X-35?

TERENE (*terrified*) No—no! Not X-35!!

DICK Yes! X-35!

PETER No! not X-35!

DICK Yes! X-35!

X-35 No!—You can't—you can't mean X-35!

DICK Yes! Yes! I can—I *do* mean X-35!

TERMITE I guess it's my turn: Oh, not X-35, anybody but X-35!

DICK No—no, not anybody—just X-35!

(TERENE *turns and tries to escape in the confusion*)

DICK Hey, chicken, where do you think you're going?

TERENE Shopping!—I have to get some toilet paper—I've been using the *Village Voice.*

DICK Stop right where you are or I'll bring you down with a single bullet.

TERMITE (*going over to* TERENE *to comfort her*) There, there, honey. Get hold of yourself. Show these bullies who really wears the pants. Oh, excuse me, I see you *are* showing them.

PETER See here, Private Dick, nobody knows the identity of X-35. You're wasting your time.

X-35 See here, privates, X-35 isn't anywhere in the vicinity.

DICK Everybody shut up! I know for a fact that X-35 is someone in this very shower room.

TERMITE It could be you, Private Dick. That would be the usual switch.

DICK Yes, it would. Only, I'm sorry to disappoint you because *I* ain't X-35. Okay, we'll start with you, Termite: tell me what you know.

TERMITE Well, I know for a fact that the part of Dick is played by ——————.

DICK Thank you kindly.

TERMITE You are very welcome, I am sure.

DICK And, now, you, Terene: *Qui est* X-35?

TERENE Pardon?

DICK *J'ai dit, "Qui est* X-35?"

TERENE I'm sorry, I only speak English.

DICK Only English? How long have you been in this country?

TERENE Twenty-two years.

DICK Twenty-two years and you only speak English? Why, I'm just a cop on the beat and I speak English, French, German, Sanskrit, and Coptic!

TERENE Really? You ought to get a promotion.

DICK Okay, Mark Anthony Stark Naked: What do you know?

X-35 I only know that this scenario was written by Ronald Tavel and that the director is ——————.

DICK And you, Peter Pecker: What have you to say?

(PETER *panics suddenly, turns about and tries to escape. Everybody screams; much confusion;* DICK *waves his gun wildly.* X-35 *and* MISS TERMITE *catch* PETER *and bring him back, each holding one of his hands so that he can not move.* DICK *takes aim very carefully and fires his gun off directly in* PETER'S *face.* TERENE, X-35, *and* MISS TERMITE *cry out in horror.* PETER *drops lifeless to the floor*)

DICK (*turning to* DUMMY) Hey, Dummy, get rid of this stiff pecker, will you? (DUMMY *lifts* PETER, *but is uncertain of what to do*) Oh, just drop him in that shower over there, will you?

(DUMMY *carries* PETER *to the right stall and dumps him in; he draws the curtain and sits to the side*)

TERMITE Well, that was curtains for one more stud!

DICK Yes, and that just about rounds up this case.

TERENE How do you mean?

DICK Well, Peter Pecker was obviously the secret spy, X-35. If he wasn't, why would he have tried to escape?

X-35 Hmmmmmmmm. I never thought of that.

DICK Naturally. But the police get paid to think of just such things.

TERMITE Why, Officer, you're a genius!

DICK Thank you, madame.

TERMITE In fact, I'm getting to like you better all the time.

DICK Do you think we two could get together—I mean, now that we're not enemies any more?

TERMITE I'm sure we two could get together. I always wanted to be somebody's old lady. And I might as well be a dick's as a dyke's.

DICK (*holding* TERMITE'*s hand*) Bye, everybody, see youse at the wedding.

X-35 Congratulations, Dick.

TERENE Congratulations, Dyke.

(*All four shake hands, pat backs, and kiss, and* DICK *and* MISS TERMITE *exit, happy in each other's company*)

X-35 Oh, Terene, would you excuse me?

TERENE What for?

X-35 Oh, I have to take a piss.

TERENE Use the sink. It's closer than the throne.

X-35 Thanks. I'll be back in a moment.

(*He exits*)

TERENE (*wandering back and forth*) So that was X-35! Peter Pecker was X-35! The man who was my enemy for so many years. The brute who took me in my bloom, in my flower-hood, when I was helpless. The barbarian who stole that which can never be replaced. If he kneels now on the hot sulphurs of Hell for thrice three millenniums, he can never

repay the theft, could never restitch the ripped membrane.
(*sitting near the stalls*)
What I believed was secret, volition, or hate that consciously
directed hurt and dearth, was only how the handsome wind
can whirl around the goat-clung ledges of a precipice, or
how the sun can with a constancy that tires ponderance, keep
course across the violet ceilings of the sky . . . or some such
habiled principality. . . .
(TERENE *meanders like the mad* Ophelia)

PETER (*come inexplicably back to life, pokes his head into view,
rubs his hands juicily, and proclaims with great evil*) Sweet
little Mary Lou Lambkins—she carelessly culled daffodillies
while *he* sharpened the axe!!!
(*He disappears.* x-35 *is heard from offstage*)

x-35 Enter again, distraught, with your hair down.
I think I'd like to see that scene replayed.
God knows, but the Director certainly
Seems satisfied the way the reel was made,
Would hate to draw an extension on our stay
And keep us stuck in town another week.
And yet I think we ought at least to take
Advantage of our filming of the play.
It's not as if I didn't want to break,
Race off to rendezvous with all the rest,
The brand-new script, the salary we'd make
And all—it's simply that I'm not at peace
With every scene we've shot: they're not our best.
Particularly the one where you come in,
Distraught, your hair all down, tangled, and wild:
I think it isn't all it might have been
And shouldn't like to quit until I see
What else it could contain. It's just too mild,
Too limited; I'm sure you're meant to mean much more . . .
That, somehow, you've become all Elsinore.
And that's just what I can not figure out.
Because if that's the case, why should I talk
Anent my readiness and wrack in doubt,
Wondering whether I shall thrust or balk.

The Quality is waiting in the hall.
The script makes very plain, if you'll recall,
It's dirty work that caused the sparrow's fall.
(*x-35 enters, relieved*)

TERENE (*regarding him curiously*) Mark, did you read that narration?

x-35 What?

TERENE I thought I heard someone narrating this film. Oh, never mind.

x-35 I don't mind, if you don't mind.

TERENE That's it—the same voice! You have the same voice as the narrator.

x-35 I suppose I do.

TERENE What are you narrating this film for? Do you think it really needs narration?

x-35 No.

TERENE Then will you stop it right now?!

x-35 I hear and obey!

DUMMY Help me to rise: I wish to make a statement.

TERENE Did you say something, Mark Stark?

DUMMY Help me to rise: I wish to make a statement.

x-35 Did you say something, Terene?

TERENE Yes, I said, "Did you say something, Mark Stark?"

x-35 No, I mean (*turning around*) Look, it must have been Dummy!
(TERENE *and* x-35 *rush back to where* DUMMY *is sitting by the stall. They kneel next to him and bend their ears*)

DUMMY In my youth I was a notable scholar and a reputed penman. . . . But nowadays my mind wanders from the subject (*long, painful pause*) Help me to rise: I wish to make a statement.
(TERENE *and* x-35 *lift* DUMMY *to his wobbly feet. He collapses and they lift him up again. He coughs violently; his entire frame shakes. He clears his throat and finally speaks*)

DUMMY I just thought I'd tell you two I am not deaf and dumb as you have so confidently esteemed me. And, oh, by the way, this man is secret spy X-35.

TERENE (*screaming*) What!!! You—you are X-35!

x-35 No! No, I am not X-35! I—

DUMMY He's obviously. Examine yourself, my child.

x-35 No, no—don't.

(TERENE *pulls out the waistband on* x-35*'s underpants and stares in;* x-35 *is helpless;* DUMMY *takes a peek, too*)

TERENE (*hysterical*) Yes, yes! You *are* X-35! I can tell by your circumcision!

x-35 (*furious*) Oh, you stink every twenty-eight days!

(TERENE *begins to cry in earnest.* x-35 *stands perplexed*)

DUMMY Well, I guess my work here is finished. I'll leave you two lovebirds to yourselves

(*He waves good-by and hobbles off*)

x-35 So what if I am X-35? What difference does that make? What's in a name? A rose by any other would smell the same every twenty-eight days. Don't you know that I love you.

TERENE Oh, get away from me! Get away from me!

x-35 Is it because I'm a spy for thirty-five millimeter movies?

TERENE Oh, who cares about movies! Who cares what movies you spy for! You know less about movies than Bosley Crowther does.

x-35 Then what is it, then? What, then, is so horrible about me?

TERENE (*drying her tears*) Look at me, X-35, look very closely at me. . . .

x-35 Er—I—what f—

TERENE X-35, do you not recognize who I am?

x-35 You are Terene the Terrible Tart of Terra Cotta. Everybody knows th—

TERENE No, O short-memoried one, I am not Terene the T.T. of T.C. I am . . .

x-35 (*slowly recognizing her*) You are . . . you are . . .

TERENE I am Lulu LaGoulu, the Lady from La LaLuna!!!

x-35 The innocent, helpless virgin whom I seduced oh so many years ago!

TERENE Yes, the very same she!!!

x-35 Well, I certainly am glad I found you. I've been meaning to return your cherry to you for the longest time!

(TERENE *screams and falls in a faint to the floor*)

x-35 (*staring blankly down at her*) Some tarts take their cherries
so seriously.
(*He shakes his head sorrowfully, turns and enters the left
stall; he draws the curtain*)

TERENE (*Waking up and drying her tears*) How many names he
had. Mark . . . Mark Stark . . . Mark Stark Naked . . .
Tony . . . Mark Antony . . . Mark Antony Stark Naked
. . . X-35 . . . Isn't it funny? But I love him. Lady spies
always love the guy who copped their cherry. . . . Oh,
Mark, I have a closeness to you that no one new now can
have. That no one hereafter can have when your true identity
becomes general knowledge. I will be able to surprise those
people then. I can even shock those close to you now. . . .
Oh, and Mark, dear, don't show any new girl your circum-
cision. . . . (*she stands and walks back into the right stall.
repeating the name "Mark" several times over; then she
breaks into song*)
No ship shall ever sail
Anywhere at all,
But I'll hear your call.
No swift departure fail—
No ship shall ever sail.

No gull recalled from sea,
From any far port,
But it will escort
Your sad call back to me;
Your proud sad call for me.

Yet I, Love, though listening to those birds
With clean, impatient acclaims,
Hear your same thoughts, hear unchanged your words:
I know your homes and your names.

No cargo in the bay,
Anchored to the dock,
But in its bound rock
Seems somehow to betray

Your call from far away.

Ah, yes, your call is clear,
Every note I hear,
Nothing sounds more dear—
Yet not a thought has changed,
No word been disarranged
By something I once cried
Before my leaving lied
To me about your claims—
I know your homes, your fames,
I remember all your names.

(*She draws the curtain of her shower, tosses her towel to the audience*)

DUMMY (*hobbling back, announces*) My, my, how my mind does wander these days from the subject. I forgot to say that the part of Dummy was played most marvelously by ——————.
(*Sounds of singing and the shower-water running*)

CURTAIN

ALDEN VAN BUSKIRK[*]

❧

Last Will And

If I die in sleep it will be in a convulsion whose "terror"
and "beauty" proved irresistible at last. I rise, the
quivering bud afraid to blossom.
It comes out of dreams where music,
color and objects interchange
but for their continual flame. It is within this flame-
flower I am drawn up sweating half awake and
horizontal. Spine arches in short
spasms. I see nothing above.
Darkness everywhere or are my eyes gone out.
Before now: I gave in to life and awoke
Trembling—a coward.
But every time more rigid,
every time more pull, I
hurt with desire to
explode and vow no more retreats.
God wants to fuck me too,
and death will be my final lover.
I give her all.

     9/7/61
     Dave this is true
     Recall N.Y.C. Xmas last, one night alone.

* ALDEN VAN BUSKIRK, *born in 1938 in Rutland, Vermont, took his bachelor's degree at Dartmouth, and later did graduate work at Washington University in St. Louis. He died in 1961 of a rare blood disease; his friend David Rattray collected his poems, most of which were written in the last year of his life, in* Lami *(1963).*

TOM VEITCH*

❦

The Luis Armed Story

I am sitting in the park watching a spider weave his tiny web back and forth across my fingers. Got to stop that tank from making this Easy's Last Stand. Listen to my last words anywhere. Luis Armed was born in 1917 a sickly little kid with a rheumatic heart and many other complications that made him ill for the most part of his life which ended in July 1926, when he was 9, and the nuns of St. Louis de France Parochial School were at his bedside to take down his dying words because they'd heard his astonishing revelations of heaven delivered in catechism class on no more encouragement than that it was his turn to speak—Shutup.

In the dimness of the café, the manager is arranging the tables and chairs, the ashtrays, the siphons of soda water; it is six in the morning. I awoke early, shaved, dressed, draped myself with cameras and equipment, and went on deck to record our entry into the port of Gothenburg. In the beginning was the Word, and the Word was with God; and the Word was God. The Agon, then. In her tight fitting Persian dress, with turban to match, she looked ravishing.

This is the story of a man, one who was never at a loss. I can feel the heatv . . . heatv closing in, feel them out there making their moves, setting up their devil doll stool pigeons, crooning over my spoon and dropper I throw away at Washington Square Station, vault a turnstile and two flights down the iron stairs,

* TOM VEITCH, *born in Tulsa, Oklahoma, in 1941, worked as an auto mechanic and drove transcontinental cargo transport before studying for two years at Columbia College. His stories and poems have appeared in* Art and Literature, C, Lines, Fuck You, Kulchur, Cabbage, Theology Digest, *and other magazines.*

catch an uptown A train. . . . For the reader familiar with analytical psychology there is no need of any introductory remarks to the subject of the following study. An eight-year decline of syphilis ended in 1955. "For a pansy." The purpose of this book is to provide a concise yet comprehensive guide to the history and understanding of philosophy for the general reader.

As a lifelong student of sexual criminality, I have yet to encounter a treatise upon the subject so expertly written as this one by two laymen. Raymond C. needs your help. In a stone tower in witch-haunted Salem lives a man known to his world as—Doctor Fate! (To our world he is simply Luis Armed.)

I am blind but I must never reveal it. Don't ask why, all I can tell you is that it is important. It is a masquerade, but a masquerade which serves a purpose. Part of that purpose is to supply me with heroin, which I need badly to maintain a balanced metabloism . . . bloism. . . .

Recently I took a trip around the world in search of new supply lines to the sacred drug. . . . I made this trip with the aid of a special cane constructed for me by a friedn . . . edn . . . of mine who works for the National Radar Manufacturing Combine and Equi-Trust Foundation. . . . Without this cane I would never have made a step beyond my doorstep on East Ninth street in New York City. . . . A familiar address? Perhaps it rings a bell? Maybe if I gave you the house number? 630 E. 9th Street? Does that help?

Yes, my name is Luis Armed, and I work for Consolidated Edison as a roving research man. . . . My travels take me everywhere. . . . And with the sight-seeing, the women, the exotique foods and wines . . . goes the marf . . . marf . . . marvelous spledors of . . . spledors . . . of *the drug*—heroin by name. You see, I, Luis Armed, am an addict. A junkie. I take into my system as much as forty centigrams of heroin a day, and that is not grass. That is H. The Big H. I did not lick The Big H. The Nig H licked me. Si.

. . . I will tell you something of my experiences in Saudi Arabia, where the dates and figs grow in abundance, where the women where the va . . . vails . . . where a man can become filthy rich overnight in the oil business . . . or die trying . . .

(many the busted opportunist whose committed suicide by tying himself to the cap of his last oil well about to burst . . . an ugly death . . .). . . .

So I'm working the oil well routine out of St. Louis with four old bags and a dead dog on a leash. . . . This guy named "Rio" along with us, handling the wheel, had a big gat under his shirt. . . .

So I say to my borther . . . borhter . . . Robert whose flaked out in the back seat. . . . "Listen Robert, what you say we ditch this outif . . . outif . . . outfit . . . when we hit New York? I know a guy whose got a stash on eighty-first street. . . . He'll set us up for awhile . . . what you say?"

So I leave Rosa at the candy store and walk on down town to the plant where I used to work. I see the boss there he says "Hi, Luis," I say "Hi, boss," then I go over to the soda machine and plop in a dime. The coke comes clonking down the spout, bottle and all. I pick the bottle of coke out of the rubber bin its in. . . . The boss is talking to someone: "So I closed that deal yah see, now we got plenty of moola to operate on, everything is jake. We'll fly straight from here on in. . . . Without eyes looking over our shoulders. . . ."

I catch the picture. He's pulled a fasty this guy, told a little lie or shaded the truth a bit to get what he was after. Smart fellah my old boss. . . .

So I'm walking out of the place, it's starting to thunder and lightning, quite a wind blowing up. Rain starts coming down, wetting everything, making the music I love against the pavement. . . . The rain is bringing back memories to me of Mexico and Yucatan where I was born. . . . I am thinking of life when I was a child it was so carefree and happy. . . . And now a tragedy like this. . . .

So these two guys are standing there talking, one of them is a salesman for the plant. "Listen," he says, "I had to lie to that guy a little to get his order. Told him we could get the thing out in three weeks. Actually it may take us months. . . . Now I find out we didn't really need the order that bad, the boss has already got us on our feet. . . . Oh well, the business wont hurt us any. . . ."

So they are standing on the platform under a roof, and I walk past, looking for some nice place to get out of the rain, maybe the church where I can kneel down and say a pray to the Virgen and ask her to help my sister Rosa who is in much trouble. . . . So this priest comes up beside me, "Goodafternoon my son," he sya . . . sya . . . says. "Hello father," I say, "nice weather we are having isn't it?" "Yes," he says, "I like the storms myself, they remind me of God and how large is his power. . . ." Yes, that is true I think, and the rain begins to come harder. . . .

I'm sitting in the café, which one I don't know, I think it was the one across from the café. A kid comes by hawking the evening paper—I flip him a dime, take one of his rags. The paper falls open as I let it slip by accident from my grasp. . . . I bend over to pick it up. These words hit me like a torch between the eyes:

ARMED BROTHERS ARRESTED IN CAPITAL—

Good Lord, what are those bastards been up to? I read on—

"Police arrested today the two Armed brothers—one carrying a shotgun, the other a carbine—about an hour before President Johnson droned to the Capitol for his swearing-in—

"The two youths calmly stated they planned to assassinate the President at the exact moment of his assassination. 'What has he done for our native land of Puerto Rico,' they shouted at hysterical police. 'What has he done for starving Puerto Ricans everywhere?' "

I read on:

ARMED BROTHERS SEIZED IN CAPITAL—

"Police said today that the notorious Armed brothers were seized today in Washington D.C. by fits of sneezing and laughing. Under questioning and the probing finger of the law the only words the two insane Mexicans would emit were 'Real Life Real Death . . . Real Life Real Death.' Police were at a loss to explain. . . . The brothers were released into their own custody. . . ."

I read on:

"Señores! Come to Mexico! The land of Enchantment! Tu es muy loco if you pass up your big chance to drive down south this

summer and see the bullfight and the cockfight and the pretty
senioritas of Old Mexico. . . . Why not come on down today?
Do you know what you is missing? Do you know all the mira-
juana and other goodies you can find in the street down here? Do
you know about the beautiful Mexican putas, las putas muy
hermosas, y las chingalitas to be had on any streetcorner? Little
one, 12 years old, so sweet. . . . Come on down and stick it into
one of our little ones. . . . They love it. . . ."

We are approaching where the church is and I ask the father if
there is anything he can do for my poor sister Rosa, who has
caught the sickness from being with many bad men. . . . For her
poor mother she has done this, and to feed the tiny ones that seem
to keep popping from our mother's womb. . . .

"Yes, I'll speak to God," said the father. "And I'll talk to my
friend the doctor. Certainly we must do something for your sister. She is such a nice girl. . . ."

I think of the story we used to tell. The story we sang of Rosa,
our sister:

> When she cries it is with one eye only. . . .
> Rosa Armed was her own name not mine. . . .
> With love she was generous
> Having lain with every manner of man and beast. . . .

It was funny to us to sing this song (in Espanish we sang it). But
now I see it is not so funny. . . . I am sorry my poor Rosa, I am
sorry for our cruel funny childish ways. . . .

The priest and eye come to the church. The doors are open,
and we run up the stairs to get in out of the rain. There are others
with us, others who have fallen in beside us along the way. . . .

As we enter the church there are many people who are there
praying. All seem to be standing, facing the altar. And where are
the pews? I am thinking as we enter, what if God were to strike
this church now with his lightning?

And lo there is an electric crackle of sound and a brilliant
explosion of light from the center of the church. I can see that a
figure has appeared among the people, the figure of the Virgen—I
can see her feet and her blue gown which falls loose about her
feet—someone is standing so I cannot see the face. . . . I think:

something is about to happen—a thought in my head: someone here is to be exalted now. . . . And lo I find it is myself rising in the air, above the heads, into the dome of the church, and my mind is laughing. . . .

The first shots of what planned to be a long war. A headline in the *World-Telegram and Sun* of January 19. Will conduct a Review of the Press. These editorials have been published by clean hands. More than any other city newspaper. The Armed brothers myth. What does "rehabilitation" mean? Hail to the Chief—

Washington Jan 20—Police today picked up the two Armed brothers—one carrying a shotgun, the other a carbine—walking across Pennsylvania Ave. about an hour before President Johnson droned to the Capitol for his swearing-in ceremony.

The two youths said they came from Alexandria, Va., home by bus and were walking to another bus station en route to Centerville Va., for a little hunting trip.

Police said the brothers held valid hunting licences. They were identified as Luis R. Armed, 17, and William "Robert" Armed, 24. They carried guns. They were held for questioning. They will be released tomorrow.

Police said they carried a double-barrelled, 12-gauge shotgun, a 22-caliber carbine and ammunition. Police were at a loss to explain the weight of dog-dust on their foreheads or the strange lightness of their words. Police were puzzled by the continued resistance of the two youths to any form of coercion. Police were satisfied that the two boys did not intend to assi . . . assi . . . assassinate the President, Mr. LBJ.

When asked to comment upon the situation, Mr. Johnson is supposed to have said: "Real life real death, am I to ask for anything more than that?"

Police were not overly satisfied with this comment of Senior Johnsons. There was some thought of running the old boy through a third or fourth degree. However, that plan was soon squelched when Mrs. Johnson indicated that Mr. Johnson already was a very busy man. He had time for other things.

Police Chief James E. Clark commented: "Well if Johnson doesn't care about what's going on in Washington, then I don't see why we should worry about it either." The Armed boys refused to comment on this. Luis was seen to spit and gnash his teeth.

"Luis," the others say, "it is young Luis. . . ."

But I am laughing and can feel the eyes of the Virgen upon me although I can still not see them—

And then I am waking on my bed, I know it has been a holy dream, and my whole body is alive with some new chemical, some holy electricity burning and laughing in every part of me. . . .

For hours I lay thinking, wondering what I can give her who has given me this dream. . . .

I am in the subway waiting for the doors to close. There is a girl sitting across from me who is very beautiful. I look at her face and at her eyes, thinking: this girl is very beautiful I would love her if I could. Now she raises her eyes to mine. Lo! they do not turn away but continue to look at mine and it is I who must turn away or give up the ghost at this moment—

In one version of what happened I turned my eyes from hers after a moment or two, smiling to myself, feeling my penis rise in my pants. She was so beautiful, and I was so afraid to let the eyes take me away from myself. . . .

In another version of what took place I continued to look into the eyes of this beautiful girl who did not stop looking back into my eyes. . . . I was smiling at her but her mouth stayed the same and her eyes melted and my face melted and ran down the front of my shirt—

And when it came to our stop I got up and she got up. And I took her hand and we left the subway car. And we stood on the platform while the heavy rattling train clambered away up the trakcs . . . trakcs. . . .

And lo! she was my sister Rosa who I had not recognized and who had not recognized me, and we had loved each other as two lovers meeting by chance in a crowd of people. . . . And lo from that day forward we could never think of each other as merely brother and sister but as two secret lovers, fated never to marry, fated to love and be apart from one another. . . .

When Rosa cried it was with one eye only. . . .
Rosa Armed was her name not mine. . . .

When she went uptown everyone else went downtown. It was that bs . . . bas . . . bad. The body odor I mean. Change your clothes fifteen times a day and still does no good, the green drek still oozing out the veins at incredible rate . . . photofade out into fantasy, let not this dark reality destroy you Roy. . . .

So Robert, the younger of the brothers, discovers himself standing alone on one end of dusty mainstreet, Colt 45 strapped to his left, left leg. . . . He is right handed, but the butt of the gun is turned around, Western style, he will . . . twoill reach for it with his right hand, pull it out easy gliding motin . . . a stark motif of courage painted against the desert winds. . . . Four blasts will erupt from the blistering end of the nozzle. . . . The gun will scream vengeance down the silent broken streets, the blasted streets of shame, the way it was—old west a tight with fear and greed, drinkin' into infernos of fear and hate, goin' out there into the raw windswept streets, Colt strapped to your waist, tumbleweeds, little tumbles romping past you in the hazy warm western afternoon—heat building up to firecracker in the brain . . . kill that motherfucker who called you "yellow."

So here he is, The Yellow Kid, standing with his back to the empty red Arizona dessert, pissing his pants cause he knows in three minutes the shit is going to fly I mean everything is going into the fire—Black Bob has come to town. . . .

"Call it, stranger—"

"Shit, Kid, this is yourn—you hit leather when you is ready—I go plenty o' time after that to blast you fool head off. . . ."

"OK, stranger, you asked for it—"

The ground heaves up under them they are riding gray horses suddenly in the clouds aching hihgh . . . hihgh above the desert . . . moving the winds down off the raw mountains into the sea. . . . An Indian stands alone on a pony, feathers rustling slightly in the breeze. . . . His sad eye looks deep into the world, across the plains the horizon sees the ghosted figures of the black cowboys . . . peeps

"What do you do?" he said.

"I don't know," I said, watching him watch me with his eyes. . . . "I have a few girlfridns . . . fridns. . . ."

"Hah ha—" his eyes speaking then, the famous twinkle saying I get the message, man, we'll have no more of this then will we?

"Listen, Luis," I said, placing my arm across the table to rest against his. . . . "Listen, I feel a little sick inside, I don't te . . . te . . . really want to discuss this with you, in the least, or at least right now. . . . Sabe ustedes?"

"Si. Yo se." He grinned a big foolish grin at me and pulled out a gold cigarette case. I was a little astounded at the brilliance of it, the way it refracted the light into my cold undersea eyes. . . .

"Tu es loco, mi amigo," he said, still grinning. "Tu es muy loco. . . ."

"Si." He was that way. I always got that kind of reaction from him when it came to hitting terms and realities. . . . Strange fellow this Luis. . . .

"Sometimes I think you must be Spanish," I said.

"Am I not the Spanish? Am I not the Indio and the Spanish?"

"Si. I guess so."

"Yes, I am the Spanish, I speak with my own words but I am the Spanish. And I am muy loco . . . but i . . . i . . . like it. It's fun, you know. Allthat tommyrot. Old chap. Tallyho."

"Listen," I said, "what you say we ditch this 'getup' thing and make it down to Moe's Place for a few beers? Like music, man, like music. . . ."

"Hokay. Like Music. We speak the same language, but t . . . t . . . not to each other, is that it? Is that it?"

"Yes, I guess that is it. Non of your grope-scenes, non of your pleasure scenes, non of your sewer-scenes. Stage plant regurgitations. Prophecy on the cool desert, the strange blasted features of the Super Conmna . . . mna . . . working down to your level to feel you in. . . ."

"This will be a strange novel," I told them. "Skip around, start at any point, continue to page 24, etc. . . . Do as you please, don't read it at all—"

"Yes, but what about the meaning of the work as a whole, sir?" they inquired.

"Yes," I said. "There is a meaning of the work as a whole. It is there. Believe me. Seek and ye shall find.—But—and here's the catch—it's cloaked in a new form, you see, a new and beautiful assemblage of reality, you see? It comes to you red hot and alive, you see? In new words, new breakdowns of the old forms, kill and be killed, a rewriting of old truths to keep them fresh as sparks in the brain centers? Do you see?"

They understood—in a way. But as usual, as is always true with the young ones, the thinkers, as usual they understood in a way which was not exactly the way it was. . . . They saw a distorted image of truth as it were, and I was in a fix to fix it different, because it simply couldn't be done—at all. . . .

And so it goes, dear folks, my dear dear dear dear folks. I am in love with all of you, mad with love of you, and yet afraid to write these few simple words to you, mes parents, to tell you that I am now in the jail of the city. With the many bandidos sleeping on the floor and the manager with the long dirty moustaches. . . . One wants to die. . . .

4¢

Mr. Mrs. Fernando Armed
630 E. 9th St.
NYC

your son,
Luis

Luis was there. He knew what I was talking about. But he too had his own idead . . . idead . . . ideas. . . .

"But sir, is it not the truth that what I imagine is what I say and likewise what I say is not what you indeed imagine nor say, therefore what either of us says is only related to what the other one says in so to speak as it may in some way intersect by some common image term or abstraction?"

"Yes, Luis." Bless him.

"And is it not true sir that at this very moment you are beating into our heads something that is merely the construction or sifting out of your own energy fumes or ashes from the meeting of electrodes, consequently it is not absolutely necessary that we listen to you at all exd . . . exd . . . except as our own thoughts images ideas formulations interpretations abstractions phot phot photo word tickle agrees or sets up some compensatory charged

faco . . . faco . . . faco . . . factor which finds unification
with that which it agrees? Or vice versa?"

The thought within breaks—like this—putting on the
"breaks—" And I became the biggest empty space in New York
—No floor, no chore—no shore, float up the beach eating apples
die in the morning wind float down off the coast carrying pollen
dust from the meadows high in the mountains—

Rosie Armed. She's a nice girl. Too nice for your type. If you
know what I mean? She's needed a good talking to for some time.
Been around them hoodlum brothers of hers too long. They just
tell her how to do. And force her hand—up their ass. "I don't
please to go," she would say, smiling at us through the teeth. "I
don't please to go with you at all." Of course, and we understood.
We never let the wind of bad thought get between us. . . .

We were the brothers. Brought up in Peurto Peurto, raised on
the old chicken farm my fathers raised out of the dust. . . .
Adam had no navel but he was born vaccinated. You read such
things in these American papers. I prefer not to struggle with
words. They tend to overpower me. At all times I am the victim,
never the master. Like in the knife game. . . . You know how it
goes. . . .

You thought she was French. But she was born in Los Angeles.
And her skin was very very yellow. Like the t3333 three tears
that fall on the face of the animal. . . . And the voice—incredible. Next slide.

The oink milk of the pig is very sickening to drink. And yet
the young pigs they like it very much. I wonder why is that? Can
anyone tell me why is that? Perhaps not. . . .

Do you remember the winter of no snows, when the steady
rhythm of the black forest rain drove the rats out of the cellars?
Do you remember how bad we all felt during that time? It was
most elaborate the stories we told then to ourselves, to keep away
the sickness. . . . But now it has come back, blwoing yes blw
OOoo ing up the chambers that sink beneath the mountain. . . .

FILL IN THE ....
    Luis .... for his .... doing what .... Rosa said.
"Cuss .... feek .... to do this .... and please."

"Shit, Robert, ... was the answer too?"
"Of course. Tomorrow .... break it pugh."
They .... and .... fill for does that. Pusher ....
mock fought .... and do .... put it. . . . Pleasant ....
rose .... garden .... was .... all .... Luis, who was the
big fat one, ... wanted.

Rosa ate it up. She opened her .... and laid the .... into
the .... Robert .... He .... Fifteen times he ....

"Quite an ....," he said, coughing.
"TheseY .... get too serious .... and don't."
"Yes."

When she cries is with one eye only. . . . Disgusting to say
the least, expecially since one can never be sure which eye it will
be. . . . A sort of "Genius" hoax. . . . Signals from the stars.
. . . Watch it today. . . . The constellations of meaning, bub.
. . . 8:23 P.M. NYC hello it's only a paper *you.*

But to get back to her eye(s). . . . Rosa Armed was her own
name not mine. . . . She was anal-retentive about everything
. . . except love— In that she was generous, having lain w/
every manner of man and beast. . . . Afterward afterward she
would light a cigarette and start weeping. . . . The spectacle her
eye presented to her dead lover was disgusting, especially Rosa
Armed. Let me tell you about her men and her beast. . . . Both
genres are disgusting. . . .

"Castor oil flops" we used to call them. They never cried. Outside the rain continued to fall on a plot of ground the size of a
quarter. Rosa used to go down for a quarter of an hour and then
come back up soaked in briny tears. . . . Wouldn't touch her
with a ten foot pole. . . . She was only a few feet tall—and Rosa
Armed was her name.

She laughed. She .... her .... over his .... and ....
sitting up and .... with a .... sound.

"Do you get the picture?"
ROSA ARMED SEIZED IN CAPITAL—
"Seized by convulsions of lust. That .... is .... is .... and
.... of .... for .... beyond .... into .... before

.... after .... because .... but .... instead you
.... so there.

"Strange .... you have."

"Si. Tu es muy .... por .... y .... todo ....
cucho .... para .... me tiene .... constedes ....
pues .... mi amigo .... chinga .... putalita ....
biene .... mucho .... pres .... culo. . . ."

"Stick it up your ass?"

I had the courage to look back having a strained neck . . . father in ruins mother totting in a hospital. . . . Never did like it . . . what do you mean, *my eye!* I mean 8:23 P.M. is gone once. Rosa 823 lbs. No ident.

Ça

Continue ↑

Hi folks . . . (undecipherable hieroglyphs)

(Thus ends the books of Rosa.)

I put two tinted book ends—one on either (both) side(s) of rose Rosa Armed—into my pocket—fat and contue continue. . . .

"Hi Rosa," said one of them. She called one of the book ends "Mother" the other "Father" and whatever was inbetween them (vide the equator) was their perpetual progeny. Help! It is 8:32 between them. . . . String along them and you'll gee, you paper you

FOR EXAMPLE

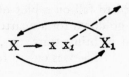

"T.D. says" blue voice box

X = Rosa

X_1 = Armed

xx_1 = the luscious member

Nix to sex says Mule (Rosa in disguise)

For example

spleling:
fiend
feind
feend
fiind
feind

Break it break it break it (la mule) automatic Rosa equipment
nada . . .
(significance)

THE END

So I heave Rosa on the floor and step on an ant that looked like
a Turk. I pee in the moss there, it says "Hi, Luis," I say "Hi,
moss." Then I lay her over the Pepsi machine and pop her lime.
The gook comes oinking down the spout, mottled and pale. The
little stranger. She's been fucking, Japs, and I, Doctor Luis Armed,
am left holding the afterbirth. . . .

"Shit, Rosa, couldn't you muck with somethin' more decent?"

"Listen, you dirty Greek," she yodels, sounding like an old lady
with oil in her lungs, "you filthy greaseball, I'll have you arrested
if you touch me again!"

"Shit, I'm you brother aint I?"

"Brother my ass. To me you're just 'Doc,' and that's as far as it
goes."

So I threw the placenta in the wastebasket and sat down to have
a smoke. Rosa lay stretched out on the table, bleeding like a pig,
exhausted with the dubber din of it all. . . . Strange old lady
electric thoughts ran in her mouth. . . . Couldn't be helped, it's
always like this, I know, I've seen em' all. . . .

I pick the little gook up off the floor and gather a gander of his
dead eye. The moss is caking his hairy mucous face. Funny, these
gooks, all look the same when you let em' out of the chlorine
trenches. . . .

"Well, sis, so I closed this deal, yah see? Now we got plenty of
moola to operate on, everything is jake. We'll fly straight from
here on in. . . ."

"You mean I don't have to hustle my gut so you can fill
yours?"

"At's right. I closed this deal, yah see? Now ee . . . ee we got plenty of the ready cash. . . . Fly straight as a hawk from here on in. . . . Destination moon. . . ."

"That's good. We'll move back to Mexique. Little hacienda by the sea. I'll be your wife, you can fuck me all you want, nobody will know the distance. . . . We'll get some of them pills. . . ."

"You're a hard woman, Rosa, but soft inside, and I like you." I got up and smiled into her careworn features. . . . Now I'll lay her back and slough it in. . . .

LEWIS WARSH*

❦

Moving Through Air

A stone falls,
and the expedient path
is blocked. We hide
in the bushes
because we are certain of being attacked
from behind, from the boat
we are lifting our bows into the air
watching the arrows splash   taking
aim   repeating the fire.

The wind on top of the gull streak, hindering
advances
we repeat   after an hour
you are immune
you see them die
like cubes of sugar in a tumbler
where you sit
the waiters, trays at hips, brush
through the aisles
you look at your watch and the angle of the tray
the growth of the long invigorating marrow
inside the rock
that vein you know now must be mined

* LEWIS WARSH, *born in the Bronx in 1944, graduated from the City College of New York in 1966. He founded* Angel Hair, *an occasional poetry journal which also published books. His poems have appeared in* Paris Review, Poetry, Wild Dog, Spice, *and other magazines, and he has finished a novel.*

you smoke and you look at the air and you wonder
about the water, the boat, the cooler
water under the pier,
you even enter the various waters
to test my judgment   yet
you are the only mind I ever desired
desire now out of habit
in the thread a fret sustains us, benches
under the trees,
the beach, gum on the sandals, the net raised
because you cheat.

EUGENE WILDMAN*

❦

The Subway Singer

When did I know? When did I begin to sing? When did the
songs begin in me? Once again we reach for the turning point. I
have always had this feeling, this association of song and bird.
So then, this singing, and a first song with a first bird. So. The
first was on a clear day. My father was taking me to the peacock garden, we were standing on the platform waiting for the
train. Down the track on which the fast express runs, a heavy
boxer dog came lumbering. It seemed alone within itself, exerting
all its concentration to stay on the deadly track. I wanted to shout,
call out to it: stupid. And then it dawned on me: it was stupid.
What was horrifying was its concentration. It passed out of sight
and I remained there, waiting for what would come, staring at the
tracks and embankment. Our train did not arrive. After ten minutes the dog reappeared, lumbering in the opposite direction with
the same concentration as before. Then our train pulled in and
we were soon at the peacock garden where, full of the glory of
colors, we thought no more of the brown dog. But it seems important now to insist that the dog was a boxer. It was not a Dober-
man, it was not a Shepherd. What a different thing that would
have been.

We returned home in the evening. It was six o'clock and the
avenue was dark, as we walked toward our house a shout grew
at the end of the street. It was a long, narrow avenue, the shouts

* EUGENE WILDMAN, *born in Brooklyn, New York in 1938, edited the*
Chicago Review *during 1966 and 1967. He has published fiction and*
criticism in that journal, the Northwest Review, *and other magazines.*
Currently teaching at Northwestern, he is working on a book of stories,
two novels, and a study of "Tragic Space."

rose, louder and more strained, and through the darkness a tremendous motion was perceptible, a thrashing about and a circle of shadows off to the side. At once the street became luminous, the evening streetlamps went on. At the end of the long street, illumined, the twins Nathan and Daniel Ein were rolling furiously on the ground, fighting. The two most studious boys I knew. Wondrous. Simply. The spectators along the side were bent as willows, the twins were shouting as they fought each other. The whole street seemed to fly by me, rushing to that point. Perhaps then was the beginning of the songs, though I could not have known it yet. Abruptly it ended. From a doorway behind me their mother emerged. She cupped her hands to her mouth to call. For an instant everything seemed separate, absorbed, within itself. The quietly glittering stars, myself, the crowd, the woman behind me, the imperturbable houses, my father beside me, even the twins furiously tumbling. It was all stopped. Everything was that moment. Even the two recollections of the successive passages of the dog, even the bursting of the peacocks upon my sight. It was all then. Within each separate thing was a peaceful gulf as wide as the space between the stars and us.

The problem is that we never know what we are waiting for. And it takes a disciplined man to refrain from drawing conclusions. As for myself, there are few things that I am certain of, but those I treat with respect. I put my faith in trains and in the Star of David; in trains because something that big compels belief, and in the Star of David because it has one more point than anybody else's star. After that, it is all chance; you play your options and try not to think of what is catching up with you. Fate moves in its own time and has its own ways; but an honest man would have to admit that he is never taken entirely by surprise.

The distance began to break. Her voice began a rising call that shattered the peaceful gulfs. "Ein! Ein!" she shouted. The moment became bizarre. The shouting was gone, the twins disengaged themselves. The first one stood and looked up the street. "Ein zwei!" he shouted at his mother. For a moment longer he stared, immobile, then he was in motion, approaching in the direction of his house. The second brother stood up, not moving now either, and looking at his twin. The stillness had begun to settle again, everything was charged. "Ein ein!" I yelled. The words came flying out of me, though I tried to hold them back.

Time flowed. We had jumped to another track, like leaping from a train. As when summer came and we would walk through neighborhoods where we did not live, through gardens that were not our own. From garden to garden we moved, and at the end of the day we arrived home laden with sprigs and blossoms of yellow. My mother would accept offerings in silence. One day we were moving through the yards of the people who hated us, summer was ending, from the street a voice began.

> Green, green fields at home
> I am dying in the green, green sea

Melodyless, it was a song. A white-haired man stood before the curtained windows of the indrawn houses, of the people who saw it all and whose doors had never opened. In the street he stood, a song that was sad, a sea song without any melody, rising up out of him. We gave him sprigs of primulas, which he took, though he never looked, and the song he sang never broke. All through the summer we would move through the city, going on busses, then entering the yards of the people who loathed us, breaking the stems and taking the flowers. We would come home with the yellow flowers from all the gardens of the city. Once the singer was on our own street. He sang a Russian song, never even noticing us. In the fall the police showed up at the school one day. I was sent for, with the Eins, with Ash, with Gold, with Rosethorn. "You have stolen flowers," a detective said. We said nothing. "I compel you to admit it," the detective said. "All right," Daniel Ein said, "we stole flowers." The detective wrote in his book. "Much better," he said, and snapped it shut. That was all. "We can never take flowers again," Ein said. "Of course we can," I argued. "The Flower Ring is done with," he said.

We were like the wind, moving among the spaces of the lampposts, moving toward our sanctuaries. I remembered for some reason a portion of an old English sea chant I had read. The lines were themselves like the wind and the water as they rose and fell in my imagining.

> God bless them all who die at sea
> If they must sleep on restless waves
> God make them dream they are ashore
> With grass above their graves

It was all in flux. "Fackel!" the second twin called to me, eyes riveted, his expression uninterpretable. I said nothing, I could think of nothing. The lamps were cool buds that floated impossibly above us. I kept wanting to reach up and touch the light, my arms and fingertips were enormously long, I could leap high above all the lights. My father had not spoken the entire while. "God's will," he said, a smile upon his face, and turned abruptly and went into the house.

There was no father, there was my name only. I believe in names, I believe that names burn, I believe that history is only the record of how names have come into the world, have flowed into the universe like the pain of Christ, like the outcries of ten billion angry redeemers, never to be separable from it again. Which is why I find myself drawn to that name, but I will speak of that in its proper place.

Had I been born Frederick Six, had I begun life as Frederick Six I would surely have done things differently, it would all have been different from the first. I have no doubt of how noble I would have been. Or had it turned out Freddie Six. As Freddie Six I would have had a sneer, I should calmly have faced the doom of the world with a trumpet or a saxophone held lightly in my hands. We are what we are. It has come about twice in the capitols of my travels, I will tell about that in its place too, that I have had to become Freddie Six, and the name did not fail either time of its magical transformation.

Something was born in the world that night, I was born to the world that night. There was something about it: the shouts, the twins fighting at the end of the street, the crying out of the names. The brothers too entered life then. Ein one and Ein two they became from that night on. Watch the rain against the window pane, how it searches out the empty places. The greatest surprise is that we find who we are; when you get over that, over the surprise of yourself, there are very few things that can surprise you again. I walked into my father's house, the incorrigible fingers convulsed. There were two clouds above the lampposts.

It is not as if we could be accused of surprise. All of us knew that a world was ended; but we agreed to *seem* as though we did not understand. We consented to act like Germany's victims as they willed to dream of our agonies. It was an achievement of the imagination: Germany and we. We had succeeded in alchemizing the time, had achieved in collaboration somehow, some fusion of sign and vessel. We are moving now together through a landscape cluttered with broken and incomprehensible symbols, and the trains were to become for us all a kind of ultimate prayer and answer. Aberrant steaming metallic deities they appeared. Signs and vessels they were, the attraction of destiny to destiny as they swept over Europe in the night to claim their offering of Jews. We could only make of this an ancient malevolence that we sought to placate with familiar useless rituals. But our explanations were only spells, and we could no longer believe either in our questions or our magic. "What will become of us?" we would cry. "We will be delivered," we would answer ourselves.

And so the rabbis vainly conjured their God and offered prayers that the redeemer be sent. "He will surely come," Rabbi Jacob Cranach proclaimed to a crowded congregation. "He *could* come," whispered Ein one, Nathan Ein. "The last messiah brought us two thousand years of persecution," said Ein two, the twin Daniel. "Maybe he came and went," said Petel Keppek, sitting to his right. "He got lost," the man in front of Petel said, turning to address Nathan Ein. A man three rows back craned his head forward and shouted: "We should have had fancy uniforms, instead he would be on our side." Captain Nazeruth himself was drawn in by the power of our spells. "If God had not wanted this to happen, He would not have permitted it to be," his heavy voice boomed from the rear. There was a moment of awkward silence. "This is true," a woman in the balcony said.

It was as though nothing had been lacking except the proper interpretation. It was all a matter of interpretation, and we did not fail to observe that the oracles had already been at work on the other side. Daniel Ein's voice took up. "It might be that the deliverer just forgot after he came." His face was a caricature of belief. "I look around me, I see that nothing has been forgotten," came back Nathan Ein. "There are too many unemployed philosophers," a voice from up front said. "That also is true," the woman in a balcony said.

We accustomed ourselves to Captain Nazeruth and to the crowds that were wherever we were; that watched us when we entered our shops, that gathered in the streets outside our homes; or that defaced the walls of the synagogue, for the time remaining that there was a synagogue. I have memorized their faces. And in their invariable presence I found an admission, almost, of a kind of collusion between us. Some of those faces I could not dispense with. Schippel, the engineer. Kammer, the merchant who once had done business with Petel. Reider, unemployed, one leg four inches shorter than the other. Harmann, bricklayer. Four others whose membership was irregular and whose names I did not know, but whose faces were unmistakable. As we passed them their mouths would open. "Bolsheviks," they would say in rasping unison. Never many of them but always sufficient. And I would think: So my fine Reider, so my Schippel, so my Kammer and you others. One day you will come to gawk and there will be no me to be seen. I will have gone. Where I customarily was, nothing will be. And in some space where your own lives are emptinesses, there I will quite distinctly exist. Then we would enter the synagogue. "Nordic imbeciles," we would mutter. "Bolsheviks," they would shout again as we filed in. I bear those faces within me today.

For a time there was even talk of resistance. We would form an espionage group; we would blow up the train that took us away; we would smuggle Jews out of the country. We even imagined that we were led by Nathan Ein; and so for a time we could indulge in a fantasy of tragedy. But we were so prepared to die stoically that we had first to mythologize the one truth of our history: we had survived, we were *there*.

"It is God's language," Rabbi Eli Benjamin instructed us, "the Lord speaks in time and through events." "The divine alphabet is history," Rabbi Cranach said. "Exactly," Captain Nazeruth agreed, standing at the rear, cigarette held between two fingertips, elegantly emitting a puff of smoke. "God wants this to happen," he said. "It is God's way of speaking," Rabbi Benjamin added. "You Jews have entirely childish notions of salvation," Captain Nazeruth went on, ignoring him. "You imagine things and leave yourselves open to despair. If you tie yourselves to such unworldly hopes, you will never get on in this world. I tell you this as someone who has come to know you quite well." "He has a very good point," said Nathan Ein. "What point?" asked Rabbi Benjamin. "Yes, what point is he making?" asked Daniel Ein. "He is making the point," said Nathan Ein, "that there is no savior who is going to save us." "How does he know that," said Petel, "when all the stories speak of one and stories are all we have anyway?" "Then I will tell you," Nathan Ein answered, "so you will know once and for all what goes on with saviors. I will even grant that there is one, and I will grant you even more that he got here and didn't get lost. Is that fair enough?" "Go on!" we all shouted. "Fair enough," said Rabbi Cranach. "So then. I don't know when we should agree the savior must have appeared. Perhaps a long time ago. But his name, as you can imagine, when he first came among us must have been on everyone's lips." "Now *there* is a point," interrupted Daniel Ein. "It *must* have been," agreed Rabbi Benjamin. "If there is a savior, what is his name?" Hornstein the grocer challenged "Well?" the woman from the balcony reinforced him, "go and give the name." "Let the speaker finish," Rabbi Cranach pacified. "We may imagine," Nathan Ein continued, "that even the children must have run about the streets shouting it. At that time there would have been no one to whom the name would not have been known. The sound itself would have conveyed such joy to people that men might well have taken to using it as a greeting or as a conventional term of affection." "Interesting," said Captain Nazeruth, "interesting. But the authorities would have had to intervene at that point then." "What on earth for?" said Rabbi Benjamin. "There would be impersonations and other unscrupulous uses of the name. Parents would take to naming their children after the savior. Eventually too many people would have the same name. It couldn't be allowed. But more important than that even, a divine name might very well convey power, and an indiscriminate use of it would of course have to be prevented. In my opinion it would be necessary to prohibit use of the name altogether and to adopt an official circumlocation instead." "It would not even be necessary to go to such lengths," Nathan Ein said. "The name would be known throughout the world. From mouth to mouth, from region to region, from nation to nation the name would be passed. We may even consider the possibility that this would go on for generations. In all the inevitable profusion of names the savior would naturally become confused. In time his memory of it would become dimmed." "He would forget even that he was the savior," Petel stated, but in a voice that refused to credit the thought. "Perhaps at times it would come back," Nathan Ein went on, "he would attempt to speak in his own name. But of course he would be hooted down. Eventually, from lack of use, he would forget completely." "A probable conclusion," Captain Nazeruth said. "Quite probably he is somewhere among us now, using whatever circumlocution is fashionable." "And never even knowing that he is the savior," Rosethorn the cantor added wonderingly. "That being the case," Captain Nazeruth took up, "it would be for the good of the people to prohibit any sort of reference to him. It could only lead to waste and discontent, and the severest penalties should have to be enforced." "That could never work," Rabbi Cranach exploded. "By random chance the name is bound to be uttered. You can never obliterate it from history, nor prevent it from reappearing in time." His eyes were alight with feeling. "Nothing difficult in that," Daniel Ein countered. "It strikes a chord; but since it is meaningless, it is forgotten almost instantly." "You place too heavy a burden on random chance and not enough on what is necessary," Nathan Ein lectured Rabbi Cranach.

"Ein one is right," I said one evening at dinner. "We are better off believing in trains." And the trains did become the recipients of our beliefs. "We must look upon them as God's telegrams," Rabbi Benjamin had pronounced. "What is He trying to say?" my mother burst out at the table. But it was no longer possible not to believe in them, so many of us had already been delivered

—including finally Petel and his improbably lovely daughter Frischa. I had said to him once in Yiddish, "Petel, how does a man like you, basically the most ordinary of men, come to have such a daughter as Frischa? It wouldn't seem that such a thing could be." Frischa was his all, and he delighted in such teasing. "Speak German when in public," he said this time, shifting his feet nervously. "Petel!" I went on, "you of all people. What kind of airs are you putting on? Are you setting up to enter Frischa into our German burgher class? These are not the times for it, let me tell you." "More than anything else," he said, "I want not to be conspicuous. Just a shade worse than everybody else." Then suddenly they were gone. Along with Daniel Ein. There was no longer the subterfuge of spiriting us away in the night. One day the police showed up, accompanied by a soldier. "You are Petel Keppek, the tailor's assistant?" the police officer asked. "Formerly an exporter of furs," Petel, aware by now of what was occurring, corrected him with dignity. The soldier slapped him in the face. "What is that for?" said Petel. The soldier looked uncomfortable for a moment. "How dare you speak German?" he said finally. A crowd began to gather. Someone stood on tiptoe at the rim of an expanding circle. "What happened?" a man passing by asked. "He spoke German," someone said. "I'll break his neck," the man said. And then Petel was gone. With Frischa, and Daniel Ein, and forty-one others.

In another life we would have married, that improbable girl and I. But there were barely occasions for this life, and to speak of another would have been far too sad. The last time we met we walked by the lake near that same peacock garden I had gone to as a boy with my father. The feeling of time was strongly upon me, perhaps because there was so little left to us. There was nothing we could say, and certainly nothing that was on our minds. We walked aimlessly, occasionally our eyes meeting, our fingers touching. And then tacitly, agreeing, eyes or fingers would separate, withdraw. We returned to ourselves, to our absence of thoughts, and mingled with the swans along the water's edge.

They were inviolate in their aloofness, in their claim to purposelessness, in their rights of possession of the water and its banks. We were inferior to such strength and legitimacy. "Touch it," a woman, smiling, taunted her husband, pointing to one of the large males. The powerful neck flashed forward, twice the heavy wings flapped. The birds were gigantic, white; we suddenly became aware of how few there were of us. The beak snapped. The swan hissed like an angry cat, the wings flapped again. Another hissed and snapped its beak at the air. Three swans began to walk upon the lake, candles borne upon the water. The remainder, there must have been more than twenty we realized all at once, sullenly drove us from the bank. We left the park, I recall the reddish flaring of the sun.

Then the forty-three were gone. We met that night at Nathan Ein's. "Animals," I said. "Not animals," he corrected, "logicians. They are doing all this for logic." "You are right," I agreed, "it has been reasoned out. They have books on the subject." He walked to the window and flung it open. "Logicians!" he called out. I lit a cigarette. "Show me a man who reasons, I will show you a fascist," I said." And I will show you a pig," he answered, "a philosophical pig. A pig who writes a treatise. *Books!*" he shouted out the window. By way of answer someone threw an apple in. He began to laugh. "The first fruit of philosophy," he declaimed. "My greatest fear is that they will kick me in the head," Rosethorn the cantor said. "You admire the brain?" Ein demanded. "With a concussion you're helpless," Rosethorn protested. Ein merely glared. "Like a prizefighter," Rosethorn explained weakly. "Thank God for philosophy and for Max Schmeling," Ein said and turned away. "The world must have more systems in it."

Three nights later it was Ein who was beaten in the head. He was walking to the synagogue when a teen-age boy threw a mushy, overripe pear at him. It fell at his feet. Ein continued walking, another fruit hit him, this time in the chest. Five boys of about sixteen barred the way in front. He recognized Kammer's son among them. A crowd of adults had quickly formed, an ever-distending albumen filled with many eyes, giving the youths occasion and encouragement. A young man, perhaps twenty, with enormous hands pushed his way to the fore of the crowd. Behind the young man a girl with pale blue eyes, of the same age as the boys, looked at Ein vacantly. From behind, a hand pushed him. The half-circle parted, as if the albumen had volition, willed this, and he began to obey. At six feet away a third fruit hit him, this time in the back of the head. Before him were the five youths. Ein stopped. Indecisively he turned toward the adults, as if intending to appeal to that. Intention, any thought, deserted him. "My mind!" he said in a hideous voice. In every doorway stood a son of one of these adults. Then he was hit again in the head. "You are damaging my mind!" he shouted. The young man with the enormous hands detached himself from the crowd and walked over to Ein, who was watching him come and could not decide what to do. For a moment he glimpsed the utterly vacant eyes of the girl, and the lips, which were slightly open. The young man looked at Ein briefly, and then with one great hand gripped Ein's head and squeezed it. His scream seemed to be audible only inward.

The crowd dispersed quickly and we took Ein into the synagogue. He was shaking and had to be helped to walk. "No cuts," Rabbi Cranach pronounced after we had sat him down. "They haven't drawn blood this time," I said to him. "I feel it inside," he said. "You're all right," I answered. "But inside I can feel it," he said. "What?" we asked. "What do you feel?" "Something is seeping out. I know that I am hurt and I can feel it. Something that I am losing. Slowly. Drop by drop. I can feel my intelligence running out."

Then the journey, the exodus, began for the rest of us. But Ein was already a song within me. Now we sat in the cramped darkness of the train, each one of us locked within a fantasy of his own. We did not speak much because there was nothing that one person could say that meant anything to another. There was little awareness of bodily extension, only a sensation of being enveloped in darkness. Each of us was less than himself, and yet each of us was in a deeper way all of the others. "How can this be?" a voice ventured once. "Don't bother with how, we're *here*," all the other voices corrected. A voice near me recalled, "Don't be conspicuous, Petel used to say." From the other end of the car a new voice began to laugh.

When we reached the new diaspora we discovered that our

former neighbor Petel was in charge of us. "It was Frischa," he tried to explain, stiffening himself to meet our eyes. We could only turn away with contempt. "There was no choice," his voice was pleading. "They were going to make Frischa a doll." We could neither punish nor forgive enough, so we chose to leave him to himself. But it was not sufficient for me. "I don't judge him," I said later, though as I did so a memory of the swans massed by the bank came vividly into my mind: of Frischa and I silently contending against them, and of that candlelike passage upon the water. "I don't judge him," I said, "but I cannot see how such a man lives with himself. It isn't as if they torture them there, it isn't as if they perform their experiments. To so betray our people is beyond my understanding." A voice that I knew well was beside me explaining. "She was the first one they made him send through." It was Daniel Ein speaking.

We talked only about getting away. New York was the favorite escape. Everyone thought he had relatives there and that Jews owned the city. They would force America to intervene, every one of us would be rescued. I would laugh at that and they would laugh at me. "New York?" I would say. "Palestine." "Nonsense," they would say. "The British." And then we would all laugh. "But first we have to get out," I would remind them. Often Petel would come by while we were talking. He would squat down in a corner of the room, eyes fixed on us and listening intently. He never made a move to join us and we never invited him. Nor did his expression ever indicate that he had heard a word; but when we were finished talking he would get up at once and leave.

"God help me," I said to Daniel Ein one time, "your brother was absolutely right. I have never heard of a piece of bestiality that was not preceded by reasons. *Petel!*" I shouted. There was no answer. "It sets my mind at rest, it *relieves* me to know, that whatever happens to me, I will have been enabled to take part in the great systematizing achievement of my age. In two months, due to the nature of *the work*, I will probably not have strength to say this again. It *gratifies* me, therefore, to have this a matter of record. Reasons. Is that all it takes? Reasons? Then the wonders of antiquity already pale. Logic: there is the European soul. Logic and Efficiency, and above all Magnitude. The Great Wall? The Pyramids? The Tower to Heaven? How many reasons did they cost in the making? Don't you see, it is merely Platonism. How do we measure the value of an idea? How many reasons are given for the sake of it." Petel had begun to walk away. In my mind an image caught of the apple that had flown through the window. "It was half eaten," I thought aloud. *"Petel!"* I shouted. He looked back for what seemed minutes. "I was afraid she would like it," Petel said.

So there is a connection that you will learn between laughter and song. Only that, softly. Petel himself stood tremulous on the brink. The world had ended and we were all dissembling. Within us each some vision was coiled that only waited to be unleashed. "You have too many illusions, Petel," I said. Petel and I walked toward each other. "We are going to New York," I told him.

DATE DUE
